Zehn Jahrzehnte
REVISED

Zehn Jahrzehnte
REVISED

1870-1970

FRANK G. RYDER

Indiana University

HOLT, RINEHART AND WINSTON, NEW YORK, TORONTO AND LONDON

Printed in the United States of America

Library of Congress Card Number: 66-10526

37659-0216

To A.G.R. and S.S.R.

Foreword

This collection is designed to provide the student of intermediate German with reading of real literary significance. It is also, in its short compass, a true anthology, selected and arranged to give him some feeling for an important genre of German literature, its historical development, its greatest writers, and the themes which have occupied their attention.

The title of the book indicates its plan: one story or *Novelle* for each of the last ten decades, chosen to represent the writing of the time and to serve, within the limits of length and difficulty, the purposes mentioned above.

The authors represented here are figures of the first rank in modern fiction. Keller, Ebner-Eschenbach, Mann, Rilke, Kafka, Ernst, and Wiechert are all securely established in the canon of great German writing. The last three decades are purposely represented by "new" writers, all of whom began their careers after World War II, rather than by late works of older authors. This makes the test of greatness more difficult. Borchert, however, seems certain to retain his sudden fame. Gaiser has already confirmed the high praise accorded him soon after his first appearance: "one of the great hopes of postwar German writing"; Piontek is associated with and representative of the youngest generation. These are names that the student will encounter again and again if he goes on to further study of German and German literature. Encouraging him to do so is one of the fundamental aims of this text.

Every work stands in its full original form. Nothing is changed, substituted, or deleted. This is of particular importance when critical attention centers on the story as a literary work of art. Such emphasis implies fairly extensive annotation. Rather than take refuge in inferior stories because they are simple, it is preferable, within reason, to provide more help in reading the best. Fortunately much of the best is also linguistically simple.

Two sorts of apparatus are provided. What is necessary for an immediate understanding of the text (mostly difficult non-recurrent vocabulary) is given in the inside margins. All extra assistance—in matters of syntax, idioms, and informational background—appears separately at the bottom of the page. The entire text has been put through a data processing procedure using a computer, to produce a complete concordance of all vocabulary items from *und* to nonce words. The end vocabulary was thoroughly revised using the concordance. Its use, especially in a revision which involved dropping one story, adding another and making one substitution, was particularly crucial and has greatly enhanced the accuracy and reliability of the apparatus.

The format of the book is designed to make all annotation as accessible as possible, and at the same time to preserve the impression of "genuineness" in the reading matter itself. The German text appears intact and unencumbered, with no numbers or signs to interrupt the reading—in other words, exactly like a complete page in a German book.

Personages, places, allusions, etc. are all identified, though briefly. The editor believes that comprehension and critical appreciation of the work itself is the first task—hence, the nature of the apparatus. Occasionally, interpretations of specific passages are suggested in the notes—or raised by implication in the "Fragen" that follow the text—particularly when the brief remarks in the introduction to the story might do little to resolve a doubtful point.

To meet the criteria of greatness in author and story, historical continuity, *and* increasing linguistic difficulty would be an improbable *tour de force*. The annotation of each text takes into account its level of difficulty, and somewhat more attention is given those which come first (Keller, Ebner-Eschenbach) or which offer particular difficulties in vocabulary (Piontek, especially his terms related to mountain climbing). In any case, there is a simple solution for those who want to read in ascending order of difficulty. Careful polling of the students at Dartmouth who read the texts of the original edition in "unedited" form, with a dictionary—together with the editor's own experience and the advice of others—indicates that the stories, coincidentally, grade themselves. One can take advantage of this, with only slight loss in sense of historical development, by starting with the decade of the 1920's (Ernst), proceeding to the end, and then covering the previous decades in their order. To see how early in the study of German one might start the use of this text, following such a course, the teacher need only look at the Ernst and Borchert stories.

For each author there is a page of biographical and literary orientation, and for each story a brief foreword. In matters of interpretation I have often preferred to raise questions or suggest avenues of approach rather than supply answers. The "critical foreword"—to use a somewhat inflated term—should really be read after the story, the biographical sketch before.

Two specific points of editing: The student should note that the principal parts of strong and irregular verbs are given separately (in uncompounded form) at the end of the vocabulary. The dagger after a verb refers to this list. Daggers are not used in the footnotes since verbs given there are usually parts of idioms and phrases and are themselves listed in the vocabulary.

A separate list of exact and nearly exact cognates is appended to the vocabulary. The student will have no trouble translating these words but may wish to check details of stress and inflection.

All the copyright holders concerned have been most cooperative and kind in granting permission to print these stories. I should like to thank

for Heinz Piontek's *Rote Pfeile*, the author

for Gerd Gaiser's *Fehleisen*, Carl Hanser Verlag, München

for Wolfgang Borchert's *Die lange lange Straße lang*, Feuilletondienst im Rowohlt Verlag G.m.b.H., Hamburg. (From: Wolfgang Borchert, *Das Gesamtwerk*, Rowohlt Verlag G.m.b.H., Hamburg)

for Ernst Wiechert's *Der Todeskandidat*, Verlag Kurt Desch, München-Wien-Basel

for Paul Ernst's *Der geraubte Brief*, C. Bertelsmann-Verlag, Gütersloh

for Franz Kafka's *Das Urteil*, Shocken Books, Inc., New York

for Rainer Maria Rilke's *Die Weise von Liebe und Tod des Cornets Christoph Rilke*, Insel Verlag Anton Kippenberg, Wiesbaden

for Thomas Mann's *Tobias Mindernickel*, S. Fischer Verlag, Frankfurt am Main. (Copyright by Thomas Mann with the kind permission of S. Fischer Verlag, Frankfurt a.M.)

I am most grateful to Professor Emeritus Willem Graff for his help in connection with Rilke's *Cornet;* also to my colleagues at Indiana, Professors Dorrit Cohn and Ferdinand Piedmont, for numerous suggestions and comments. For their generous assistance in answering my questions about their stories, I am particularly indebted to Gerd Gaiser and Heinz Piontek.

A final word of gratitude belongs to my late colleague at Dartmouth, Professor Merle C. Cowden, and to his students and mine, who read these works *in deserto*.

F. G. R.

Introduction

The following pages offer a summary view of literary trends in the period covered by our stories. Such an undertaking must be approached with caution, and not only because of its brevity. Too often we tend to picture literary history as an orderly progression of definable movements, each one ending decently before the other begins. Worse still is the temptation to take a literary category for the bed of Procrustes, and cut off or stretch the writer and his work to assure a good fit.

Classifying is nonetheless inevitable and necessary, if only to deal systematically with a vast body of material. Writers often make the task easier by joining forces and announcing their purpose, or even naming themselves, like the Expressionists.

Wherever a writer takes his stand, however individual, he is bound to find himself in some company. The basic ways of looking at life are few. In new situations the old polarities are shifted and recombined: rationalism and irrationalism, objectivity and subjectivity, optimism and pessimism, the absolute or the relative view, belief in purpose or chance, style as mirror or style as order, etc. It is not surprising that even in a period of profound change clear and familiar trends appear. We must try to get the best view of them we can in a short space.

The term "Poetic Realism" has a vaguely contradictory sound, yet it characterizes well the dominant mood of German prose from the middle of the nineteenth century until almost 1890. The familiar reality of life is the subject, but the spirit in which it is viewed is still both individual and lyric and thus to a degree reminiscent of the subjectivity of Romanticism. More important perhaps, the Realist's view is closely allied to the idealist philosophies and an absolute, rather than relative, system of values.

The Realists were almost by definition not a school. They did not theorize like the Romanticists nor band together and issue manifestos like the Naturalists and the Expressionists. Their purposes must be inferred from their work. They were independent, even solitary figures. Two of the finest of them have their place in this anthology: Keller and Ebner-Eschenbach.

The whole of life is too vast for any palette. All Realists choose some segment of observable reality for their portrayal. The choice made by the Poetic Realists is consistent enough to permit a general characterization of their subject matter—and, ironically, to keep their influence from being felt in foreign lands or even from continuing uninterrupted in German literature.

Most of them either ignored or actively resisted the growing industrialization and urbanization of Europe. They dwell upon the common verities and the hallowed details of the "middle range" of life. The locale of their writing is limited in two senses. They write typically of an area they know intimately (Keller, for example, of rural and small-town Switzerland). They write primarily of a single class or a vertical section of society, with whose ways they are familiar (Ebner-Eschenbach of the Moravian landed estate in all its ramifications: nobility, small townsmen, and peasants). Within these limits their subjects may be either contemporary or historical.

There are many styles in Poetic Realism, depending on the solution each writer found for problems of selection and technique. Keller's irony has virtually no parallel in other writers of the period. There are differences, too, in the ultimate verdict they pass on life, though by and large it is an affirmative one. Where the pervading temper is pessimistic, it is not voiced in strident complaint but in the dignity of resignation or in courageous assertion of human values in a troubled world.

In their speech they are conservative. They do not explore the periphery of language for new modes of expression. Their medium is the commonly understood idiom, however carefully wrought and individualized. It reflects a basic confidence that reality is as it seems to be. What happened when men were no longer sure of this is evident in Kafka and the Expressionists.

The Poetic Realists are not themselves the center of their own artistic concern. They do not report on their inner states, like the Expressionists. They do not faithfully record every shade of their own sense impressions, like the Impressionists. Nor do their characters serve as vehicles of social criticism, as with the Naturalists.

Though the Realist's viewpoint is that of an independently creative individual, it is the (selected) reality that speaks for itself, and the beauty or the pain resides in the persons and things described and speaks from them.

During the 1880's a conjunction of revolutionary forces in European life and thought produced an upheaval in literature, too. Not the least of these was the social and economic fact of industrialization and its accompanying urban poverty. With it came Marx's determinism and the crusades of the Socialists, Darwin's concept of struggle for survival, his concentration on heredity and environment as shaping forces, the increasing rejection of absolute systems of morality, including Christianity, and the questioning of individual responsibility for choices and decisions. This complex of forces directed attention to the lower classes, to the by-ways of human suffering and the distortions of human behavior. It emphasized the pathetic, not tragic, situation of man in a universe of which he was rather an accidental product than a master.

Into this vortex of change moved the Naturalists. They had a social message and an absorbing interest in the nether regions of society. This was for them the proper area of literary concern, and the place where "truth" was to be found. In Naturalism and the considerable expanse of modern literature it affected there is always a certain tendency to say that the seamy side is the better (or at least more fascinating) half of reality. More positively, the Naturalists opened to literature whole reaches of life hitherto largely unexplored and unfashionable. Foreign exponents speeded the trend: the early Tolstoy, Ibsen, Dostoevsky, and Zola.

In some ways, the Naturalists do not represent so much a break with Realism as a drastic tightening of its scope and a specialization of its language. The "poetic" mood must make way to a rigorously "scientific," unadorned reproduction of actual speech and behavior. In style as in subject the Naturalist finds it unworthy to impose too much harmony upon reality. There were several extremes in this development: a sort of tape-recorder style, reproducing everything in speech down to the hems and haws; the use of dialects to achieve genuineness; a notable increase in the incidence of bad words (a current which has not yet entirely lost its momentum).

It might be inquired why so much time is given to a movement of which no strict representative is included here. The answer is that the heritage of Naturalism is to be found whenever an effort is made to attain strict reproduction of reality in language, in all systematic avoidance of poetic idealization and heroism. In this sense, legions of modern authors follow the Naturalists. This is true of the early Thomas Mann. In language at least it is true of Wiechert, Ernst, Gaiser, and Piontek. Even the concentration of modern taste upon prose fiction or, to a lesser degree, the drama, is part of the Naturalist legacy. American writing in particular remains strongly Naturalistic.

With most new developments in human thought, there is a good deal of adventitious association. The seamiest reaches of the working class are not the only possible scene for an undistorted rendering of reality. It would be no great exaggeration to say that an accident of historical association produced the proletarian twist to Naturalism. But this doctrinaire line was a central factor in the shift away from Naturalism to Impressionism. Writers did not want to be forever trammelled by a social mission. More important, however, is the return to the individual artistic consciousness as a point of origin in the creative process.

For the Impressionists of the turn of the century the reality to be reproduced is now the sense impression, the picture left by life upon the sensitive screen of an artist's mind. Bierbaum, one of their pioneer theoreticians, declared that the Impressionists did not deny what they had learned from Naturalism; they simply placed the individual imagination and perception ahead of external observations. This is a fundamental difference.

Freud is a frequent companion of the Impressionists, with perhaps more artistic necessity than that which associated the Naturalists with Marx or Darwin. The stream of consciousness technique is an obvious mode of expression for such finely tuned creative instruments. However much Rilke may differ from the Impressionists in other respects and in other works, his *Cornet* offers certain definite Impressionist characteristics. It is the recording of swiftly passing reality on a sensitive mind, more Rilke's perhaps than that of the young and simple *Cornet*. In related but differing ways, Schnitzler speaks for his Leutnant Gustl and Joyce for his characters in the *Dubliners* and *Portrait of the Artist*.

The advancing symptoms of extreme Impressionism were soon obvious. It became hyperrefined, exotic, attenuated, and melancholy. In the bittersweet decadence of *fin-de-siècle* Vienna the Impressionists seemed most at home. It is easy to see why the movement, in its strict form, is dated.

Impressionism had two main characteristics: more or less passive openness to sense impression and the paramount position of the individual artistic consciousness. The Expressionists rebelled against the first but carried the latter to its ultimate extension.

Expressionism appeared as a literary term and a school shortly before the first World War. The Expressionists knew the explosion was coming. They even seemed for a time to have an answer to the paralyzing shock of the war and the shattering crisis of European thought which the war helped to make visible.

It is hard for the modern mind, confronted with different urgencies, to encompass the dimensions of that crisis. What all Europe had lost was incredible, and the sense of loss was understandably acute among the Germans, who also lost the war. Middle-class optimism, that stalwart faith in the inevitability of progress, was finally and utterly erased. Free will, firm values, traditional standards, had not only been questioned, they seemed to have been eliminated. Science had promised to free man from some of his shackles but as it did so it cut him adrift, a purposeless accident in time and space. Or it cast him into a new prison of hereditary and environmental forces, of unmanageable urges and ids. Religion was reeling from a number of blows, some of them administered by theologians.

The Expressionists promised nothing less than a new life, out of the creative powers of the individual soul. Theirs would not be the passive sensitivity to external stimuli, however brilliantly recorded, but a dynamic, intense, creative ego, producing a new reality out of itself, and a new set of values. Expressionism had an almost ecstatic determination to reform everything, concomitantly a tendency to resist or deny all former values. In such a mood, and with an infinite concept of the power of the word and the role of the artist, the movement was enormously productive of experimentation in style and language. This is perhaps its most important legacy, for the fine hopes of reforming life were soon dimmed by the intransigence of history and human nature.

Expressionism was visionary, subjective, mythic, universal, and revolutionary. It was with its kindred or dependent movements, the principal representative in the twentieth century of the subjective-irrational side of the Western mind. The typical utterance of the Expressionists is emotionally charged — they themselves called it a *Schrei*. They cultivated an intensity of rapture or of torment, a boundless, unrestrained revelation of the interior of the soul. The Dionysiac doctrine of Nietzsche, his revaluing of everything, was in part their inspiration, and Freud served as their guide to the unmasking of levels within the psyche.

It must be apparent that the natural medium of the Expressionists and their descendants was not prose but the lyric, that genre which the Naturalists almost entirely eschewed. But their techniques and their attitude were important in prose, too. Although no doctrinaire Expressionist is represented in our selections, the unveiling of inner states in Kafka, and certain stylistic aspects of Borchert are clearly Expressionist. Where revelation of intense psychic states, of fantastic and supernatural imaginings becomes the task of prose fiction, the Expressionist idiom appears. It also appears where two or more levels of reality coexist, or where mythic significance is to be read from the novel or story, in general where we see no longer the conventionally understandable, sequential development of action and consequence familiar in Realistic fiction.

Expressionism promised too much. In form it left an inheritance of the highest value, but as a new star to steer life by it barely survived the first Great War. The reactions which followed were in some cases extensions of Expressionist doctrine to new extremes, as if the fault of the first movement had been that it was too modest. Various forms of Dadaism and Surrealism result, but they have little meaning for the *Novelle*. The later Symbolists joined unrelated aspects of reality in weird, mysteriously significant combinations. The *neue Sachlichkeit* (New Matter-of-Factness) returned to the rendering of undifferentiated reality, but not with the missionary conviction of the Naturalists, rather with the pessimistic conviction that life was full of chaotic details and empty of meaning. The Neo-Classicists like Paul Ernst rebelled more constructively. They attempted a return to the tightly drawn, ethically centered narration of exemplary human actions, couched in the clear, restrained forms of an earlier day.

Through all of this confusion of movements and trends the common style of Realism and Naturalism never disappears. It is after all basically congenial to the genres of narrative prose—a recreated reality bearing the closest affinity to the world we know around us. Sometimes the story so written carries the obvious symbolic weight of a parable, as in Gaiser. Sometimes it brings forth a moral issue, as with Wiechert. At other times, as in Piontek, the seemingly "impartial" narrative is a subtle paradigm of some essential aspect of the relationship human beings bear to one another. In general, the best German writing of most recent times has been eclectic. It has employed predominantly the language of Realism or Naturalism, but it has not abandoned, only tempered, the sensitivity of Impressionism, the moral concern and symbolic intent of Expressionism.

Contents

Zehn Jahrzehnte
REVISED

Gottfried Keller

Gottfried Keller is a Swiss, one of the giants of nineteenth-century German literature, one of his country's greatest writers. His novel, *Der grüne Heinrich*, strongly autobiographical, is one of the half dozen finest in German. (It was not immediately recognized as such—Keller stoked his stove one winter with the unsold copies of the first edition.) His *Novellen* are masterpieces, most of them portraying man and his foibles, ironically but not without affection.

Keller was born in Zürich in 1819, the son of a cabinet maker. The circumstances of his early life were neither affluent nor serene. His formal education began in the poor-school of which his father had been an administrator, and ended with his expulsion in 1834 from the Cantonal Industrial School in Zürich. He was alleged to have taken part in a minor uprising, the target of which was an incompetent teacher. The expulsion covered all the state schools of Zürich. Keller said later, "Excluding a child from public education amounts to nothing more nor less than cutting off his inner development, his intellectual and spiritual life."

He spent the next years in idleness and discontent, living in his widowed mother's house. Finally he went to Germany, where for two years (1840-1842) he studied art at Munich, desperately unsuccessful and always poor, even when he had persuaded his mother to mortgage the house to help him. He spent time in the beer halls and even tried to edit a bar paper. He was finally reduced to painting flagstaffs for a royal wedding. Disillusioned, he returned to Zürich.

In Munich, however, Keller had begun to write. His first substantial publication—a book of poetry, in 1846—brought him critical approval, though little else. He was still dependent on his mother, whose patience and support is an epic of self-sacrifice in what must often have seemed a lost cause.

In 1848 he went to Heidelberg for two years, with a Cantonal fellowship. He studied widely and effected two sweeping changes in his own philosophy, the one roughly from Romanticism to Realism, the other an abandonment of conventional religious belief (though he was no atheist). Life became more intense and challenging, he said, when he no longer had any hope of making up for what he had missed, "in irgendeinem Winkel der Welt."

For the next five years he studied in Berlin, writing much, planning more (including our story), but making no tangible progress. He called Berlin his "house of correction." Bouts of despair and long silences—for two years he did not write his mother—marked his life in the Prussian capital. Yet people had faith in him. His fellowship was renewed, and he was offered the professorship of literature at the new Polytechnic in Zürich. He refused it. In the end he was nearly imprisoned for debt. Friends saved him, and his mother sent her last money to bring him home.

The hard years were almost over. He had already published, he was respected in Zürich as a writer, he contributed political and patriotic articles to the better journals. In 1861 he became First Secretary of the Canton, one of the highest positions in the civil service. After a difficult start, he filled the job with high distinction. In 1876 he retired, to write. His literary reputation, already large in Switzerland, grew phenomenally in Germany. He was often compared, in breadth of achievement and in literary distinction, with Goethe.

Keller was a little man, highly unsocial, with a prickly exterior which belied the affectionate irony of his writings. He knew the literary great of his day but was close friends with none. He fell in love more than once, with women who were too beautiful or already engaged or otherwise unattainable. He once proposed to a woman and almost in the same breath advised her not to marry him. Only his mother, and later his sister Regula, stood by him. To the end of his life (in 1890) he remained a bachelor.

Die Jungfrau als Ritter

(1872)

This story is one of the *Sieben Legenden*—"legend" to be taken in its technical ecclesiastical sense of a saint's life. These are, however, extraordinary legends. Keller professed, in his little introduction to the whole collection, to have read many saints' lives and to have detected in them a great bent for story-telling, both churchly and profane. Actually, he was so distressed by the foolishly naive style and the murky pedantry of the principal collection he had read (done by a certain Theobul Kosegarten in 1804) that he determined to restore life to the genre. In this he succeeded.

Keller is usually classed among the Realists. A better designation—or sub-species: Ironic Realist. He achieves his particular ironic effect by holding his characters at a distance, pointing in humor—sympathetic, not sarcastic—to their manifest weaknesses. Or he may cause them to behave in an outrageous fashion—which behavior he solemnly records. Or, as a counterpart, he may take a warmly humorous view of their solemnity. He may show how virtue wins out, not by dint of its virtue—it is often shaky—but because of confusion, strife, and corruption in the ranks of the opposition.

Such an approach to reality requires a special style, and that style is not easy. Detail is piled on more or less relevant detail until the accumulation becomes hilarious. High-flown words associate with reasonably low-flown actions or humble and unworthy things, elevated expressions with undignified motives. Between premise and conclusion in a single sentence lies a logical gulf—to fill it and restore flawless logic we need only a dollop of human frailty. The second sentence in our story is a good example: "Bertrade was so sweet and gracious that every suitor wondered why she wasn't already his." Sometimes he gets the same effect from the simple gap between intent and effect in human actions. Keller is a particular master of another humorous device: letting a character say everything he happens to be thinking, in the usual jumble of inconsistency, thus convicting himself of mixed motives or of keeping a disorderly mind.

All these aspects of Keller's ironic realism appear in exemplary fashion in the story of Zendelwald and Bertrade. Even Zendelwald's rundown little fief is a marvelous parody, a quick glimpse of the true state of things "when knighthood was in flower." Zendelwald is a tower of indecision, his mother a paragon of over-zealous energy. In the two champions another and rarer element of Keller's humor appears, the delight in sheer caricature, in the grotesque.

To find this legend sacrilegious would be to miss the point utterly. There is true mystery and miracle in it, although, to paraphrase Coleridge, it requires a certain "willing suspension of belief." It is a curious mirror-image of the usual divine grace, one very common in Keller, and deserving of more attention than it has received. One can compare Zendelwald with Parzival, the "perfect fool," but Parzival does reform, his receiving of grace and his investiture can be explained as merited reward. He has suffered and labored for his own redemption. As for Zendelwald, he falls asleep. His granting of grace (through the Virgin Mary, who fights his battle) is in effect completed when he arrives, and all he has to do is confirm it. It is a sort of grace in spite of the fact, a demonstration that in life there is a sort of beatitude even for the foolish, the contrary, or the indolent.* True, in his unearned victory Zendelwald demonstrates, at some risk to himself, one of Keller's favorite virtues: honesty.

*** Those who know other stories by Keller will recognize a common situation. The tailor Strapinski in *Kleider machen Leute* omits and commits everything he can to seal his own undoing. Yet he gets his sweetheart and his good life. Of course he "pays" for his foolishness by an episode of intense humiliation. In our legend there is not even the humiliation, only the act of grace.**

DIE JUNGFRAU ALS RITTER

Extra vocabulary: **Gezelt** canopy, **Arche** ark, **Brunn** spring, **Morgenröt** dawn

Maria wird genenn't ein Thron und Gott's Gezelt,
Ein' Arche, Burg, Turm, Haus, ein Brunn, Baum, Garten, Spiegel,
Ein Meer, ein Stern, der Mond, die Morgenröt, ein Hügel:
Wie kann sie alles sein? sie ist ein' andre Welt. 1
(Angelus Silesius, *Cherub. Wandersmann 4. Buch, 42.*)

die Grafschaft, -en *translate* earldom

männiglich one and all

das Lehen, - fief

Gebizo 2 hatte zu seinen früheren Besitzungen noch so viele neue erworben, daß Bertrade über eine bedeutende Grafschaft gebot und sowohl ihres Reichtums als ihrer Schönheit wegen 3 im deutschen Reiche berühmt wurde. Da sie zugleich eine große Bescheidenheit und Freundlichkeit gegen jedermann kund tat, so schien das Kleinod ihrer Person allen unternehmenden und schüchternen, kühnen und furchtsamen, großen und kleinen Edelleuten 4 gleich leicht zu gewinnen, und männiglich, wer sie einigemal gesehen, 5 wunderte sich, warum er sie eigentlich nicht schon an der Hand hätte. Dennoch war mehr als ein Jahr verflossen, ohne daß man von einem vernahm, 6 der wirkliche Hoffnung gewonnen.

Auch der Kaiser hörte von ihr, und da er wünschte, daß ein so ansehnliches Lehen in die Hand eines rechten Mannes käme, beschloß er, auf einer Reise die berühmte Witwe zu besuchen, und zeigte ihr dies in einem gar wohlgeneigten und freundlichen Briefe an. Diesen gab er einem jungen Ritter Zendelwald,

- 1 -

[1] **Angelus Silesius** (real name: **Scheffler**) was a German mystic of the 17th century, the most famous of whose religious aphorisms—paradoxical visions of the nature of the divine and man's relation to it—are contained in the collection *Cherubinischer Wandersmann.* In many ways he is the precursor of Rilke (**Was wirst du tun, Gott, wenn ich sterbe?**).

[2] **Gebizo:** The previous story begins: **Es war ein Graf Gebizo, der besaß eine wunderschöne Frau, eine prächtige Burg . . . und so viele ansehnliche Güter** (*possessions*), **daß er für einen der reichsten und glücklichsten Herren im Lande galt.** At the end of the story, Gebizo falls into a mountain gorge and dies. Bertrade is his widow.

[3] **wegen** (*prep., gen.*) here in postposition: *for; for her wealth as well as for her beauty*

[4] **allen . . . Edelleuten** is dative object of **schien.**

[5] **gesehen** supply **hatte**

[6] Take **. . . man von einem vernahm** as "passive substitute" and remember that **ohne daß** is English *without . . . -ing.*

welcher gerade des Weges zu reiten hatte. Der wurde von Bertrade huldreich empfangen und bewirtet wie jeder, der auf ihrer Burg einkehrte; er besah sich ehrerbietig die herrlichen Säle, Zinnen und Gärten und verliebte sich nebenbei heftig in die Besitzerin. Doch blieb er um deswillen nicht eine Stunde länger auf der Burg, sondern als er seinen Auftrag verrichtet und alles gesehen, nahm er kurzen Abschied von der Frau und ritt von dannen, der einzige von allen, die je hier gewesen, der nicht daran dachte, diesen Preis erringen zu können.

Überdies war er träg in Handlungen und Worten. Wenn sein Geist und sein Herz sich eines Dinges bemächtigt hatten, was immer vollständig und mit Feuer geschah, so brachte es Zendelwald nicht über sich, den ersten Schritt zu einer Verwirklichung zu tun, da die Sache für ihn abgemacht schien, wenn er inwendig damit im reinen war. Obgleich er sich gern unterhielt, wo es nicht etwa galt, etwas zu erreichen, redete er doch nie ein Wort zur rechten Zeit, welches ihm Glück gebracht hätte.[7] Aber nicht nur seinem Munde,[8] auch seiner Hand waren seine Gedanken so voraus, daß er im Kampfe von seinen Feinden öfters beinahe besiegt wurde, weil er zögerte, den letzten Streich zu tun, den Gegner schon im voraus zu seinen Füßen sehend. Deshalb erregte seine Kampfweise auf allen Turnieren Verwunderung, indem er stets zuerst sich kaum rührte und nur in der größten Not mit einem tüchtigen Ruck obsiegte.

In voller Gedankenarbeit, deren Gegenstand die schöne Bertrade war, ritt dieser Zendelwald jetzt nach

- 2 -

gerade *here* just by chance
des Weges that way
huldreich gracious

ehrerbietig respectful
die Zinne, -n (crenelated) battlement
um deswillen for that (reason)

es über sich bringen† bring oneself to

im reinen sein† have made up one's mind

das Turnier′, -e tournament, joust

mit einem tüchtigen Ruck *translate;* with a sudden and vigorous move
ob-siegen conquer, prevail

[7] **hätte** here and frequently *might have* (*would have*)

[8] **seinem Munde** is dative with **voraus sein**

der Köhler, - charcoal burner (*see below*)

handlich *here* handy, active

übertrie'ben geltend machen assert in an exaggerated fashion

an den Mann kommen† catch a husband

überhet'zen overwork (*e.g., a hunting dog*), rush

erhaschen snatch, catch up with

die Ziege, -n goat

die Armbrust, ⸚e cross-bow

das Waldhuhn, ⸚er capercaillie (*a game bird resembling the black grouse*)

nach Gelüsten to (her) heart's desire (*or* content)

die Forel'le, -n trout

der Kalk *here* lime

seinem Heimatschlößchen, das in einem einsamen Bergwalde lag. Nur wenige Köhler[9] und Holzschläger waren seine Untertanen, und seine Mutter harrte daher jedesmal seiner Rückkunft mit bitterer Ungeduld, ob[10] er jetzt endlich das Glück nach Hause bringe.

So lässig Zendelwald war, so handlich und entschlossen war seine Mutter, ohne daß es ihr viel genützt hätte, da sie ihrerseits diese Eigenschaft ebenfalls jederzeit übertrieben geltend gemacht und daher zur Zwecklosigkeit umgewandelt hatte.[11] In ihrer Jugend hatte sie so bald als möglich an den Mann zu kommen gesucht und mehrere Gelegenheiten so schnell und eifrig überhetzt, daß sie in der Eile gerade die schlechteste Wahl traf in der Person eines unbedachten und tollkühnen Gesellen, der sein Erbe durchjagte, einen frühzeitigen Tod fand und ihr nichts als ein langes Witwentum, Armut und einen Sohn hinterließ, der sich nicht rühren wollte, das Glück zu erhaschen.

Die einzige Nahrung der kleinen Familie bestand aus der Milch einiger Ziegen, Waldfrüchten und aus Wild. Zendelwalds Mutter war eine vollkommene Jägerin und schoß mit der Armbrust wilde Tauben und Waldhühner nach Gelüsten; auch fischte sie Forellen aus den Bächen und pflasterte eigenhändig das Schlößchen mit Kalk und Steinen, wo es schadhaft geworden. Eben kehrte sie mit einem erlegten Hasen heim und schaute, als sie das Tier vor das Fenster ihrer hochgelegenen Küche hing, nochmal ins Tal hinaus;[12] da sah sie ihren Sohn den Weg heraufreiten und ließ freudig die Brücke nieder, weil er seit Monaten fortgewesen.

- 3 -

[9] **Köhler** were proverbial for their poverty. This touch alone serves to establish the inconsequential nature of the Zendelwald estate—a quality not usually emphasized in feudal fiction.

[10] **ob** *wondering whether, to see if*

[11] That is, she was so vigorous and decisive that she had lost by it.

[12] Think of the sentence first without the **als** clause.

Sogleich begann sie zu forschen, ob er nicht irgendein Schwänzchen oder eine Feder des Glücks erwischt und mitgebracht hätte, woran sich kluglich zu halten wäre, und als er die wie gewöhnlich unerheblichen Ergebnisse seiner letzten Kriegsfahrt erzählte, schüttelte sie schon zornig den Kopf; als er aber vollends seiner Botschaft zur reichen und reizenden Bertrade erwähnte und deren Huld und Schönheit rühmte, da schalt sie ihn einen Faulpelz und Bärenhäuter wegen seines schimpflichen Abzuges. Bald sah sie auch, daß Zendelwald an nichts dachte als an die ferne Herrenfrau, und nun wurde sie erst recht ungeduldig über ihn, da er mit einer so trefflichen Leidenschaft im Herzen gar nichts anzuwenden wüßte, während ihm die schwere Verliebtheit eher ein Hemmnis als ein Antrieb zum Handeln war.

So hatte er nicht die besten Tage; die Mutter schmollte mit ihm und aus Ärger, um sich zu zerstreuen, besserte sie das zerfallene Dach des Schloßturmes aus, so daß es dem guten Zendelwald angst und bange ward, als er sie oben herumklettern sah. Unwirsch warf sie die zerbrochenen Ziegel herunter und hätte fast einen fremden Reitersmann totgeschmissen, welcher eben in das Tor zog, um sich ein Nachtlager auszubitten.

Es gelang diesem aber, die Freundlichkeit der herben Dame zu wecken, als er beim Abendbrot viel gute Dinge erzählte und besonders, wie der Kaiser soeben auf der großen Burg der schönen Witwe weile, wo ein Fest das andere dränge und die wonnige Frau vom Kaiser und seinen Herren unablässig bestürmt

irgendein Schwänzchen oder eine Feder (*good fortune being thought of as a bird*) some tiny part of the tail or a feather
erwischen catch
woran' sich klüglich zu halten wäre which one might, with some prudence, hang on to
unerheblich inconsequential
die Huld graciousness
der Faulpelz, -e lazybones
der Bärenhäuter, - sluggard
schimpflich disgraceful
erst recht really
nichts anzuwenden wüßte could think of nothing useful to do
das Hemmnis, -se obstruction
schmollen be peeved with
angst und bange werden† be(come) anxious and fearful
der Ziegel, - tile
herb austere, acid, sharp
ein Fest drängt das andere one banquet (fete) comes close on the heels of the other

werde, unter diesen sich einen Gemahl zu wählen. Sie habe aber den Ausweg ergriffen, ein großes Turnier auszuschreiben und dem Sieger über alle ihre Hand zu reichen, fest vertrauend, daß ihre Beschützerin, die göttliche Jungfrau, sich ins Mittel legen und dem Rechten, der ihr gebühre, den Arm zum Siege lenken werde. [13] [14]

„Das wäre nun eine Unternehmung für Euch", schloß der Mann, sich an Zendelwald wendend, „ein so hübscher junger Ritter sollte sich recht daran hinmachen, das Beste zu erwerben, was es nach irdischen Begriffen in diesen Zeitläufen gibt; auch sagt man allgemein, die Frau hoffe, es werde sich auf diesem Wege irgendein unbekanntes Glück für sie einfinden, so ein armer tugendlicher Held, welchen sie alsdann recht hätscheln könnte, und die großen bekannten Grafen und eiteln Freier seien ihr alle zuwider." [15]

Als der Fremde weggeritten war, sagte die Mutter: „Nun will ich wetten, daß niemand anders als Bertrade selbst diesen Boten hergesandt hat, dich auf die richtige Spur zu locken, mein lieber Zendelwald! Das ist mit Händen zu greifen; was hätte der Kauz, der unser letztes Krüglein Wein zu sich genommen hat, sonst zu tun und zu reisen in diesem Wald?" [16]

Der Sohn fing über ihre Worte mächtig an zu lachen und lachte immer stärker, teils über die offenbare Unmöglichkeit der mütterlichen Einbildungen, teils weil ihm diese Einbildungen doch wohlgefielen. Der bloße Gedanke, Bertrade könnte wünschen, seiner habhaft zu werden, ließ ihn nicht aus dem Lachen

- 5 -

aus-schreiben† proclaim, appoint

die göttliche Jungfrau *is, of course,* the Virgin Mary

sich ins Mittel legen intercede

sich hin-machen an set about, put one's mind to

in diesen Zeitläufen in these days

so . . . like, for example

hätscheln pamper, spoil

der Freier, - suitor

wetten bet

das ist mit Händen zu greifen that is perfectly plain

der Kauz, ¨e fellow, "bird"

das Krüglein, - little jug

habhaft werden† gain possession of

[13] Phrase division: **über alle/ihre Hand**

[14] **dem Rechten** may best be taken as "dative of possession" with **den Arm:** (*guide to victory*) *the arm of the right man* (*the one who . . .*).

[15] **Tugend,** in the scale of chivalric values, was not so much "*virtue,*" as "*high merit, distinction.*" That is, the ethical connotation was restricted. Keller may be using the word in either the medieval or the modern sense.

[16] **was . . . sonst** should be taken together.

herauskommen. Doch die Mutter, welche glaubte, er lache, um sie zu verspotten, geriet in Zorn und rief: „So höre denn! Meinen Fluch gebe ich dir, wenn du mir nicht gehorchst und dich von Stund an auf den Weg machst, jenes Glück zu erwerben; ohne dasselbe kehre nicht zurück, ich mag dich dann nie wiedersehen! Oder wenn du dennoch kommst, so nehme ich mein Schießzeug und gehe selbst fort, ein Grab zu suchen, wo ich von deiner Dummheit unbelästigt bin!"

So hatte Zendelwald nun keine Wahl; um des [17] lieben Friedens willen rüstete er seufzend seine Waffen und ritt in Gottes Namen in der Richtung nach Bertradens Wohnsitz hin, ohne daß er überzeugt war, wirklich dort anzukommen. Doch hielt er den Weg so ziemlich inne und je näher er dem Ziele kam, um so deutlicher gestaltete sich der Gedanke, daß er das Ding eigentlich wohl unternehmen könnte, so gut wie ein anderer, und wenn er mit den Rivalen fertig geworden sei, so werde es den Kopf auch nicht kosten, mit der schönen Frau ein Tänzchen zu wagen. Zug für Zug fand jetzt in seiner Vorstellung das Abenteuer statt und verlief auf das beste, ja er hielt bereits tagelang, während er durch das sommergrüne Land ritt, süße Zwiegespräche mit der Geliebten, worin er ihr die schönsten Erfindungen vorsagte, daß ihr Antlitz in holder Freude sich rötete, alles dies in seinen Gedanken.

Als er eben wieder eine erfreuliche Begebenheit innerlich ausmalte, sah er in Wirklichkeit an einem blauen Höhenzuge die Türme und Zinnen der Burg in der Morgensonne erglänzen und die vergoldeten

- 6 -

von Stund an from this very moment

das Schießzeug *here* bow and arrow

rüsten prepare, make ready

so ziemlich more or less
inne-halten† keep to

einen Tanz wagen try a turn (*in sense of* battle *or* contest)

der Höhenzug, ⸚e ridge

[17] **um des lieben Friedens willen** translate *for the sake of peace and quiet.*

zerstieben† (ist) vanish, scatter
zag timorous, timid

der Zauderer, - hesitant person
das nämliche the same one, the very one

gereichen zu redound to, contribute. *Translate:* contributed in no small measure to the decorative aspect of the little congregation
der Pfaff, -en, -en priest (*colloquial*)
der Küster, - sexton

verdorrt dried up
das Reisig brushwood

das Wirrsal confusion, mess
gucken look (*colloquial*); peek

Geländer aus der Ferne herüberfunkeln und erschrak so darüber, daß all sein Traumwerk zerstob und nur ein zages, unschlüssiges Herz zurückließ.

Unwillkürlich hielt er das Pferd an und schaute, nach Art der Zauderer, rings nach einer Zuflucht aus. Da gewahrte er ein zierliches Kirchlein, das nämliche, welches einst Bertrade der Mutter Gottes erbaut und in welchem sie jenen Schlaf getan hatte.[18] Sogleich beschloß er, da einzukehren und sich vor dem Altare ein wenig zu sammeln, besonders da es der Tag war, an welchem das Turnier abgehalten wurde.

Eben sang der Priester die Messe, welcher bloß zwei oder drei arme Leute beiwohnten, so daß der Ritter der kleinen Gemeinde zur nicht geringen Zierde gereichte; als aber alles vorbei war und Pfaff und Küster das Kirchlein verlassen, fühlte Zendelwald sich so wohl in diesem Aufenthalte, daß er ganz gemächlich einschlief und Turnier und Geliebte vergaß, wenn er nicht davon träumte.

Da stieg die Jungfrau Maria wieder von ihrem Altare herunter, nahm seine Gestalt und Waffenrüstung an, bestieg sein Pferd und ritt geschlossenen Helmes,[19] eine kühne Brunhilde,[20] an Zendelwalds Statt nach der Burg.

Als sie eine Weile geritten, lag am Wege ein Haufen grauen Schuttes und verdorrten Reisigs. Das kam der aufmerksamen Jungfrau verdächtig vor und sie bemerkte auch, daß etwas wie das Schwanzende einer Schlange aus dem Wirrsal hervorguckte. Da sah sie, daß es der Teufel war, welcher, noch immer verliebt,[21] auch in der Nähe der Burg herumgeschlichen

- 7 -

[18] In the previous story it is related that Bertrade had built a chapel and dedicated it to the Virgin. The night before the Witches' Sabbath Gebizo is about to take her, unknowing, to a rendezvous with the Devil, to whom, in desperate desire for worldly goods, he had promised her. She goes into the chapel to pray. Here she falls asleep, the Virgin takes her place and goes with Gebizo to meet the Devil. In an extraordinary contest the Devil is bested. Bertrade awakes and returns home, Gebizo having expired as explained earlier.

[19] **geschlossenen Helmes** *helmet closed* (genitive absolute)

[20] **Brunhilde,** in Norse mythology and in the Middle High German *Nibelungenlied*, a Valkyrie, semi-divine and possessed of vast strength.

[21] Alluding again to the previous story, in which the Devil declares he can bear his banishment from Heaven only if some mortal woman will love him.

war und sich vor der Jungfrau schnell in das Gerölle versteckt hatte. Scheinbar achtlos ritt sie vorüber, ließ aber geschickt das Pferd einen kleinen Seitensprung tun, daß es mit dem Hinterhufe auf jenes verdächtige Schwanzende trat. Pfeifend fuhr der Böse hervor und davon und machte sich in dieser Angelegenheit nicht mehr bemerklich.

Durch das kleine Abenteuer erheitert, ritt sie voll guten Mutes vollends auf die Burg Bertrades, wo sie eben ankam, als die zwei stärksten Kämpen übriggeblieben, um die Entscheidung unter sich herbeizuführen.

Langsam und in nachlässiger Haltung, ganz wie Zendelwald, ritt sie auf den Platz und schien unentschlossen, ob sie sich beteiligen wolle oder nicht.

„Da kommt noch der träge Zendelwald", hieß es, und die zwei starken Ritter sagten: „Was will uns der? Laßt uns ihn noch schnell abtun, ehe wir's unter uns ausmachen!"

22 Der eine nannte sich „Guhl der Geschwinde". Er pflegte sich mit seinem Rosse wie ein Wirbelwind herumzutummeln und suchte seinen Gegner mit hundert Streichen und Listen zu verwirren und zu besiegen. Mit ihm mußte der vermeintliche Zendelwald zuerst den Kampf bestehen. Er trug einen pechschwarzen Schnurrbart, dessen Spitzen so steif gedreht waagrecht in die Luft ragten, daß zwei silberne Glöckchen, die daran hingen, sie nicht zu biegen vermochten und fortwährend klingelten, wenn er den Kopf bewegte. Dies nannte er das Geläute des Schreckens für seine Feinde, des Wohlgefallens für seine

- 8 -

der Kämpe, -n, -n champion

es hieß† the word went around, people said
was will uns der what does he think he's going to do to us

tummeln wheel, dash

pechschwarz pitch-black
der Schnurrbart, ⸚e mustache

das Geläute chiming, tinkling

[22] **Guhl** is said to be in some features a caricature of the French soldiery in the Franco-Prussian War, the **Sieben Legenden** having been completed just after that war. **geschwind** means *swift*, but it might be better to keep the alliteration and think of *Guhl the Glorious*.

der Helmbusch, ⸚e plume

der Hahnenschwanz cock's tail (*coq gaulois*)

zu verstehen geben† let it be understood, imply

der Zoll, -e inch

das Zöpfchen, - braid

flechten† plait, twist

die Bandschleife, -n bow of ribbon

das Mausfellchen, - little mouse skin

die Fledermaus, ⸚e bat

aus geschlitzten Augen from the slits of his eyes

der Turnier'platz, ⸚e jousting field

Dame! Sein Schild glänzte, je nachdem er ihn drehte, bald in dieser, bald in jener Farbe, und er wußte diesen Wechsel so rasch zu handhaben, daß das Auge davon geblendet wurde. Sein Helmbusch bestand aus einem ungeheuren Hahnenschwanz.

Der andere starke Ritter nannte sich „Maus der Zahllose", womit er zu verstehen gab, daß er einem ungezählten Heere gleich zu achten sei.[23] Zum Zeichen seiner Stärke hatte er die aus seinen Naslöchern hervorstehenden Haare etwa sechs Zoll lang wachsen lassen und in zwei Zöpfchen geflochten, welche ihm über den Mund herabhingen und an den Enden mit zierlichen roten Bandschleifen geschmückt waren. Er trug einen großen weiten Mantel über seiner Rüstung, der ihn fast samt dem Pferde verhüllte und aus tausend Mausfellchen künstlich zusammengenäht war. Als Helmzierde überschatteten ihn die mächtig ausgebreiteten Flügel einer Fledermaus, unter welchen er drohende Blicke aus geschlitzten Augen hervorsandte.

Als nun das Signal zum Kampfe mit Guhl dem Geschwinden gegeben wurde, ritt dieser gegen die Jungfrau heran und umkreiste sie mit immer größerer Schnelligkeit, sie mit seinem Schilde zu blenden suchend und mit der Lanze hundert Stöße nach ihr führend. Inzwischen verharrte die Jungfrau immer auf derselben Stelle in der Mitte des Turnierplatzes und schien nur die Angriffe mit Schild und Speer abzuwehren, wobei sie mit großer Kunst das Pferd auf den Hinterfüßen sich drehen ließ, so daß sie stets dem Feinde das Angesicht zuwendete. Als Guhl das bemerkte, ritt er plötzlich weit weg, kehrte dann um

- 9 -

[23] **Maus** is said, continuing the allegory, to represent the hordes of Slavs on the opposite side of Germany (= **Zendelwald**) from France (= **Guhl**). The word theme is continued (in German) in **Fledermaus** below.

und rannte mit eingelegter Lanze auf sie ein, um sie über den Haufen zu stechen. Unbeweglich erwartete ihn die Jungfrau; aber Mann und Pferd schienen von Erz, so fest standen sie da, und der arme Kerl, der nicht wußte, daß er mit einer höheren Gewalt stritt, flog unversehens, als er auf ihren Speer rannte, während der seinige wie ein Halm an ihrem Schilde zerbrach, aus dem Sattel und lag auf der Erde. Unverweilt sprang die Jungfrau vom Pferde, kniete ihm auf die Brust, daß er unter der gewaltigen Stärke sich nicht rühren konnte, und schnitt ihm mit ihrem Dolche die beiden Schnäuze mit den Silberglöcklein ab, welche sie an ihrem Wehrgehänge befestigte, indessen die Fanfaren sie oder vielmehr den Zendelwald als Sieger begrüßten.

24

Nun kam Ritter Maus der Zahllose an den Tanz. Gewaltig sprengte er einher, daß sein Mantel wie eine unheildrohende graue Wolke in der Luft schwebte. Allein die Jungfrau-Zendelwald, welche sich jetzt erst an dem Kampfe zu erwärmen schien, sprengte ihm ebenso rüstig entgegen, warf ihn auf den ersten Stoß mit Leichtigkeit aus dem Sattel und sprang, als Maus sich rasch erhob und das Schwert zog, ebenfalls vom Pferde, um zu Fuße mit ihm zu kämpfen. Bald aber war er betäubt von den raschen Schlägen, mit denen ihr Schwert ihm auf Haupt und Schultern fiel, und er hielt mit der Linken seinen Mantel vor, um sich dahinter zu verbergen und ihn dem Gegner bei günstiger Gelegenheit über den Kopf zu werfen. Da fing die Jungfrau mit der Spitze ihres Schwertes einen Zipfel des Mantels und wickelte Maus den Zahllosen

- 10 -

ein-legen couch (a lance)

über den Haufen stechen† overthrow, unhorse

das Erz, -e metal, brass

der Halm, -e straw

der Dolch, -e dagger

der Schnauz, ⸚e (*provincial or colloquial*) mustache

das Wehrgehänge, - sword-belt

an den Tanz kommen† (*see above* **einen Tanz wagen**) enter the fray

einher′-sprengen (ist) come galloping along

entge′gen-sprengen (ist) gallop to meet

[24] **flog . . . aus dem Sattel**

die Spinne, -n spider
die Wespe, -n wasp

zerdreschen† thrash
mit der flachen Klinge with the flat of her sword (**die Klinge** blade)
die Behendigkeit dexterity
das Mäusepelzchen, - little mouse pelt

hinken limp
das Zöpfchen *see above*

vergeben† *here* compromise, infringe upon; *the object* (*the quality concerned*) *is in the dative*

mit solch zierlicher Schnelligkeit selbst vom Kopf bis zum Fuße in den Mantel ein, daß er in kurzer Zeit wie eine von einer Spinne eingesponnene ungeheure Wespe aussah und zuckend auf der Erde lag.

Nun zerdrasch ihn die Jungfrau mit der flachen Klinge und mit solcher Behendigkeit, daß der Mantel sich in seine ursprünglichen Bestandteile auflöste und die umherstäubenden Mäusepelzchen unter dem allgemeinen Gelächter der Zuschauer die Luft verfinsterten, während der Ritter allmählich wieder zutage kam und als ein geschlagener Mann davonhinkte, nachdem sein Besieger ihm die bebänderten Zöpfchen abgeschnitten hatte.

So war denn die Jungfrau als Zendelwald der letzte Sieger auf dem Platze.

Sie schlug nun das Visier auf, schritt hinauf zur Königin des Festes, beugte das Knie und legte die Siegestrophäen zu deren Füßen. Dann erhob sie sich und stellte einen Zendelwald dar, wie dieser gewöhnlich zu blöde war, es zu sein. Ohne indessen seiner Bescheidenheit zu viel zu vergeben, grüßte sie Bertraden mit einem Blicke, dessen Wirkung auf ein Frauenherz sie wohl kannte; kurz, sie wußte sich als Liebhaber wie als Ritter so zu benehmen, daß Bertrade ihr Wort nicht zurücknahm,[25] sondern dem Zureden des Kaisers, der am Ende froh war, einen so tapfern und edlen Mann mächtig zu sehen, ein williges Ohr lieh.[26]

Es geschah jetzt ein großer Festzug nach dem hochragenden Lindengarten, in welchem das Bankett bereitet war. Dort saß Bertrade zwischen dem Kaiser und ihrem Zendelwald; aber es schien gut, daß jenem[27]

[25] The medieval knight was expected to excel in both branches of endeavor. Inadequacy in battle or in courtly love was not to be excused.
[26] The structure of the sentence becomes obvious if the relative clause (**der . . . froh war, . . . zu sehen**) is abstracted.
[27] In English we should take **jenem** (*the former*) as subject of the passive construction, *had been provided with. . . .*

für eine zweite muntere Nachbarin gesorgt worden; denn dieser ließ seiner Braut[28] nicht viel Zeit, mit andern zu sprechen; so geschickt und zärtlich unterhielt er sie. Er sagte ihr augenscheinlich die feinsten Dinge, da sie ein Mal um das andere glückselig errötete. Heitere Wonne verbreitete sich über alle; in den grünen Laubgewölben in der Höhe sangen die Vögel um die Wette mit den Musikinstrumenten, ein Schmetterling setzte sich auf die goldene Krone des Kaisers, und die Weinpokale dufteten wie durch einen besonderen Segen[29] gleich Veilchen und Reseda.

Aber vor allen fühlte sich Bertrade so glücklich, daß sie, während Zendelwald sie bei der Hand hielt, in ihrem Herzen ihrer göttlichen Beschützerin gedachte und derselben ein heißes, stilles Dankgebet abstattete.

Die Jungfrau Maria, welche ja als Zendelwald neben ihr saß, las dies Gebet in ihrem Herzen und war so erfreut über die fromme Dankbarkeit ihres Schützlings, daß sie Bertraden zärtlich umfing und einen Kuß auf ihre Lippen drückte, der begreiflicherweise das holde Weib mit himmlischer Seligkeit erfüllte; denn wenn die Himmlischen einmal Zuckerzeug backen, so gerät es zur Süße.

Der Kaiser aber und die übrige Gesellschaft riefen dem vermeintlichen Zendelwald ihren Beifall zu, erhoben die Becher und tranken auf das Wohl des schönen Paares.

Indessen erwachte der wirkliche Zendelwald aus seinem unzeitigen Schlafe und fand die Sonne so stark vorgeschritten, daß das Turnier wohl vorbei sein mußte. Obgleich er nun des Handelns glücklich

- 12 -

das Laubgewölbe, - bower (of foliage)
um die Wette in competition, vying
der Schmetterling, -e butterfly
der Wein' pokal', -e wine goblet
das Veilchen, - violet
die Rese' da, -s mignonette

ab-statten offer up

Zuckerzeug backen† make candy
zur Süße geraten† turn (come) out sweet

auf . . . Wohl trinken† drink to the health of

[28] **die Braut** is either *bride* or *fiancée,* here of course the latter.

[29] Indeed there was a "special grace" involved.

enthoben war, fühlte er sich doch sehr unglücklich und traurig, denn er hätte doch die Frau Bertrade gar zu gerne geheiratet. Auch durfte er jetzt nicht mehr zu seiner Mutter zurückkehren, und so entschloß er sich, eine immerwährende freudlose Irrfahrt anzutreten, bis ihn der Tod von seinem unnützen Dasein erlösen würde. Nur wollte er vorher noch einmal die Geliebte sehen und sich ihr Bild für die übrigen Tage einprägen, damit er stets wüßte, was er verscherzt habe.

Er legte also den Weg bis zur Burg vollends zurück. Als er das Menschengedränge erreichte, hörte er überall das Lob und das Glück eines armen Ritters Zendelwald ausrufen, der den Preis errungen habe, und bitterlich neugierig, wer dieser glückliche Namensvetter sein möge, stieg er vom Pferde und drängte sich durch die Menge, bis er am Rande des Gartens einen Platz gewinnen konnte, und zwar an einer erhöhten Stelle, wo er das ganze Fest übersah. 30

Da erblickte er in Schmuck und Glanz und unweit der funkelnden Krone des Königs das in Glück strahlende Antlitz der Geliebten, aber Haupt an Haupt bei ihr zu seinem bleichen Erstaunen seine eigene Person, wie er leibte und lebte. Wie leblos starrte er hin, just sah er seinen Doppelgänger die fromme Braut umfangen und küssen; da schritt er, unbeachtet in der allgemeinen Freude, unaufhaltsam durch die Reihen, bis er dicht hinter dem Paare stand, von seltsamer Eifersucht gepeinigt. In demselben Augenblicke war sein Ebenbild von Bertrades Seite verschwunden und diese sah sich erschrocken nach ihm um. Als sie aber Zendelwald hinter sich sah, lachte

- 13 -

die Irrfahrt, -en wandering (*as of a knight-errant*)

sich ein-prägen impress upon one's memory

verscherzen lose through one's folly, throw away

wie er leibte und lebte as he lived and breathed

[30] hörte . . . **ausrufen** = English heard . . . proclaim*ed*

sie voll Freude und sagte: „Wo willst du hin? Komm, bleibe fein bei mir!" Und sie ergriff seine Hand und zog ihn an ihre Seite.

So saß er denn, und um den vermeintlichen Traum recht zu probieren, ergriff er den vor ihm stehenden Becher und leerte ihn auf einen Zug. Der Wein hielt stich und strömte ein zuversichtliches Leben in seine Adern; wohlaufgelegt wandte er sich zum lächelnden Weibe und sah ihr in die Augen, worauf diese zufrieden die trauliche Unterhaltung fortsetzte, in welcher sie vorhin unterbrochen worden war. Allein Zendelwald wußte nicht, wie ihm geschah,[31] als Bertrade ihm wohlbekannte Worte sprach, auf welche er einige Male, ohne sich zu besinnen, Worte erwiderte, die er auch schon irgendwo gesprochen hatte; ja, nach einiger Zeit merkte er, daß sein Vorgänger genau das nämliche Gespräch mit ihr geführt haben mußte, welches er während der Reisetage phantasierend ausgedacht hatte, und welches er jetzt bedächtig fortsetzte, um zu sehen, welches Ende das Spiel eigentlich nehmen wolle.

Aber es nahm kein Ende, vielmehr wurde es immer erbaulicher, denn als die Sonne niederging, wurden Fackeln angezündet und die ganze Versammlung zog auf den größten Saal der Burg, um dort des Tanzes zu pflegen. Nachdem der Kaiser den ersten Gang mit der Braut getan, nahm Zendelwald sie in den Arm und tanzte mit ihr drei- oder viermal um den Saal, bis die Erglühende ihn plötzlich bei der Hand nahm und zur Seite führte in ein stilles Erkergemach, das vom Mondschein erfüllt war. Dort warf sie sich an

- 14 -

fein *adds to the imperative only a touch like our* be good and . . ., be a good boy and . . .

stich halten† stand the test
zuversichtlich confident
die Ader, -n vein
wohlaufgelegt in a happy frame of mind
traulich intimate, cozy

erbaulich edifying
die Fackel, -n torch

der Gang, ⸚e *here* turn, dance

das Erkergemach, ⸚er room jutting out into a bay window; *translate simply* bay

[31] **wie ihm geschah** *what was happening to him*

seine Brust, streichelte ihm den blonden Bart und dankte ihm für sein Kommen und seine Neigung. Der ehrliche Zendelwald aber wollte jetzt wissen, ob er träume oder wache, und befragte sie um den richtigen Sachverhalt, besonders was seinen Doppelgänger betraf. Sie verstand ihn lange nicht; doch ein Wort gab[32] das andere, Zendelwald sagte, so und so ist es mir ergangen, und erzählte seine ganze Fahrt, von seiner Einkehr in das Kirchlein und wie er eingeschlafen sei und das Turnier versäumt habe.

Da ward Bertraden die Sache soweit klar, daß sie abermals[33] die Hand ihrer gnädigen Patronin erblickte. Jetzt erst aber durfte sie den wackern Ritter keck als eine Himmelsgabe betrachten, und sie war dankbar genug, das handfeste Geschenk recht ans Herz zu drücken und demselben den süßen Kuß vollwichtig zurückzugeben, den sie vom Himmel selbst empfangen.

Von jetzt an verließ aber den Ritter Zendelwald alle seine Trägheit und träumerische Unentschlossenheit; er tat und redete alles zur rechten Zeit, vor der zärtlichen Bertrade sowohl als vor der übrigen Welt, und wurde ein ganzer Mann[34] im Reiche, so daß der Kaiser ebenso zufrieden mit ihm war als seine Gemahlin.

Zendelwalds Mutter aber erschien bei der Hochzeit hoch zu Roß und so stolz, als ob sie zeitlebens im Glück gesessen hätte. Sie verwaltete Geld und Gut und jagte bis in ihr hohes Alter in den weitläufigen Forsten, während Bertrade es sich nicht nehmen ließ, sich alljährlich einmal von Zendelwald in dessen einsames Heimatschlößchen bringen zu lassen, wo sie auf dem

- 15 -

der Sachverhalt state of affairs

keck without fear

handfest substantial, solid

es sich nicht nehmen lassen† insist on

sich bringen lassen† *literally* have oneself taken, *here* be(ing) taken

[32] **gab** *led to*
[33] **abermals:** The Virgin had, as we know, aided Bertrade in the previous story, too.
[34] **ein ganzer Mann** *a real person*

grauen Turme mit ihrem Liebsten so zärtlich horstete wie die wilden Tauben auf den Bäumen umher. Aber niemals unterließen sie, unterwegs in jenes Kirchlein zu treten und ihr Gebet zu verrichten vor der Jungfrau, die auf ihrem Altar so still und heilig stand, als ob sie nie von demselben heruntergestiegen wäre.

horsten (live in a) nest

- 16 -

Marie von Ebner-Eschenbach

The productions of the famous Burgtheater in Vienna inspired in the young Countess Marie Dubský her first literary ambitions, and the encouragement of the great dramatist Grillparzer outweighed any opposition her family could bring to bear. She was then seventeen. In 1848, at the age of eighteen, she married her gifted cousin, Baron Moritz Ebner von Eschenbach, the engineer, inventor, physicist, and later field-marshal. Thereafter she was able to devote herself, unopposed, to writing. After a few unrewarding ventures into historical drama under Schiller's influence, and modest success in the lyric, she found her field of greatest creativity and originality in the *Novelle*. She and Annette von Droste-Hülshoff are usually considered the finest women writers in German literature.

Marie von Ebner-Eschenbach was throughout her life a pronounced and conscious aristocrat. Her father's family, Dubský von Třebomyslic, was of the ancient Bohemian Catholic nobility. Her mother's family, originally Saxon Protestant, had been raised to noble rank in the eighteenth century. Whatever her pride of class, her mind was above "nationalism," and she had a strong, though paternalistic, social conscience. "Es gäbe keine soziale Frage, wenn die Reichen von jeher Menschenfreunde gewesen wären." Her portraits of Moravian peasants are as warm and true as those of the Viennese nobility.

Her life as a girl, in a large and wealthy family—summers at Castle Zdislawitz in Moravia, winters in Vienna—might have prepared her for little more than the pleasant routine and amiable leisure of the old Austrian aristocracy. She showed her independence, however, by adding to the customary training of girls of her class a sound classical education. Her knowledge and attainments were an excellent match for her distinguished husband's, but success came later to her than it did to him. When she and her husband finally settled in Vienna in 1863—which was her principal residence the rest of her life, excepting only a few trips to Rome and to Paris—she had still not established a literary reputation.

In 1879, her story, *Lotti, die Uhrmacherin*, was published in the *Deutsche Rundschau*, an influential monthly to which Keller and many other writers of the time contributed. This was the beginning of her rapidly growing recognition. Her *Neue Erzählungen* were published in 1881, her *Dorf- und Schloßgeschichten* (including *Krambambuli*) in 1883, followed by a considerable body of separate works, and in 1893 by her first *Gesammelte Schriften*. Until her death in Vienna in 1916, the stream of stories continued, interspersed with autobiographical essays, aphorisms, selections and "collected works."

Marie von Ebner-Eschenbach was a reverent person, strongly inclined to mysticism, and basically optimistic. Her warmth and humanity are extraordinary, and they know no limits of class. She once said it was her ambition to "portray a noble trait in the countenance of the depraved, a flash of spirit in the eye of the simple man."

Krambambuli

(1883)

The psychological insight which helps to make *Krambambuli* a favorite story can be appreciated by anyone who reads it. Connected with it, however, is a remarkable footnote to the acumen of creative perception. (From the standpoint of literary criticism it is perhaps irrelevant, but it is fascinating nonetheless.) The episode which directly inspired the story was only half finished when the story was completed, and the rest of the episode occurred in the way the story had "predicted."

The original of *Krambambuli*, as the authoress's nephew tells us, was an emaciated beast belonging to a gypsy who camped on the grounds of Zdislawitz. Hopp's counterpart was Marie's brother, and the story was written as the dog was in the throes of becoming accustomed to his new master. A year later, with the story long since published, the dog made his choice, to be sure without the dramatic confrontation, but under obvious strain and with every sign of intense conflict.

It is unfortunate that space permits only so bare an outline of the events at Zdislawitz because this transition from reality to story is in fact more than a gratuitous note. It is a clear example of the distillation and concentration, the removal of adventitious elements and the imposing of symmetry, which characterize the relation of literature to "undifferentiated" life.

The triumph of *Krambambuli* as a story lies in the portrayal of a classic tragic conflict—one of the highest manifestations of human nature—in the mind of an animal. This is probably the key to its effectiveness: not so much that it is a great "dog story," but that it is a perfect demonstration of the elemental nature, the inevitability and essential beauty of tragic conflict itself. For as soon as any being admits of values beyond itself or its own self-interest, to which it gives its loyalty, it also admits of the possibility of a conflict between two of them, equally demanding and valid. Such conflicts are the heart of great tragedy. Faced by them, men must choose, and in choosing destroy or injure one of the conflicting ideals—or rationalize their way out (the Romanticist's way). This is the source of tragic guilt. For the dog, of course, rationalization is impossible. Only the agonizing necessity of choice remains.

The terrible clash of conflicting loyalties is not the sole feature that links this *Novelle* to high tragedy. In his final, desperate resolution of his conflict the dog becomes the agent of his unworthy master's destruction, his Nemesis. "Der Gelbe" is destroyed by the very loyalty he once callously betrayed.

In an analysis of the tragedy, it is immaterial that the protagonist is a dog. Yet *Krambambuli* has its undeniable appeal *as* a dog story. This appeal lies in the high tribute of saying that a dog is capable of such a conflict—and saying it without sentimentality, the besetting vice of animal stories.

Even in this short compass, the distinguishing marks of the writer's art are apparent. There is a fine balance of detail and economy in all her descriptions. The portraits drawn from the humbler classes of society are concise and clear, there is an unsentimental distribution of good and bad. In this Marie von Ebner-Eschenbach is firmly rooted in the best traditions of Realism, for one of the fallacies of Naturalism is the tacit notion that the lower you go in the class structure the closer you get to "truth."

The picture of nature, the portrayal of "works and days" in the forest or the small town, is eloquent and accurate. There is a sureness of touch in the writing, and an impressive familiarity that comes only from the unusual combination Ebner-Eschenbach represents: a woman of sophistication and great talent, as much at home in the feudal domain of fields and woods and settlements as in the castle that commands it. (The milieu of the story is of course forever past. Even in its own time it was something of a benevolent archaism. Castle Zdislawitz is now a workers' vacation retreat in the Czech Communist state.)

KRAMBAMBULI

Vorliebe empfindet der Mensch für allerlei Dinge und Wesen. *Liebe*, die echte, unvergängliche, die lernt er—wenn überhaupt—nur einmal kennen. So wenigstens meint der Herr Revierjäger Hopp. Wie viele Hunde hat er schon gehabt, und auch gern gehabt, aber lieb, was man sagt lieb, und unvergeßlich ist ihm nur einer gewesen—der Krambambuli.[1] Er hatte ihn im Wirtshause „Zum[2] Löwen" in Wischau[3] von einem vazierenden Forstgehilfen gekauft oder eigentlich eingetauscht. Gleich beim ersten Anblick des Hundes war er von der Zuneigung ergriffen worden, die dauern sollte bis zu seinem letzten Atemzuge. Dem Herrn[4] des schönen Tieres, der am Tisch vor einem geleerten Branntweingläschen saß und über den Wirt schimpfte, weil dieser kein zweites umsonst hergeben wollte,[5] sah der Lump aus den Augen. Ein kleiner Kerl, noch jung und doch so fahl wie ein abgestorbener Baum, mit gelbem Haar und gelbem spärlichem Barte. Der Jägerrock, vermutlich ein Überrest aus der vergangenen Herrlichkeit des letzten Dienstes, trug die Spuren einer im nassen Straßengraben zugebrachten Nacht. Obwohl sich Hopp ungern in schlechte Gesellschaft begab, nahm er trotzdem Platz neben dem Burschen und begann sogleich ein Gespräch mit ihm. Da bekam er es denn bald heraus, daß der Nichtsnutz den Stutzen und

- 1 -

der Revier'jäger district (forest and game) ranger, warden

vazie'ren be unemployed
der Forstgehilfe, -n, -n forester's assistant

das Branntweingläschen, - small glass of brandy

heraus' -bekommen† find out, get it out of someone
der Stutzen, - (short) rifle

[1] **Krambam'buli** is the name of a cherry brandy associated with Danzig, though the word is applied to other, related liquors. It is also the title of a famous German student song. The word itself is an 18th-century formation, from a stem meaning "juniper."
[2] **zu,** in such names: *at the sign of*
[3] **Wischau** is a small town (and district) formerly in the Austro-Hungarian Empire, now in Czechoslovakia.
[4] **dem Herrn** is dative, thus clearly not the grammatical subject; here, by accident, it may be rendered as the subject: *the man had the look of a scoundrel in his eyes*
[5] **der . . . wollte,** the full relative clause, may be omitted to get a view of the structure of the main clause.

die Jagdtasche dem Wirt bereits als Pfänder ausgeliefert hatte und daß er jetzt auch den Hund als solches hergeben möchte; der Wirt jedoch, der schmutzige Leuteschinder, wollte von einem Pfand, das gefüttert werden muß, nichts hören.

Herr Hopp sagte vorerst kein Wort von dem Wohlgefallen, das er an dem Hunde gefunden hatte, ließ aber eine Flasche von dem guten Danziger[6] Kirschbranntwein bringen, den der Löwenwirt[7] damals führte, und schenkte dem Vazierenden fleißig ein.—Nun, in einer Stunde war alles in Ordnung. Der Jäger gab zwölf Flaschen von demselben Getränke, bei[8] dem der Handel geschlossen worden—der Vagabund gab den Hund. Zu seiner Ehre muß man gestehen: nicht leicht. Die Hände zitterten ihm so sehr, als er dem Tiere die Leine um den Hals legte, daß es schien, er werde mit dieser Manipulation nimmermehr zurechtkommen. Hopp wartete geduldig und bewunderte im stillen[9] den trotz der schlechten Kondition, in der er sich befand, wundervollen[10] Hund. Höchstens zwei Jahre mochte er alt sein, und in der Farbe glich er dem Lumpen, der ihn hergab, doch war die seine um ein paar Schattierungen dunkler. Auf der Stirn hatte er ein Abzeichen, einen weißen Strich, der rechts und links in kleine Linien auslief, in der Art wie die Nadeln an einem Tannenreis. Die Augen waren groß, schwarz, leuchtend, von tauklaren, lichtgelben Reiflein umsäumt, die Ohren hoch angesetzt, lang, makellos. Und makellos war alles an dem ganzen Hunde von der Klaue bis zu der feinen Witternase; die kräftige, geschmeidige Gestalt, das über jedes Lob erhabene

-2-

das Pfand, ⸚er pledge, pawn, security

der Leuteschinder, - extortioner, cheat, skinflint (**schinden** skin)

der Kirschbranntwein, -e cherry brandy
fleißig *here* liberally

tauklar clear as dew
das Reiflein, - little ring, ringlet
hoch angesetzt high-set

die Klaue, -n *here* paw
die Witternase, -n hunting dog's nose (*from* **wittern** scent, sniff)
geschmeidig supple

[6] **Danzig,** the former German seaport city on the Baltic, now Polish (*Gdansk*)
[7] **der Löwenwirt** is the owner of the Lion Inn.
[8] **bei** here *over*
[9] **im stillen** *silently*
[10] Here the "participial" construction, or extended modifier, has as its central modifier a simple adjective rather than a participle: . . . *dog, wonderful in spite of. . . .*

das Piedestal', -e pedestal; *here* legs and feet

der Lauf, ⸚e *here* leg

der deutsche Ordensritter, - Teutonic Knight (*see below*)

lauten sound; *here* come, be

tüchtig *here* good, sound

knebeln gag, muzzle

Piedestal. Vier lebende Säulen, die auch den Körper eines Hirsches getragen hätten und nicht viel dicker waren als die Läufe eines Hasen. Beim heiligen Hubertus![11] Dieses Geschöpf mußte einen Stammbaum haben, so alt und rein wie der eines deutschen Ordensritters.[12]

Dem Jäger lachte das Herz im Leibe[13] über den prächtigen Handel, den er gemacht hatte. Er stand nun auf, ergriff die Leine, die zu verknoten dem Vazierenden endlich gelungen war,[14] und fragte: „Wie heißt er denn?"—„Er heißt wie das, wofür Ihr ihn kriegt: Krambambuli", lautete die Antwort.—„Gut, gut, Krambambuli! So komm! Wirst gehen? Vorwärts!"—Ja, er konnte lang rufen, pfeifen, zerren—der Hund gehorchte ihm nicht, wandte den Kopf dem zu, den er noch für seinen Herrn hielt, heulte, als dieser ihm zuschrie: „Marsch!" und den Befehl mit einem tüchtigen Fußtritt begleitete, suchte aber sich immer wieder an ihn heranzudrängen. Erst nach einem heißen Kampfe gelang es Herrn Hopp, die Besitzergreifung des Hundes zu vollziehen. Gebunden und geknebelt mußte er zuletzt in einem Sacke auf die Schulter geladen und so bis in das mehrere Wegstunden entfernte Jägerhaus getragen werden.[15]

Zwei volle Monate brauchte es, bevor Krambambuli, halb totgeprügelt, nach jedem Fluchtversuche mit dem Stachelhalsband an die Kette gelegt,[16] endlich begriff, wohin er jetzt gehöre. Dann aber, als seine Unterwerfung vollständig geworden war, was für ein Hund wurde er da! Keine Zunge schildert, kein Wort ermißt die Höhe der Vollendung, die er erreichte, nicht

- 3 -

[11] **der heilige Huber'tus,** *St. Hubert* (died 727), the patron saint of hunters. He was the steward to Theoderich, King of the Franks, later Bishop of Liège. While hunting he met a stag with a cross between its antlers. Taking this as a miraculous sign, he turned Christian.

[12] *Teutonic Knight,* member of the religious and military order, founded in connection with the crusades, which in large part was responsible for the colonization of eastern Germany, along the Baltic. The order remained powerful and wealthy for centuries. Its high point was perhaps the 14th century.

[13] **im Leibe** *within him*

[14] *which the unemployed man had finally succeeded in tying*

[15] **geladen und . . . getragen werden**

[16] **an die Kette legen** *chain*

nur in der Ausübung seines Berufes, sondern auch im täglichen Leben als eifriger Diener, guter Kamerad und treuer Freund und Hüter. „Dem fehlt nur die Sprache", heißt es von andern intelligenten Hunden—dem Krambambuli fehlte sie nicht; sein Herr zum mindesten pflog lange Unterredungen mit ihm. Die Frau des Revierjägers wurde ordentlich eifersüchtig auf den „Buli", wie sie ihn geringschätzig nannte. Manchmal machte sie ihrem Manne Vorwürfe. Sie hatte den ganzen Tag, in jeder Stunde, in der sie nicht aufräumte, wusch oder kochte, schweigend gestrickt. Am Abend, nach dem Essen, wenn sie wieder zu stricken begann, hätte sie gern eins dazu geplaudert.

„Weißt[17] denn immer nur dem Buli was[18] zu erzählen, Hopp, und mir nie? Du verlernst vor lauter Sprechen mit dem Vieh das Sprechen mit den Menschen."

Der Revierförster gestand sich, daß etwas Wahres an der Sache sei; aber zu helfen wußte er nicht. Wovon hätte er mit seiner Alten[19] reden sollen? Kinder hatten sie nie gehabt, eine Kuh durften sie nicht halten[20], und das zahme Geflügel interessiert einen Jäger im lebendigen Zustande gar nicht und im gebratenen nicht sehr. Für Kulturen aber und für Jagdgeschichten hatte wieder die Frau keinen Sinn. Hopp fand zuletzt einen Ausweg aus diesem Dilemma; statt *mit* dem Krambambuli sprach er *von* dem Krambambuli, von den Triumphen, die er allenthalben mit ihm feierte, von dem Neide, den sein Besitz erregte, von den lächerlich hohen Summen, die ihm für den Hund geboten wurden und die er verächtlich von der Hand wies.

Zwei Jahre waren vergangen, da erschien eines

-4-

auf-räumen clean (house)
stricken knit

eins *here* a bit

Revierförster = Revierjäger

etwas Wahres an der Sache some truth in the point, in what she said

im gebratenen (Zustand); braten† roast

die Kultur', -en *here* reforestation, tree nursery

der Sinn *here* taste

allenthal'ben everywhere

von der Hand weisen† turn down

[17] **du weißt**
[18] **was = etwas**

[19] **die Alte** *old lady; old woman;* here *wife*
[20] **halten** here *keep*

Tages die Gräfin, die Frau seines Brotherrn, im Hause des Jägers. Er wußte gleich, was der Besuch zu bedeuten hatte,[21] und als die gute, schöne Dame begann: „Morgen, lieber Hopp, ist der Geburtstag des Grafen . . .", setzte er ruhig und schmunzelnd fort: „Und da möchten hochgräfliche Gnaden dem Herrn Grafen ein Geschenk machen, und sind überzeugt, mit nichts anderem soviel Ehre einlegen zu können wie mit dem Krambambuli." „Ja, ja, lieber Hopp." Die Gräfin errötete vor Vergnügen über dieses freundliche Entgegenkommen und sprach gleich von Dankbarkeit und bat, den Preis nur zu nennen, der für den Hund zu entrichten wäre. Der alte Fuchs von einem Revierjäger kicherte, tat sehr demütig und rückte auf einmal mit der Erklärung heraus: „Hochgräfliche Gnaden! Wenn der Hund im Schlosse *bleibt*, nicht jede Leine zerbeißt, nicht jede Kette zerreißt, oder wenn er sie nicht zerreißen *kann*, sich bei den Versuchen, es zu tun, erwürgt, dann behalten ihn Hochgräfliche Gnaden umsonst—dann ist er *mir* nichts mehr wert."

Die Probe wurde gemacht, aber zum Erwürgen kam es nicht; denn der Graf verlor früher die Freude an dem eigensinnigen Tiere. Vergeblich hatte man es durch Liebe zu gewinnen, mit Strenge zu bändigen gesucht. Er biß jeden, der sich ihm näherte, versagte das Futter, und—viel hat der Hund eines Jägers ohnehin nicht zuzusetzen—kam ganz herunter. Nach einigen Wochen erhielt Hopp die Botschaft, er könne sich seinen Köter abholen. Als er eilends von der Erlaubnis Gebrauch machte und den Hund in seinem Zwinger aufsuchte, da gab's ein Wiedersehen uner-

-5-

schmunzeln grin, look pleased

hochgräf'liche Gnaden, *formula of deferential address (note the plural);* your Grace

ohnehin apart from that, besides

zu-setzen lose, spare

der Köter, - cur

der Zwinger, - dungeon, cage

[21] **zu bedeuten haben** *mean*

22 meßlichen Jubels voll. Krambambuli erhob ein wahnsinniges Geheul, sprang an seinem Herrn empor, stemmte die Vorderpfoten auf dessen Brust und leckte die Freudentränen ab, die dem Alten über die Wange liefen.

Am Abend dieses glücklichen Tages wanderten sie zusammen ins Wirtshaus. Der Jäger spielte Tarok mit dem Doktor und mit dem Verwalter, Krambambuli lag in der Ecke hinter seinem Herrn. Manchmal sah 23 dieser sich nach ihm um, und der Hund, so tief er auch zu schlafen schien, begann augenblicklich mit dem Schwanze auf den Boden zu klopfen, als wollt er melden: „Präsent!" Und wenn Hopp, sich vergessend, recht wie einen Triumphgesang das Liedchen an- 24 stimmte: „Was macht denn mein Krambambuli?" richtete der Hund sich würde- und respektvoll auf, und seine hellen Augen antworteten:

„Es geht ihm gut!"

Um dieselbe Zeit trieb, nicht nur in den gräflichen Forsten, sondern in der ganzen Umgebung eine Bande Wildschützen auf wahrhaft tolldreiste Art ihr Wesen. Der Anführer sollte ein verlottertes Subjekt sein. Den „Gelben" nannten ihn die Holzknechte, die ihn in irgendeiner übelberüchtigten Spelunke beim Branntwein trafen, die Heger, die ihm hie und da schon auf der Spur gewesen waren, ihm aber nie hatten beikommen können, und endlich die Kundschafter, deren er unter dem schlechten Gesindel in jedem Dorfe mehrere besaß.

Er war wohl der frechste Gesell, der jemals ehrlichen Jägersmännern etwas aufzulösen gab, mußte

- 6 -

der Tarok' *or* **Tarock'** tarot, *a card game using an enlarged pack (78 cards in all, 22 trumps)*

würde- und respekt'voll full of dignity and respect

tolldreist brazen
Wesen treiben† carry on
verlottert debauched, disreputable
das Subjekt' *here* character
übelberüchtigt infamous
die Spelun'ke, -n *literally* cave, *here like our* hole, pit, dive, *specifically a low-grade tavern*
der Heger, - forester
der Kundschafter, - informer
das Gesindel riff-raff, trash

[22] **voll,** here postposed, is usually a preposition
[23] **so . . . auch** (like the concessive use of **auch** in **wenn auch**) *however . . .*
[24] **was macht . . .?** *how is . . . doing?*

vom Handwerk of the profession, familiar with the trade

der Wild- und Waldschaden, = loss (damage) to game and forests

der Waldfrevel, - offense against the game laws

exempla'risch as a special example, exemplary

in den Wind schlagen† shrug off, belittle

die *or* **der Schneid** (*from* **schneiden**) 'guts'; push

gähnen yawn

das Weidwerk sport of hunting

auch selbst vom Handwerk gewesen sein, sonst hätte er das Wild nicht mit solcher Sicherheit aufspüren und nicht so geschickt jeder Falle, die ihm gestellt wurde, ausweichen können. [25]

Die Wild- und Waldschäden erreichten eine unerhörte Höhe, das Forstpersonal befand sich in grimmigster Aufregung. Da begab es sich nur zu oft, daß die kleinen Leute, die bei irgendeinem unbedeutenden Waldfrevel ertappt wurden, eine härtere Behandlung erlitten, als zu anderer Zeit geschehen wäre und als gerade zu rechtfertigen war. Große Erbitterung herrschte darüber in allen Ortschaften. Dem Oberförster, gegen den der Haß sich zunächst wandte, kamen gutgemeinte Warnungen in Menge zu. Die Raubschützen, hieß es, [26] hätten einen Eid darauf geschworen, bei der ersten Gelegenheit exemplarische Rache an ihm zu nehmen. Er, ein rascher, kühner Mann, schlug das Gerede in den Wind und sorgte mehr denn je dafür, daß weit und breit kund werde, wie er seinen Untergebenen die rücksichtsloseste Strenge anbefohlen und für etwaige schlimme Folgen die Verantwortung selbst übernommen habe. Am häufigsten rief der Oberförster dem Revierjäger Hopp die scharfe Handhabung seiner Amtspflicht ins Gedächtnis und warf ihm zuweilen Mangel an „Schneid" vor, wozu freilich der Alte nur lächelte. Der Krambambuli aber, den er bei solcher Gelegenheit von oben herunter anblinzelte, gähnte laut und wegwerfend. Übel nahmen er und sein Herr dem Oberförster nichts. Der Oberförster war ja der Sohn des Unvergeßlichen, bei dem Hopp das edle Weidwerk erlernt, und Hopp

- 7 -

[25] **aufspüren und . . . ausweichen können**

[26] **hieß es** *the report went*

hatte wieder ihn als kleinen Jungen in die Rudimente des Berufs eingeweiht. Die Plage, die er einst mit ihm gehabt, hielt er heute noch für eine Freude, war stolz auf den ehemaligen Zögling und liebte ihn trotz der rauhen Behandlung, die er so gut wie jeder andere von ihm erfuhr.

Eines Junimorgens traf er ihn eben wieder bei einer Exekution.

Es war im Lindenrondell, am Ende des herrschaftlichen Parks, der an den „Grafenwald" grenzte, und in der Nähe der Kulturen, die der Oberförster am liebsten mit Pulverminen umgeben hätte. Die Linden standen just in schönster Blüte, und über diese hatte ein Dutzend kleiner Jungen sich hergemacht. [27] Wie Eichkätzchen krochen sie auf den Ästen der herrlichen Bäume herum, brachen alle Zweige, die sie erwischen konnten, ab, und warfen sie zur Erde. Zwei Weiber lasen die Zweige hastig auf und stopften sie in Körbe, die schon mehr als zur Hälfte mit dem duftenden Raub gefüllt waren. Der Oberförster raste in unermeßlicher Wut. Er ließ durch seine Heger die Buben nur so von den Bäumen schütteln, unbekümmert um die Höhe, aus der sie fielen. Während sie wimmernd und schreiend um seine Füße krochen, der eine mit zerschundenem Gesicht, der andere mit ausgerenktem Arm, ein dritter mit gebrochenem Bein, zerbläute er eigenhändig die beiden Weiber. In einer von ihnen erkannte Hopp die leichtfertige Dirne, die das Gerücht als die Geliebte des „Gelben" bezeichnete. Und als die Körbe und Tücher der Weiber und die Hüte der Buben in Pfand genommen wurden und Hopp den Auftrag bekam, sie

- 8 -

bei einer Exekution′ as he was meting out punishment
das Lin′denrondell′, -e round grove of lindens
herrschaftlich belonging to the lord of the manor, manorial; *here* the count's
der Grafenwald Count's Forest
das Eichkätzchen, - squirrel
der Heger *see p. 6*
nur so simply
zerschinden† skin
aus-renken dislocate
zerbläuen thrash
leichtfertige Dirne wanton hussy
in Pfand nehmen† take as security

[27] The scene which unfolds here can be understood only if one realizes the rigor of both law and custom concerning forests in Germany, their park-like neatness, the fact that *only* fallen branches may be gathered up and that *all* of these are.

aufs Gericht zu bringen, konnte er sich eines schlimmen Vorgefühls nicht erwehren.

Der Befehl, den ihm damals der Oberförster zurief, wild wie ein Teufel in der Hölle und wie ein solcher umringt von jammernden und gepeinigten Sündern,[28] ist der letzte gewesen, den der Revierjäger im Leben von ihm erhalten hat. Eine Woche später traf er ihn wieder im Lindenrondell—tot. Aus dem Zustande, in dem die Leiche sich befand, war zu ersehen, daß sie hierher, und zwar durch Sumpf und Gerölle geschleppt worden war, um an dieser Stelle aufgebahrt zu werden.[29] Der Oberförster lag auf abgehauenen Zweigen, die Stirn mit einem dichten Kranz aus Lindenblüten umflochten, einen ebensolchen als Bandelier um die Brust gewunden. Sein Hut stand neben ihm mit Lindenblüten gefüllt. Auch die Jagdtasche hatte der Mörder ihm gelassen, nur die Patronen herausgenommen und statt ihrer Lindenblüten hineingesteckt. Der schöne Hinterlader des Oberförsters fehlte und war durch einen elenden Schießprügel ersetzt. Als man später die Kugel, die seinen Tod verursacht hatte, in der Brust des Ermordeten fand, zeigte es sich,[30] daß sie genau in den Lauf dieses Schießprügels paßte, der dem Förster gleichsam zum Hohne über die Schulter gelegt worden war. Hopp stand beim Anblick der entstellten Leiche regungslos vor Entsetzen. Er hätte keinen Finger heben können, und auch das Gehirn war ihm wie gelähmt; er starrte nur und starrte und dachte anfangs gar nichts, und erst nach einer Weile brachte er es zu einer Beobachtung, einer stummen Frage:—„Was hat[31] denn der Hund?“

- 9 -

der Sumpf, ⸚e swamp
auf-bahren place on a bier (*here ironic*)
der Schießprügel, - shooting iron

[28] The "sinners" are of course the boys who were shaken down from the tree.
[29] The symbolic character of this vengeance is amply clear in the following lines.
[30] **sich zeigen** *be revealed, develop*
[31] **was hat . . .** *what's the trouble with . . .*

Krambambuli beschnüffelt den toten Mann, läuft wie nicht gescheit um ihn herum, die Nase immer am Boden. Einmal winselt er, einmal stößt er einen schrillen Freudenschrei aus, macht ein paar Sätze, bellt, und es ist gerade so, als erwache in ihm eine längst erstorbene Erinnerung . . .

„Herein", ruft Hopp, „da herein!" Und Krambambuli gehorcht, sieht aber seinen Herrn in allerhöchster Aufregung an, und—wie der Jäger sich auszudrücken pflegte—*sagt* ihm: „Ich bitte dich um alles in der Welt, siehst du denn nichts? Riechst du denn nichts? . . . O lieber Herr, schau doch! riech doch! O Herr, komm! Da her komm! . . ." Und tupft mit der Schnauze an des Jägers Knie und schleicht, sich oft umsehend, als frage er: „Folgst du mir?" zu der Leiche zurück und fängt an, das schwere Gewehr zu heben und zu schieben und ins Maul zu fassen, in der offenbaren Absicht, es zu apportieren.

Dem Jäger läuft ein Schauer über den Rücken, und allerlei Vermutungen dämmern in ihm auf. Weil das Spintisieren aber nicht seine Sache ist, es ihm auch nicht zukommt, der Obrigkeit Lichter aufzustecken, sondern vielmehr den gräßlichen Fund, den er getan hat, unberührt zu lassen und seiner Wege—das heißt in dem Fall *recte* zu Gericht—zu gehen, so tut er denn einfach, was ihm zukommt.[32]

Nachdem es geschehen und alle Förmlichkeiten, die das Gesetz bei solchen Katastrophen vorschreibt, erfüllt, der ganze Tag und auch ein Stück der Nacht darüber hingegangen sind, nimmt Hopp, ehe er schlafen geht, noch seinen Hund vor.[33]

- 10 -

nicht gescheit not in one's right mind

herein' here!

tupfen touch, nudge

apportie'ren retrieve

spintisie'ren ruminate, speculate

einem zu-kommen† *here and below,* be up to one, within one's province

Lichter auf-stecken set up lights (candles), *i.e.,* enlighten

recte (*Latin*) straight

[32] **seiner Wege gehen** *go one's way*

[33] **nachdem es geschehen (ist) . . . erfüllt . . . hingegangen sind** (i.e., **sind** serves for last two verbs)

die Gendarmerie' gendarmery, *or* police
die Streiferei', -en (reconnoitering) expedition
der Schuft scoundrel
weg-putzen (putzen clean) wipe out, polish off
der Strolch, -e tramp, bum

„Mein Hund", spricht er, „jetzt ist die Gendarmerie auf den Beinen, jetzt gibt's Streifereien ohne Ende. Wollen wir es andern überlassen, den Schuft, der unsern Oberförster erschossen hat, wegzuputzen aus der Welt?—Mein Hund kennt den niederträchtigen Strolch, kennt ihn, ja, ja! Aber das braucht niemand zu wissen, das habe ich nicht ausgesagt . . . Ich, hoho! . . . Ich werd meinen Hund hineinbringen in die Geschichte . . . Das könnt mir einfallen!" Er beugte sich über Krambambuli, der zwischen seinen ausgespreizten Knien saß, drückte die Wange an den Kopf des Tieres und nahm seine dankbaren Liebkosungen in Empfang. Dabei summte er: „Was macht denn mein Krambambuli?" bis der Schlaf ihn übermannte.

34

35

Seelenkundige haben den geheimnisvollen Drang zu erklären gesucht, der manchen Verbrecher stets wieder an den Schauplatz seiner Untat zurückjagt. Hopp wußte von diesen gelehrten Ausführungen nichts, strich aber dennoch ruh- und rastlos mit seinem Hunde in der Nähe des Lindenrondells herum.

Am zehnten Tage nach dem Tode des Oberförsters hatte er zum erstenmal ein paar Stunden lang an etwas anderes gedacht als an seine Rache und sich im „Grafenwald" mit dem Bezeichnen der Bäume beschäftigt, die beim nächsten Schlag ausgenommen werden sollten.

36

Wie er nun mit seiner Arbeit fertig ist, hängt er die Flinte wieder um und schlägt den kürzesten Weg ein, quer durch den Wald gegen die Kulturen in der Nähe des Lindenrondells. Im Augenblick, in dem er

[34] Rhetorical suggestions, the answer being 'no'
[35] **in Empfang nehmen** *receive, accept*
[36] **der Schlag** here *cutting*

auf den Fußsteig treten will, der längs des Buchenzaunes läuft, ist ihm, als höre er etwas im Laube rascheln. Gleich darauf herrscht jedoch tiefe Stille, tiefe, anhaltende Stille. Fast hätte er gemeint, es sei nichts Bemerkenswertes gewesen, wenn nicht der Hund so merkwürdig dreingeschaut hätte. Der stand mit gesträubtem Haar, den Hals vorgestreckt, den Schwanz aufrecht, und glotzte eine Stelle des Zaunes an. Oho! dachte Hopp, wart' Kerl, wenn du's bist! trat hinter einen Baum und spannte den Hahn seiner Flinte. Wie rasend pochte ihm das Herz, und der ohnehin kurze Atem wollte ihm völlig versagen, als jetzt plötzlich, Gottes Wunder![37]—durch den Zaun der „Gelbe" auf den Fußsteig trat. Zwei junge Hasen hingen an seiner Weidtasche und auf seiner Schulter, am wohlbekannten Juchtenriemen, der Hinterlader des Oberförsters. Nun wär's eine Passion gewesen, den Racker niederzubrennen aus sicherem Hinterhalt.

Aber nicht einmal auf den schlechtesten Kerl schießt der Jäger Hopp, ohne ihn angerufen zu haben. Mit einem Satze springt er hinter dem Baum hervor und auf den Fußsteig und schreit: „Gib dich,[38] Vermaledeiter!" Und als der Wildschütz zur Antwort den Hinterlader von der Schulter reißt, gibt der Jäger Feuer[39] . . . All ihr Heiligen—ein sauberes Feuer! Die Flinte knackst anstatt zu knallen. Sie hat zu lang mit aufgesetzter Kapsel im feuchten Wald am Baum gelehnt—sie versagt.

Gute Nacht, so sieht das Sterben aus, denkt der Alte. Doch nein—er ist heil, sein Hut nur fliegt, von Schroten durchlöchert, ins Gras.

- 12 -

der Buchenzaun, ⸗e hedge of beech trees

drein-schauen look

mit gesträubtem Haar hair standing on end

an-glotzen stare at

den Hahn spannen cock

die Weidtasche, -n game bag

der Juchtenriemen, - Russia leather strap

die Passion' pleasure, temptation

der Racker, - rogue, rascal

Vermaledei'ter *lit.* cursed one, *render* confound you

ein sauberes Feuer (*ironic*) a fine shot!

knacksen snap

mit aufgesetzter Kapsel with the cap in place

der, das Schrot, -e shot

[37] **Gottes Wunder!** *miraculously*
[38] **sich geben** *surrender*
[39] **Feuer geben** *fire*

Der andre hat auch kein Glück; das war der letzte Schuß in seinem Gewehr, und zum nächsten zieht er eben erst die Patrone aus der Tasche . . .

„Pack an!“ ruft Hopp seinem Hunde heiser zu: „Pack an!“ Und:

„Herein, zu mir! Herein, Krambambuli!“ lockt es drüben mit zärtlicher, liebevoller—ach, mit altbekannter Stimme . . .

Der Hund aber — —

Was sich nun begab, begab sich viel rascher, als man es erzählen kann.

Krambambuli hatte seinen ersten Herrn erkannt und rannte auf ihn zu, bis—in die Mitte des Weges. Da pfeift Hopp, und der Hund macht kehrt, der „Gelbe“ pfeift, und der Hund macht wieder kehrt und windet sich in Verzweiflung auf einem Fleck, in gleicher Distanz von dem Jäger wie von dem Wildschützen, zugleich hingerissen und gebannt . . .

Zuletzt hat das arme Tier den trostlos unnötigen Kampf aufgegeben und seinen Zweifeln ein Ende gemacht; aber nicht seiner Qual. Bellend, heulend, den Bauch am Boden, den Körper gespannt wie eine Sehne, den Kopf emporgehoben, als riefe es den Himmel zum Zeugen seines Seelenschmerzes an, kriecht es—seinem ersten Herrn zu.

Bei dem Anblick wird Hopp von Blutdurst gepackt. Mit zitternden Fingern hat er die neue Kapsel aufgesetzt—mit ruhiger Sicherheit legt er an. Auch der „Gelbe“ hat den Lauf wieder auf ihn gerichtet. Diesmal gilt's! Das wissen die beiden, die einander auf dem Korn haben, und was auch in ihnen vor-

- 13 -

40

pack an! sic 'em, get him

kehrt machen turn around, do an about-face

die Sehne, -n bow-string

die Kapsel aufsetzen *see above*

diesmal gilt's† this is it

das Korn, ¨er *here* bead, sight

[40] **auf ihn zu** a very common phrase *up to him*

gehen möge, sie zielen so ruhig wie ein paar gemalte Schützen.

Zwei Schüsse fallen. Der Jäger trifft, der Wildschütz fehlt.

Warum? Weil er—vom Hunde mit stürmischer Liebkosung angesprungen—gezuckt hat im Augenblick des Losdrückens. „Bestie!" zischt er noch,[41] stürzt rücklings hin und rührt sich nicht mehr.

Der ihn[42] gerichtet, kommt langsam herangeschritten. Du hast genug, denkt er, um jedes Schrotkorn wär's schad bei dir. Trotzdem stellt er die Flinte auf den Boden und lädt von neuem. Der Hund sitzt aufrecht vor ihm, läßt die Zunge heraushängen, keucht kurz und laut und sieht ihm zu. Und als der Jäger fertig ist und die Flinte wieder zur Hand nimmt, halten sie ein Gespräch, von dem kein Zeuge ein Wort vernommen hätte, wenn es auch statt eines toten[43] ein lebendiger gewesen wäre.

„Weißt du, für wen *das* Blei gehört?"

„Ich kann es mir denken."

„Deserteur! Kalfakter, pflicht- und treuvergessene Kanaille!"

„Ja, Herr, jawohl."

„Du warst meine Freude. Jetzt ist's vorbei. Ich habe keine Freude mehr an dir."

„Begreiflich, Herr", und Krambambuli legte sich hin, drückte den Kopf auf die ausgestreckten Vorderpfoten und sah den Jäger an.

Ja, hätte das verdammte Vieh ihn nur nicht angesehen! Da würde er ein rasches Ende gemacht und sich und dem Hunde viel Pein erspart haben. Aber so

- 14 -

das Schrotkorn, ⸚er grain (bit) of shot
wär's† schad it would be a pity (*continue the idiom here:* to waste . . .)

das Blei lead; *here* shot

der Kalfak'ter, - toady, sycophant
pflicht- und treuvergessen *literally* oblivious of duty and loyalty; *translate* faithless
die Kanail'le (-alje) scum

[41] **noch** has here the force of *managed to, was barely able to*; that is, he was still able to do this one thing before he fell dead.

[42] **der** short for **der, der**

[43] **eines toten (Zeugen)**

mark- und beinerschütterndes *literally* marrow and bone shattering; *render* by our spine-chilling *or* heart-rending

in Augenschein nehmen† inspect

die Schildwache, -n sentinel, guard

der Gerichtsdiener, - bailiff

fletschen bare, show

geht's nicht! Wer könnte ein Geschöpf niederknallen, das einen so ansieht? Herr Hopp murmelt ein halbes Dutzend Flüche zwischen den Zähnen, einer gotteslästerlicher als der andre, hängt die Flinte wieder um, nimmt dem Raubschützen noch die jungen Hasen ab und geht. [44]

Der Hund folgte ihm mit den Augen, bis er zwischen den Bäumen verschwunden war, stand dann auf, und sein mark- und beinerschütterndes Wehgeheul durchdrang den Wald. Ein paarmal drehte er sich im Kreise und setzte sich wieder aufrecht neben den Toten hin. So fand ihn die gerichtliche Kommission, die, von Hopp geleitet, bei sinkender Nacht erschien, um die Leiche des Raubschützen in Augenschein zu nehmen und fortschaffen zu lassen. Krambambuli wich einige Schritte zurück, als die Herren herantraten. Einer von ihnen sagte zu dem Jäger: „Das ist ja Ihr Hund." „Ich habe ihn hier als Schildwache zurückgelassen", antwortete Hopp, der sich schämte, die Wahrheit zu gestehen.—Was half's? Sie kam doch heraus; denn als die Leiche auf den Wagen geladen war und fortgeführt wurde, trottete Krambambuli gesenkten Kopfes und mit eingezogenem Schwanze hinterher. Unweit der Totenkammer, in der der „Gelbe" lag, sah ihn der Gerichtsdiener noch am folgenden Tage herumstreichen. Er gab ihm einen Tritt und rief ihm zu: „Geh nach Hause!"—Krambambuli fletschte die Zähne gegen ihn und lief davon, wie der Mann meinte, in der Richtung des Jägerhauses. Aber dorthin kam er nicht, sondern führte ein elendes Vagabundenleben. [45] [46] [47]

- 15 -

[44] **einen** is here the accusative of **man**
[45] **bei sinkender Nacht** *at nightfall*
[46] **gesenkten Kopfes** is genitive absolute or adverbial genitive, *with . . .*
[47] **mit eingezogenem Schwanze** *with his tail between his legs*

48 Verwildert, zum Skelett abgemagert, umschlich er einmal die armen Wohnungen der Häusler am Ende des Dorfes. Plötzlich stürzte er auf ein Kind los, das vor der letzten Hütte stand, und entriß ihm gierig das Stück harten Brotes, an dem es nagte. Das Kind blieb starr vor Schrecken, aber ein kleiner Spitz sprang aus dem Hause und bellte den Räuber an. Dieser ließ sogleich seine Beute fahren und entfloh. 49

Am selben Abend stand Hopp vor dem Schlafengehen am Fenster und blickte in die schimmernde Sommernacht hinaus. Da war ihm, als sähe er jenseits der Wiese am Waldessaum den Hund sitzen, die Stätte seines ehemaligen Glückes unverwandt und sehnsüchtig betrachtend — der Treueste der Treuen, herrenlos!

Der Jäger schlug den Laden zu und ging zu Bett. Aber nach einer Weile stand er auf, trat ans Fenster— der Hund war nicht mehr da. Und wieder wollte er sich zur Ruhe begeben, und wieder fand er sie nicht. 50

Er hielt es nicht mehr aus. Sei es wie es sei . . . Er hielt es nicht mehr aus ohne den Hund.—Ich hol ihn heim, dachte er und fühlte sich wie neugeboren nach dem Entschluß. Beim ersten Morgengrauen war er angekleidet, befahl seiner Alten, mit dem Mittagessen nicht auf ihn zu warten, und sputete sich hinweg. Wie er aber aus dem Hause trat, stieß sein Fuß an denjenigen, den er in der Ferne zu suchen ausging. Krambambuli lag verendet vor ihm, den Kopf an die Schwelle gepreßt, die zu überschreiten er nicht mehr gewagt hatte. 51

Der Jäger verschmerzte ihn nie. Die Augenblicke

- 16 -

der Spitz, -e spitz (*or* Pomeranian)

der Laden, - (*sometimes* ⸚) shutter

sich hinweg′ -sputen hasten off

verschmerzen get over losing, cease missing

[48] **umschlich** should here be thought of in terms of the English progressive form, *was . . . -ing*

[49] What is the effect of such a contrast—Krambambuli and the spitz—taken in the context of this episode?

[50] **sie** is of course **die Ruhe**

[51] **die zu überschreiten . . .** *which he had no longer dared to cross*

inne-halten† *here* stop

waren seine besten, in denen er vergaß, daß er ihn verloren hatte. In freundliche Gedanken versunken intonierte er dann sein berühmtes: „Was macht denn mein Krambam . . .“ Aber mitten in dem Worte hielt er bestürzt inne, schüttelte das Haupt und sprach mit einem tiefen Seufzer: „Schad um den Hund.“

Thomas Mann

When Thomas Mann died in 1955, the world lost a writer whom many considered its greatest, regardless of nationality. In a series of powerful novels, from *Buddenbrooks* in 1901 to *Felix Krull* in 1954, and in his masterly *Novellen* and brilliant essays, Mann had established his world-wide fame. He had received the Nobel Prize for literature and countless other honors and honorary degrees.

Mann was born in 1875, into a prosperous upper-class family of Lübeck. His father was a merchant and *Senator*. His mother, Julia da Silva-Bruhns, was the daughter of an artistically gifted Brazilian creole woman and a German father. While Mann was still in the Gymnasium he had begun to write. He worked for a short time in the insurance business (in Munich, where he and his mother had gone in 1893, after his father's death), then for the satirical magazine *Simplizissimus*. He had written a number of *Novellen* and short stories, many of the highest quality, before 1900, but his first great success was *Buddenbrooks*. (The story is easier to read than much of Mann's work, and strongly typical. In three generations the health and vigor of the Buddenbrooks declines as its cultivation increases, until the last member of the family line is so refined and sensitive as to be unfit for life.) From these works, uninterrupted, runs Mann's tremendously productive career, through the longer *Novellen*, like *Tonio Kröger*, *Der Tod in Venedig*, *Mario und der Zauberer*; through the novels —the vast symbolic pattern of *Der Zauberberg*, the panoramic allegory of civilization in the four volumes of *Joseph und seine Brüder*, the controversial study of musical genius in *Doktor Faustus*, the legend of Pope Gregorius in *Der Erwählte*, the parodistic irony of *Krull*, the confidence-man; and through all the essays. The sum of this career is nothing less than the creation of a systematic view of intellectual creativity and the problem of human isolation, an allegory of the struggle between the physical and the spiritual, and a new myth of civilization.

Out of his early work there rises a prominent and almost obsessive theme, one which Mann never entirely abandoned. It is the problem of the artist in society as well as the psychopathology of artistic creation. It is expressed in the unbridgeable gulf that separates the "normal," robust, uninspired bourgeois from the artist, the man hopelessly set apart and driven to explore the farthest reaches of creative sensitivity and suffering, sometimes a genius, sometimes a charlatan.

When Mann is criticized adversely, it is often for this pre-occupation with morbidity and degeneration, for so strong an identification of the creative process with sickness, of culture with decay. Skeptics call it a philosophical cliché. Yet in the consistent exploration of this theme lies much of Mann's inescapable power.

Though Mann never stopped writing, he was certainly not unaffected by the history of his time. In 1933, with the advent of Hitler, Mann fled to southern France, then to Switzerland, where he edited the journal *Maß und Wert*. In 1936 the Nazis paid him the unintended honor of revoking his citizenship, and the University of Bonn withdrew the honorary degree it had granted in 1919. Mann's reply is a document of our time. (In 1946 the degree was given back to him, and the dismal farce was over.) In general, his view of democracy and of public service has been a high one, though Mann, unlike Keller and Goethe, was never able to translate it into action.

By 1938 he was in the United States, first as lecturer at Princeton, then in California, where he settled in Pacific Palisades. With the principal exception of a brief visit to Germany in 1949, he remained in this country until 1952. In that year, though he kept his American citizenship, he left for Switzerland, to live near Zürich until his death.

Tobias Mindernickel

(1898)

Superficially, Tobias Mindernickel is another "story about a dog," and certain instructive comparisons might be drawn between this *Novelle* and the preceding one. Essentially, Mann is writing about psychological and spiritual degeneration. The dog, like the urchin in the street, is only a foil against which is revealed the crisis in this disintegration of a man's character.

The story presents briefly some of Mann's perennial themes. To be sure, Mindernickel is not an artist—we have no idea what he is. But he is a man set apart, isolated from society. Further, there is ample evidence that Mindernickel is the withered branch of a once sound and well-established family tree. In this he reminds us of the last of the Buddenbrooks. But he is also a cruelly twisted personality, and in this he is one with the figures of Mann's *Novellen* of decadence, figures set apart from life because they are either physical or mental cripples or both: Friedemann, Jakoby, Cipolla, and many others.

Even in the later statement of Mann's theme, where exile from bourgeois society is a function of artistic creativity, the pathological trait often remains. In this sense *Tobias Mindernickel* is a most important tale, "phylogenetically."

Mann's *Novelle* is remarkable for its compact and linear development, even in a genre marked by its strict form. The determining facts are clear. Only in the posture of superiority vis-à-vis a being more wretched than he can Tobias express either kindness or power. Accident and coincidence provide the first opportunity for the exercise of both; his own initiative the second. The third time is intense and ominous because Tobias is a coincidental cause of a more drastic development—blood and the handkerchief bind it like a leitmotif to the first incident. The fourth and last time, in a paroxysm of insane suffering and hate he creates the opportunity, creates himself the ultimate misery with which he can condole. The supreme irony is that in doing so he has destroyed the object itself. Indeed, his whole sequence of actions is ultimately self-destructive.

The portrait of an aberrant psychological state is masterly. It is difficult to draw credibly a man so warped, a man so offended and tortured by uncomplicated happiness that he must destroy any manifestation of it in things under his sway. But quite aside from its psychopathology, the story raises disturbing general questions. What is compassion? What is the role of superiority in it? What part does the will to power play in an act of kindness? Are we "sympathetic" because we feel a secret pleasure in the greater misfortune of others? Do we sometimes imprison in unhappiness a person or an animal in order to have an object for our thwarted need to feel sorry or be helpful?

In answering we place ourselves somewhere in a spectrum that runs from abysmal cynicism about human nature to pathetic naïveté. We may even wonder what position Mann himself would have us take.

In style the story is carefully wrought and typical. The symbols of frustration and barrenness are carefully marshalled, repetition of words or word classes supports the portrait of Tobias' cringing inferiority. The intrusions of the author and his subjective judgments ("über alle Maßen schändlich," "etwas so Infames, daß ich mich weigere, es ausführlich zu erzählen") are a hallmark of Mann's story-telling. The reader should note them and decide to what degree they are parallelled in the other stories in this book.

TOBIAS MINDERNICKEL

Eine der Straßen, die von der Quaigasse aus ziemlich steil zur mittleren Stadt emporführen, heißt der Graue Weg. Etwa in der Mitte dieser Straße und rechter Hand, wenn man vom Flusse kommt, steht das Haus Nr. 47, ein schmales, trübfarbiges Gebäude, das sich durch nichts von seinen Nachbarn unterscheidet. In seinem Erdgeschoß befindet sich ein Krämerladen, in welchem man auch Gummischuhe und Rizinusöl erhalten kann. Geht man, mit dem Durchblick auf einen Hofraum, in dem sich Katzen umhertreiben, über den Flur, so führt eine enge und ausgetretene Holztreppe, auf der es unaussprechlich dumpfig und ärmlich riecht, in die Etagen hinauf. Im ersten Stockwerk links wohnt ein Schreiner, rechts eine Hebamme. Im zweiten Stockwerk links wohnt ein Flickschuster, rechts eine Dame, welche laut zu singen beginnt, sobald sich Schritte auf der Treppe vernehmen lassen. Im dritten Stockwerk steht linker Hand die Wohnung leer, rechts wohnt ein Mann namens Mindernickel, der obendrein Tobias heißt. Von diesem Manne gibt es eine Geschichte, die erzählt werden soll, weil sie rätselhaft und über alle Begriffe schändlich ist.

Das Äußere Mindernickels ist auffallend, sonderbar und lächerlich. Sieht man beispielsweise, wenn er einen Spaziergang unternimmt, seine magere, auf

- 1 -

die Quaigasse (*pronounced as if spelled* käh-) dock (wharf) road; *probably a proper name*

der Krämerladen, ⸚ general store
der Gummischuh, -e (*pl.*) rubbers
das Rizinusöl castor oil

die Eta'ge, -n (**g** soft) *here* upper floor
der Schreiner, - cabinetmaker, carpenter
die Heb'amme, -n midwife
der Flickschuster, - shoe-repair man

[1] **geht man . . . über den Flur, so**
[2] **erstes Stockwerk** *second floor*
[3] **Mindernickel** is an odd name, the first part being like **minder,** *less(er),* the second reminiscent of **das Nickel,** the metal and also **der Nickel,** the formerly common 10-50 Pfenning coins—or of **der Nickel,** German diminutive of **Nicholas,** a word with a number of out-of-the-way meanings: *Santa Claus, water sprite, spoiled child, pony!* With this curious compound, **Tobi'as,** *Tobiah* (the Biblical name: "Jehovah is good") makes an incongruous combination.
[4] **über alle Begriffe** *inconceivably, unimaginably*

5 6 einen Stock gestützte Gestalt sich die Straße hinaufbewegen, so ist er schwarz gekleidet, und zwar vom Kopfe bis zu den Füßen. Er trägt einen altmodischen, geschweiften und rauhen Zylinder, einen engen und 7 altersblanken Gehrock und in gleichem Maße schäbige Beinkleider, die unten ausgefranst und so kurz sind, daß man den Gummieinsatz der Stiefeletten sieht. Übrigens muß gesagt werden, daß diese Kleidung aufs reinlichste gebürstet ist. Sein hagerer Hals erscheint um so länger, als er sich aus einem niedrigen Klapp- 8 kragen erhebt. Das ergraute Haar ist glatt und tief in die Schläfen gestrichen, und der breite Rand des Zylinders beschattet ein rasiertes und fahles Gesicht mit eingefallenen Wangen, mit entzündeten Augen, die sich selten vom Boden erheben, und zwei tiefen Furchen, die grämlich von der Nase bis zu den abwärts gezogenen Mundwinkeln laufen.

Mindernickel verläßt selten das Haus, und das hat seinen Grund. Sobald er nämlich auf der Straße erscheint, laufen viele Kinder zusammen, ziehen ein 9 gutes Stück Wegs hinter ihm drein, 10 lachen, höhnen, singen: „Ho, ho, Tobias!" und zupfen ihn wohl auch am Rocke, während die Leute vor die Türen treten und sich amüsieren. Er selbst aber geht, ohne sich zu wehren und scheu um sich blickend, mit hochgezogenen Schultern und vorgestrecktem Kopfe davon, wie ein Mensch, der ohne Schirm durch einen Platzregen eilt; und obgleich man ihm ins Gesicht lacht, grüßt er hie und da mit einer demütigen Höflichkeit jemanden von den Leuten, die vor den Türen stehn. Später, wenn die Kinder zurückbleiben, wenn man ihn nicht mehr

- 2 -

geschweift curved
der Zylin'der, - top hat
der Gehrock, ⸚e frock coat
aus-fransen fray
der Gummieinsatz, ⸚e rubber insert, elastic
die Stiefelet'te, -n gaiter (*elastic sided boot*), congress boot
der Klappkragen, - turndown collar
der Platzregen, - sudden shower

[5] **seine magere Gestalt, gestützt auf einen Stock** or **die auf einen Stock gestützt ist;** the construction is always amenable to this treatment.
[6] **sich die Straße hinaufbewegen** *move up the street*
[7] **in gleichem Maße** *equally*
[8] That is, *his hair is combed* (*smoothed*) *down over his temples.*
[9] **ein gutes Stück Wegs,** like our *a good piece: for quite a distance*
[10] **hinter ihm drein** (*along*) *behind him*

kennt und nur wenige sich nach ihm umsehen, ändert sich sein Benehmen nicht wesentlich. Er fährt fort, ängstlich um sich zu blicken und geduckt davonzustreben, als fühlte er tausend höhnische Blicke auf sich, und wenn er unschlüssig und scheu den Blick vom Boden erhebt, so bemerkt man das Sonderbare, daß er nicht imstande ist, irgendeinen Menschen oder auch nur ein Ding mit Festigkeit und Ruhe ins Auge zu fassen. Es scheint, möge es fremdartig klingen, ihm die natürliche, sinnlich wahrnehmende Überlegenheit zu fehlen, mit der das Einzelwesen auf die Welt der Erscheinungen blickt, er scheint sich einer jeden Erscheinung unterlegen zu fühlen, und seine haltlosen Augen müssen vor Mensch und Ding zu Boden kriechen . . . 11 12 13 14

Was für eine Bewandtnis hat es mit diesem Manne, der stets allein ist, und der in ungewöhnlichem Grade unglücklich zu sein scheint? Seine gewaltsam bürgerliche Kleidung sowie eine gewisse sorgfältige Bewegung der Hand über das Kinn scheint anzudeuten, daß er keineswegs zu der Bevölkerungsklasse gerechnet werden will, in deren Mitte er wohnt. Gott weiß, in welcher Weise ihm mitgespielt worden ist. Sein Gesicht sieht aus, als hätte ihm das Leben verächtlich lachend mit voller Faust hineingeschlagen . . . Übrigens ist es sehr möglich, daß er, ohne schwere Schicksalsschläge erlebt zu haben, einfach dem Dasein selbst nicht gewachsen ist, und die leidende Unterlegenheit und Blödigkeit seiner Erscheinung macht den peinvollen Eindruck, als hätte die Natur ihm das Maß von Gleichgewicht, Kraft und Rückgrat versagt, das hinlänglich wäre, mit erhobenem Kopfe zu existieren. 15 16

- 3 -

was für eine Bewandtnis hat es mit . . . what is the story behind . . .

mitgespielt werden†, *with dative of person,* be (ill) treated by fate

mit voller Faust hinein'-schlagen† hit full in the face, hit as hard as one can

das Rückgrat, -e backbone

[11] **ins Auge fassen** *look in the eye*

[12] **möge es fremdartig klingen** *strange as it may sound*

[13] **die sinnlich wahrnehmende Überlegenheit** *superiority of (bestowed by) sense perception.* The normal man, says Mann, establishes a sort of superiority over the external world by the very act of perceiving it with his senses. Mindernickel does not even have this elemental advantage.

[14] **kriechen:** Note the repetition of words like this (**ducken, beugen**) or **ärmlich, dumpfig; höhnen, Spottruf, Gelächter,** etc. What is their purpose and effect?

[15] **werden will** *is to be*

[16] Earlier refinement leading into ineffectiveness and degradation is a theme Mann will develop widely and systematically in his later fiction.

Hat er, gestützt auf seinen schwarzen Stock, einen Gang in die Stadt hinauf gemacht, so kehrt er, im Grauen Weg von den Kindern johlend empfangen, in seine Wohnung zurück; er begibt sich die dumpfige Treppe hinauf in sein Zimmer, das ärmlich und schmucklos ist. Nur die Kommode, ein solides Empiremöbel mit schweren Metallgriffen, ist von Wert und Schönheit. Vor dem Fenster, dessen Aussicht von der grauen Seitenmauer des Nachbarhauses hoffnungslos abgeschnitten ist, steht ein Blumentopf, voll von Erde, in der jedoch durchaus nichts wächst; gleichwohl tritt Tobias Mindernickel zuweilen dorthin, betrachtet den Blumentopf und riecht an der bloßen Erde.[17]—Neben dieser Stube liegt eine kleine, dunkle Schlafkammer.—Nachdem er eingetreten ist, legt Tobias Zylinder und Stock auf den Tisch, setzt sich auf das grün überzogene Sofa, das nach Staub riecht, stützt das Kinn in die Hand und blickt mit erhobenen Augenbrauen vor sich nieder zu Boden.[18] Es scheint, daß es für ihn auf Erden nichts weiter zu tun gibt.

Was Mindernickels Charakter betrifft, so ist es sehr schwer, darüber zu urteilen; der folgende Vorfall scheint zugunsten desselben zu sprechen. Als der sonderbare Mann eines Tages das Haus verließ und wie gewöhnlich eine Schar von Kindern sich einfand, die ihn mit Spottrufen und Gelächter verfolgten, strauchelte ein Junge von etwa zehn Jahren über den Fuß eines anderen und schlug so heftig auf das Pflaster, daß ihm das Blut aus der Nase und von der Stirne lief und er weinend liegen blieb. Alsbald wandte Tobias sich um, eilte auf den Gestürzten zu, beugte sich über

- 4 -

johlen hoot, howl

das Empire'möbel, - (ãpi:r) Empire piece (*period furniture from Napoleonic times*)

straucheln (ist) stumble

[17] Note the symbols of frustration and barrenness.

[18] **vor sich nieder zu Boden** *down at the ground in front of him*

ihn und begann mit milder und bebender Stimme ihn zu bemitleiden. „Du armes Kind", sagte er, „hast du dir weh getan? Du blutest! Seht, das Blut läuft ihm von der Stirn herunter! Ja, ja, wie elend du nun daliegst! Freilich, es tut so weh, daß es weint, das arme Kind! Welch Erbarmen ich mit dir habe! Es war deine Schuld, aber ich will dir mein Taschentuch um den Kopf binden . . . So, so! Nun fasse dich nur, nun erhebe dich nur wieder . . ." Und nachdem er mit diesen Worten dem Jungen in der Tat[19] sein eigenes Schnupftuch umgewunden hatte, stellte er ihn mit Sorgfalt auf die Füße und ging davon. Seine Haltung und sein Gesicht aber zeigten in diesem Augenblicke einen entschieden anderen Ausdruck als gewöhnlich. Er schritt fest und aufrecht, und seine Brust atmete tief unter dem engen Gehrock; seine Augen hatten sich vergrößert, sie hatten Glanz erhalten und faßten mit Sicherheit Menschen und Dinge, während um seinen Mund ein Zug von schmerzlichem Glücke lag . . .

das Schnupftuch, ⸗er handkerchief

Dieser Vorfall hatte zur Folge, daß sich die Spottlust der Leute vom Grauen Wege zunächst ein wenig verminderte. Nach Verlauf einiger Zeit jedoch war sein überraschendes Betragen vergessen, und eine Menge von gesunden, wohlgemuten und grausamen Kehlen sang wieder hinter dem geduckten und haltlosen Manne drein: „Ho, ho, Tobias!"

Eines sonnigen Vormittags um 11 Uhr verließ Mindernickel das Haus und begab sich durch die ganze Stadt hinauf zum Lerchenberge, jenem langgestreckten Hügel, der um die Nachmittagsstunden die

der Lerchenberg (*proper name*), *like our* Larchmont

[19] **in der Tat** *indeed, in fact*

vornehmste Promenade der Stadt bildet, der aber bei dem ausgezeichneten Frühlingswetter, welches herrschte, auch um diese Zeit bereits von einigen Wagen und Fußgängern besucht war. Unter einem Baum der großen Hauptallee stand ein Mann mit einem jungen Jagdhund an der Leine, den er den Vorübergehenden mit der ersichtlichen Absicht zeigte, ihn zu verkaufen; es war ein kleines gelbes und muskulöses Tier von etwa vier Monaten, mit einem schwarzen Augenring und einem schwarzen Ohr.

Als Tobias dies aus einer Entfernung von zehn Schritten bemerkte, blieb er stehen, strich mehrere Male mit der Hand über das Kinn und blickte nachdenklich auf den Verkäufer und auf das alert mit dem Schwanze wedelnde Hündchen. Hierauf begann er aufs neue[20] zu gehen, umkreiste, die Krücke seines Stockes gegen den Mund gedrückt, dreimal den Baum, an welchem der Mann lehnte, trat dann auf den letzteren zu und sagte, während er unverwandt das Tier im Auge behielt,[21] mit leiser und hastiger Stimme:

„Was kostet dieser Hund?"

„Zehn Mark", antwortete der Mann.

Tobias schwieg einen Augenblick und wiederholte dann unschlüssig:

„Zehn Mark?"[22]

„Ja", sagte der Mann.

Da zog Tobias eine schwarze Lederbörse aus der Tasche, entnahm derselben einen Fünfmarkschein, ein Drei- und ein Zweimarkstück, händigte rasch dieses Geld dem Verkäufer ein, ergriff die Leine und zerrte eilig, gebückt und scheu um sich blickend, da einige

- 6 -

die Haupt'allee', -n (principal) thoroughfare

die Krücke, -n *here* crook, head (*of a cane*)

die Lederbörse, -n leather purse

der Schein, -e bill; **das Stück, -e** coin; *the mark of this time bore about the same relation to the dollar as it does at present—four to one.*

[20] **aufs neue** *anew, once more*

[21] **unverwandt im Auge behalten** *keep one's eye fixed on*

[22] What is conveyed by Tobias' hesitant repetition of the price?

quieken squeal

Leute den Kauf beobachtet hatten und lachten, das quiekende und sich sträubende Tier hinter sich her.[23] Es wehrte sich während der Dauer des ganzen Weges, stemmte die Vorderbeine gegen den Boden und blickte ängstlich fragend zu seinem neuen Herrn empor; er jedoch zerrte schweigend und mit Energie und gelangte glücklich durch die Stadt hinunter.

Unter der Straßenjugend des Grauen Weges entstand ein ungeheurer Lärm, als Tobias mit dem Hunde erschien, aber er nahm ihn auf den Arm, beugte sich über ihn und eilte verhöhnt und am Rocke gezupft durch die Spottrufe und das Gelächter hindurch, die Treppen hinauf und in sein Zimmer. Hier setzte er den Hund, der beständig winselte, auf den Boden, streichelte ihn mit Wohlwollen und sagte herablassend:

„Nun, nun, du brauchst dich nicht vor mir zu fürchten, du Tier; das ist nicht nötig."

die Kommo'denschieblade, -n drawer in a bureau

schmatzen smack (lips)

Hierauf entnahm er einer Kommodenschieblade einen Teller mit gekochtem Fleisch und Kartoffeln und warf dem Tiere einen Anteil davon zu, worauf es seine Klagelaute einstellte und schmatzend und wedelnd das Mahl verzehrte.

„Übrigens sollst du Esau heißen", sagte Tobias;[24] „verstehst du mich? Esau. Du kannst den einfachen Klang sehr wohl behalten . . ." Und indem er vor sich auf den Boden zeigte, rief er befehlend:

„Esau!"

Der Hund, in der Erwartung vielleicht, noch mehr zu essen zu erhalten, kam in der Tat herbei, und Tobias klopfte ihm beifällig auf die Seite, indem er sagte:[25]

- 7 -

[23] **hinter sich her** *along behind him*

[24] **Esau:** The Bible is again the source of the name, which means "*hairy.*" See Gen. 25.25 and 27.11. Also Gen. 25.27 ". . . *and Esau was a cunning hunter.*" How much of the story of Esau and Jacob is to be read into the present tale is a matter of conjecture—or taste for allegory.

[25] **indem er sagte** *saying*

26 „So ist es recht, mein Freund; ich darf dich loben."

Dann trat er ein paar Schritte zurück, wies auf den Boden und befahl aufs neue:

„Esau!"

Und das Tier, das ganz munter geworden war, sprang wiederum herzu und leckte den Stiefel seines Herrn.

Diese Übung wiederholte Tobias mit unermüdlicher Freude am Befehl und dessen Ausführung wohl zwölf- bis vierzehnmal; endlich jedoch schien der Hund ermüdet, er schien Lust zu haben, zu ruhen und zu verdauen, und legte sich in der anmutigen und klugen Pose der Jagdhunde auf den Boden, beide langen und feingebauten Vorderbeine dicht nebeneinander ausgestreckt.

„Noch einmal!" sagte Tobias. „Esau!"

Aber Esau wandte den Kopf zur Seite und verharrte am Platze.

„Esau!" rief Tobias mit herrisch erhobener Stimme; „du hast zu kommen, auch wenn du müde bist!"

Aber Esau legte den Kopf auf die Pfoten und kam durchaus nicht.

„Höre", sagte Tobias, und sein Ton war voll von leiser und furchtbarer Drohung; „gehorche, oder du wirst erfahren, daß es nicht klug ist, mich zu reizen!"

Allein das Tier bewegte kaum ein wenig seinen Schwanz.

Da packte den Mindernickel ein maßloser, ein unverhältnismäßiger und toller Zorn. Er ergriff seinen schwarzen Stock, hob Esau am Nackenfell empor und

das Nackenfell (skin at the) nape of the neck

- 8 -

[26] **ich darf dich loben** *you deserve my praise*

hieb auf das schreiende Tierchen ein, indem er außer sich vor entrüsteter Wut und mit schrecklich zischender Stimme einmal über das andere wiederholte: 27

„Wie, du gehorchst nicht? Du wagst es, mir nicht zu gehorchen?"

Endlich warf er den Stock beiseite, setzte den winselnden Hund auf den Boden und begann tief atmend und die Hände auf dem Rücken mit langen Schritten vor ihm auf und ab zu schreiten, während er dann und wann einen stolzen und zornigen Blick auf Esau warf. Nachdem er diese Promenade eine Zeitlang fortgesetzt hatte, blieb er bei dem Tiere stehen, das auf dem Rücken lag und die Vorderbeine flehend bewegte, verschränkte die Arme auf der Brust und sprach mit dem entsetzlich kalten und harten Blick und Ton, mit dem Napoleon vor die Kompagnie hintrat, die in der Schlacht ihren Adler verloren:

der Adler, - eagle (*on the company's standard*)

„Wie hast du dich betragen, wenn ich dich fragen darf?"

Und der Hund, glücklich bereits über diese Annäherung, kroch noch näher herbei, schmiegte sich gegen das Bein des Herrn und blickte mit seinen blanken Augen bittend zu ihm empor.

sich schmiegen press close to

Während einer guten Weile betrachtete Tobias das demütige Wesen schweigend und von oben herab; 28 dann jedoch, als er die rührende Wärme des Körpers an seinem Bein verspürte, hob er Esau zu sich empor.

„Nun, ich will Erbarmen mit dir haben", sagte er; als aber das gute Tier begann, ihm das Gesicht zu lecken, schlug plötzlich seine Stimmung völlig in Rührung und Wehmut um. Er preßte den Hund mit

[27] **einmal über das andere** *one time after the other*

[28] **von oben herab** *looking down from above*

schmerzlicher Liebe an sich, seine Augen füllten sich mit Tränen, und ohne den Satz zu vollenden, wiederholte er mehrere Male mit erstickter Stimme:

29 „Sieh, du bist ja mein einziger . . . mein einziger . . .“ Dann bettete er Esau mit Sorgfalt auf das Sofa, setzte sich neben ihn, stützte das Kinn in die Hand und sah ihn mit milden und stillen Augen an.

Tobias Mindernickel verließ nunmehr das Haus noch seltener als früher, denn er verspürte keine Neigung, sich mit Esau in der Öffentlichkeit zu zeigen. Seine ganze Aufmerksamkeit aber widmete er dem Hunde, ja, er beschäftigte sich von Morgen bis zum Abend mit nichts anderem, als ihn zu füttern, ihm die Augen auszuwischen, ihm Befehle zu erteilen, ihn zu schelten und aufs menschlichste mit ihm zu reden.
30 Allein die Sache war die, daß Esau sich nicht immer zu seinem Wohlgefallen betrug. Wenn er neben ihm auf dem Sofa lag und ihn, schläfrig vor Mangel an Luft und Freiheit, mit melancholischen Augen ansah, so war Tobias voll Zufriedenheit; er saß in stiller und selbstgefälliger Haltung da und streichelte mitleidig Esaus Rücken, indem er sagte:

„Siehst du mich schmerzlich an, mein armer Freund? Ja, ja, die Welt ist traurig, das erfährst auch du, so jung du bist . . .“

31 Wenn aber das Tier, blind und toll vor Spiel- und Jagdtrieb, im Zimmer umherfuhr, sich mit einem Pantoffel balgte, auf die Stühle sprang und sich mit ungeheurer Munterkeit überkugelte, so verfolgte Tobias seine Bewegungen aus der Entfernung mit einem ratlosen, mißgünstigen und unsicheren Blick und

- 10 -

der Pantof'fel, - slipper
balgen romp

[29] **mein einziger** *what?* (German gives more evidence than English in a case like this.)

[30] **die Sache war die** *the thing was, the truth was*
[31] **der Spiel- und Jagdtrieb** *impulse to play or hunt*

einem Lächeln, das häßlich und ärgervoll war, bis er es endlich in unwirschem Tone zu sich rief und es anherrschte:

an-herrschen speak imperiously to

„Laß nun den Übermut. Es liegt kein Grund vor, umherzutanzen."

Einmal geschah es sogar, daß Esau aus der Stube entwischte und die Treppen hinunter auf die Straße sprang, woselbst er alsbald begann, eine Katze zu jagen, Pferdekot zu fressen und sich überglücklich mit den Kindern umherzutreiben. Als aber Tobias unter dem Applaus und Gelächter der halben Straße mit schmerzlich verzogenem Gesichte erschien, geschah das Traurige, daß der Hund in langen Sätzen vor seinem Herrn davonlief . . . An diesem Tage prügelte Tobias ihn lange und mit Erbitterung.

der Pferdekot horse manure

Eines Tages—der Hund gehörte ihm bereits seit einigen Wochen—nahm Tobias, um Esau zu füttern, einen Brotlaib aus der Kommodenschieblade und begann mit dem großen Messer mit Knochengriff, dessen er sich hierbei zu bedienen pflegte, in gebückter Haltung kleine Stücke abzuschneiden und auf den Boden fallen zu lassen. Das Tier aber, unsinnig vor Appetit und Albernheit, sprang blindlings herzu, rannte sich das ungeschickt gehaltene Messer unter das rechte Schulterblatt und wand sich blutend am Boden.

der Brotlaib, -e loaf of bread

Erschrocken warf Tobias alles beiseite und beugte sich über den Verwundeten; plötzlich jedoch veränderte sich der Ausdruck seines Gesichtes, und es ist wahr, daß ein Schimmer von Erleichterung und Glück darüber hing.[32] Behutsam trug er den wimmernden

- 11 -

[32] **über . . . hingehen** *pass over*

Hund auf das Sofa, und niemand vermag auszudenken, mit welcher Hingebung er den Kranken zu pflegen begann. Er wich während des Tages nicht von ihm, er ließ ihn zur Nacht auf seinem eigenen Lager schlafen, er wusch und verband ihn, streichelte, tröstete und bemitleidete ihn mit unermüdlicher Freude und Sorgfalt.

„Schmerzt es sehr?" sagte er. „Ja, ja, du leidest bitterlich, mein armes Tier! Aber sei still, wir müssen[33] es ertragen" . . . Sein Gesicht war ruhig, wehmütig und glücklich bei solchen Worten.

In dem Grade jedoch, in welchem Esau zu Kräften[34] kam, fröhlicher wurde und genas, ward das Benehmen des Tobias unruhiger und unzufriedener. Er befand es nunmehr für gut, sich nicht mehr um die Wunde zu bekümmern, sondern lediglich durch Worte und Streicheln dem Hunde sein Erbarmen zu zeigen. Allein die Heilung war weit vorgeschritten, Esau besaß eine gute Natur, er begann bereits wieder, sich im Zimmer umherzubewegen, und eines Tages, nachdem er einen Teller mit Milch und Weißbrot leergeschlappt hatte, sprang er völlig gesundet vom Sofa herunter, um mit freudigem Geblaff und der alten Unbändigkeit durch die beiden Stuben zu fahren, an der Bettdecke zu zerren, eine Kartoffel vor sich her[35] zu jagen und sich vor Lust zu überkugeln.

Tobias stand am Fenster, am Blumentopfe, und während eine seiner Hände, die lang und mager aus dem ausgefransten Ärmel hervorsah, mechanisch an dem tief in die Schläfen gestrichenen Haare drehte, hob seine Gestalt sich schwarz und sonderbar von der

- 12 -

leer-schlappen lap up (all of . . .)

das Geblaff yipping

[33] **wir** is more than the usual condescending inclusive *we;* why?

[34] **zu Kräften kommen** *gain strength*
[35] **vor sich her** *in front of him*

sich ab-heben† stand in relief, be silhouetted
gramverzerrt contorted with misery
scheel oblique, sidewise

wehleidig woeful
ausgelassen in high spirits

auf-blaffen let out a bark (yip)

grauen Mauer des Nachbarhauses ab. Sein Gesicht war bleich und gramverzerrt und mit einem scheelen, verlegenen, neidischen und bösen Blick verfolgte er unbeweglich Esaus Sprünge. Plötzlich jedoch raffte er sich auf, schritt auf ihn zu, hielt ihn an und nahm ihn langsam in seine Arme.[36]

„Mein armes Tier" . . . begann er mit wehleidiger Stimme—aber Esau, ausgelassen und gar nicht geneigt, sich ferner in dieser Weise behandeln zu lassen, schnappte munter nach der Hand, die ihn streicheln wollte, entwand sich den Armen, sprang zu Boden, machte einen neckischen Seitensatz, blaffte auf und rannte fröhlich davon.

Was nun geschah, war etwas so Unverständliches und Infames, daß ich mich weigere, es ausführlich zu erzählen. Tobias Mindernickel stand mit am Leibe[37] herunterhängenden Armen ein wenig vorgebeugt, seine Lippen waren zusammengepreßt, und seine Augäpfel zitterten unheimlich in ihren Höhlen. Und dann, plötzlich, mit einer Art von irrsinnigem Sprunge, hatte er das Tier ergriffen, ein großer, blanker Gegenstand blitzte in seiner Hand, und mit einem Schnitt, der von der rechten Schulter bis tief in die Brust lief, stürzte der Hund zu Boden—er gab keinen Laut von[38] sich, er fiel einfach auf die Seite, blutend und bebend . .

Im nächsten Augenblicke lag er auf dem Sofa, und Tobias kniete vor ihm, drückte ein Tuch auf die Wunde und stammelte:

„Mein armes Tier! Mein armes Tier! Wie traurig alles ist! Wie traurig wir beide sind! Leidest du? Ja, ja, ich weiß, du leidest . . . wie kläglich du da vor mir

- 13 -

[36] Why the flowerpot and the bare wall again?
[37] **mit am:** Two prepositions one after the other are a clue that what sort of construction is involved?
[38] **von sich geben** *utter, emit*

liegst! Aber ich, ich bin bei dir! Ich tröste dich! Ich werde mein bestes Taschentuch" . . .

Allein Esau lag da und röchelte. Seine getrübten und fragenden Augen waren voll Verständnislosigkeit, Unschuld und Klage auf seinen Herrn gerichtet—und dann streckte er ein wenig seine Beine und starb.

Tobias aber verharrte unbeweglich in seiner Stellung. Er hatte das Gesicht auf Esaus Körper gelegt und weinte bitterlich.

röcheln have a death rattle in one's throat; **und röchelte** with a, *etc.*

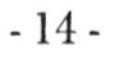

Rainer Maria Rilke

Modern German literature gained its most powerful influence on the poetry of the Western world through Rainer Maria Rilke. Other great lyricists like Stefan George were influenced from abroad, notably from France, and the extent of their own effect upon other literatures was small. Modern poets everywhere listened to and learned from Rilke, from his mystic visions, his creation of the role of poet-prophet and the new Orphic myth, from his relentless pursuit of God, his singing of things, his fear of and attempted triumph over death; and from his sensitive, sensuous verse, with its brilliant use of devices like alliteration and vowel harmonies, radical rhymes and run-on lines.

Out of Rilke's poetry come the influences which pervade his prose and make it memorable. Sometimes, as is the case with the present story, it is hard to say whether we are dealing with prose or poetry. It makes little difference, since the result is one of the notable experiments in the art of narrative writing.

Rilke was one of the great *Auslandsdeutsche*. He was born in 1875, in Prague, on Saturday, December 4 at midnight. From the association of this day with Mary and the birth of Christ came the name Maria. His first name was René, which he later Germanized to Rainer. His family, despite the illusion he cherished and on which the *Cornet* is externally based, was of modest middle-class descent. His father was a railroad employee. His mother, a woman who refused to accept reality in any form, brought him up as a girl until he was five. This, a delicate constitution, and the constant solicitude of which he was the victim, is more than enough to account for his extreme sensitivity. He was destined to be bullied as a youth and to suffer as a man.

Rilke's health was not adequate to the rigors of life at a cadet school, and he transfered to a commercial school in Austria. Occasional trips to Germany (Munich and Berlin) and a short visit to Italy pale in significance compared to his experience in Russia at the turn of the century. This was not a mere journey but a whole spiritual awakening. On the endless steppes and in the faith of the peasants he found his vision of God, God within him, growing as he grew.

In northern Germany, near Bremen, he joined a colony of artists, and there he married. The marriage was doomed. Rilke was a man apart, and he remained so. In 1902 he left Worpswede for Paris, where he became Rodin's secretary, learning much, and suffering acutely from the noise and confusion of the city.

He went to Scandinavia, back to Paris, in 1912 to Spain—where he found a patroness in the Princess of Thurn und Taxis, at whose castle at Duino on the Dalmatian coast he wrote some of his best poetry.

He was drafted in 1916 but was in no physical shape for military training. He was given a sinecure in the War Archives in Vienna. His conscience rebelled at the empty make-work of "dolling up" war reports, and he was for a time mercifully assigned to ruling large sheets of paper.

After the war he wandered about until he found a home of sorts at the Chateau of Muzot, in Switzerland, near Sierre. He died there in 1926, of leukemia brought to a crisis by the prick of a rose thorn.

Rilke stands aside from the great currents and movements of twentieth century literature—or rather he is himself one of them. His highly personal style and his mystic cult of the creative individual could influence others. They could scarcely make of him a member of a "school." In his experimentation with language, in his concentration on the word, in his ecstatic subjectivity he reminds us of the Expressionists. But it was they who learned from him. He had developed his style years before the movement or even the name existed.

Die Weise von Liebe und Tod des Cornets Christoph Rilke

(1904)

Including Rilke's *Cornet* in a collection of stories is an undertaking that involves some risk. There are many who would not call it a story at all, much less a *Novelle*. The ambiguity surrounding its form is revealed in the varying translations of its title: Lay . . ., Tale . . ., Song. . . .

Three considerations argue for its inclusion. In an age of experimentation it stands as one of the most notable ventures in the freeing and re-casting of narrative forms—and it most certainly narrates something. It has more of the characteristics of a *Novelle* than many works labelled as such: concentration upon a single striking event, a small cast of characters, a united and easily identifiable "point"; a strict, though unorthodox, construction. And finally, although this may be extraneous, it has been one of the most widely read narrative works in German literature.

Its literary merit justifies this popularity. There are few works which will so generously and quickly repay a modest amount of concentrated attention—to language, word repetitions, rhymes overt and hidden, alliterations, musicality in general, symbols and metaphors, personifications. The whole arsenal of poetic prose is here.

Let the briefest analysis of a short passage (see page 120) indicate what is meant.

Often Rilke sets the mood and scene of a new section with a single word or a brief phrase, here: *Rast!* (elsewhere: *Wachtfeuer; Ein Tag durch den Troß*). The poetic devices commence immediately, with the rhyme word *Gast*. The rhyme patterns enlarge: *fassen . . . lassen, gut . . . Mut* (here rhyme interlocks with alliteration: *gut . . . Mut . . . Muß*). Then *strecken . . . Decken* and *überschlagen . . . tragen . . . Kragen*. Note how continuity—almost a rush of excitement—is achieved. The first rhyme may end a sentence or stand at a strong pause juncture, but the second not. It leads on into more of its own sentence, at least until the bold pair of rhymes *Frauen sind . . . blauen sind*. Alliteration, much favored by Rilke, reinforces the picture: **W***ünsche . . . be***w***irten*, **k***ärglicher* **K***ost*. The dominant alliteration is sibilant—at least ten s's in clear alliterative use. Strong rhythmic patterns exist, actual scansion is possible. The most striking image is the personification of courage—even courage cannot forever brave crisis, it must stretch out and relax. The other symbols of ease and elegance are lavish: open collars, silken chairs, the ineffable pleasure of a bath. The final expression of opulence is the symbolic mention of the juice-laden fruit.

There is not even space to uncover all the resources of this small passage, and this passage represents by no means all the facets of the book's style. It is both inspiring and sobering to recall that, by Rilke's testimony at any rate, this story was the work of one night of feverish writing.

To be sure, the story is elusive. This is precisely its character. Like a ballad or a series of mood pictures it moves from one quick focus to another, omitting at will any incident, any piece of atmosphere or characterization that is extraneous to its plan. Events are hinted at or recognized from the shadows they cast. This makes them no less substantial or moving.

The heart of the work is clear: gentle youth, neither in time nor mind far removed from home and mother, lost in the vague landscape of war, coming in one swift succession of hours to the experience of first love, and of death. In this telescoping of the whole of life into a few days lies the pathos and singular appeal of Rilke's *Cornet*.

(The validity of Rilke's attitude toward war and death may be debated—indeed it should be. Is war or death in war poeticized? Why is it that this book, like few others, was a pocket companion at the front in World War I? For right reasons or wrong?)

DIE WEISE
VON LIEBE UND TOD
DES CORNETS
CHRISTOPH RILKE

„ . . . den 24. November 1663 wurde Otto von Rilke, auf Langenau, Gränitz und Ziegra, zu Linda mit seines in Ungarn gefallenen Bruders Christoph hinterlassenem Antheile am Gute Linda beliehen; doch mußte er einen Revers ausstellen, nach welchem die Lehensreichung null und nichtig sein sollte, im Falle sein Bruder Christoph (der nach beigebrachtem Totenschein als Cornet in der Compagnie des Freiherrn von Pirovano des kaiserl. oesterr. Heysterschen Regiments zu Roß . . . verstorben war) zurückkehrt . . .“

1
2

- 1 -

[1] *"On the 24th November, 1663, Otto von Rilke of Langenau, Gränitz, and Ziegra, at Linda was granted in fief that share of the estate of Linda left by his brother Christopher who was killed in Hungary; but he had to execute an agreement of reversion, according to which the enfeoffment should become null and void in the event that his brother Christopher (who according to the attached death certificate died as cornet in the Baron of Pirovano's company of the Imperial Austrian Heyster Regiment of horse) should return . . ."*

[2] **Langenau, Gränitz, Ziegra,** and **Linda** are actual places in Saxony. The date is that of the campaign launched by the Austrians (with French aid) against the Turks in Transylvania (now in Romania), an inconclusive affair which left the Porte still powerful in the area, though under a 20-year truce. **Der Cornet'** is *cornet* or *standard bearer*. The Baron of Pirovano commanded a company in the regiment of Count Sigbert of Heyster (or Heister), later Field Marshal in the Austrian armies, whose distinguished military career was then just beginning.

Reiten, reiten, reiten, durch den Tag, durch die Nacht, durch den Tag.

Reiten, reiten, reiten.

3 Und der Mut ist so müde geworden und die Sehnsucht so groß. Es gibt keine Berge mehr, kaum einen Baum. Nichts wagt aufzustehen. Fremde Hütten
4 hocken durstig an versumpften Brunnen. Nirgends ein Turm. Und immer das gleiche Bild. Man hat zwei Augen zuviel. Nur in der Nacht manchmal glaubt man den Weg zu kennen. Vielleicht kehren wir nächtens immer wieder das Stück zurück, das wir in der fremden Sonne mühsam gewonnen haben? Es kann sein. Die Sonne ist schwer, wie bei uns tief im Sommer. Aber wir haben im Sommer Abschied genommen. Die Kleider der Frauen leuchteten lang aus dem Grün. Und nun reiten wir lang. Es muß also Herbst sein.
5 Wenigstens dort, wo traurige Frauen von uns wissen.

6 Der von Langenau rückt im Sattel und sagt: „Herr Marquis . . .“

Sein Nachbar, der kleine feine Franzose, hat erst drei Tage lang gesprochen und gelacht. Jetzt weiß er nichts mehr. Er ist wie ein Kind, das schlafen möchte. Staub bleibt auf seinem feinen weißen Spitzenkragen liegen; er merkt es nicht. Er wird langsam welk in seinem samtenen Sattel.

Aber der von Langenau lächelt und sagt: „Ihr
7 habt seltsame Augen, Herr Marquis. Gewiß seht Ihr Eurer Mutter ähnlich—“

Da blüht der Kleine noch einmal auf und stäubt seinen Kragen ab und ist wie neu.

- 2 -

versumpft stagnant, mired

das Stück *here* distance, stretch

rücken shift, turn

der Spitzenkragen, - lace collar

samten velvet

[3] **der Mut ist so müde;** beginning of the alliterations so common here and in Rilke's poetry in general. What other examples on this page? What effect attained?

[4] **hocken;** note the image and compare it with that of the **Hütten** at the beginning of Raabe's story.

[5] In this barren monotony all sense of time is lost. The seasons are real at home, where women think of those who have left.

[6] **der von Langenau** *he of L.:* render simply *Langenau*

[7] **ähnlich sehen** resemble, look like

Jemand erzählt von seiner Mutter. Ein Deutscher offenbar. Laut und langsam setzt er seine Worte. Wie ein Mädchen, das Blumen bindet, nachdenklich Blume um Blume probt und noch nicht weiß, was aus dem Ganzen wird—: so fügt er seine Worte. Zu Lust? Zu Leide? Alle lauschen. Sogar das Spucken hört auf. Denn es sind lauter Herren, die wissen, was sich gehört. Und wer das Deutsche nicht kann in dem Haufen, der versteht es auf einmal, fühlt einzelne Worte: „Abends“ . . . „Klein war . . .“ [8] [9]

fügen fit, join together
spucken spit
sich gehören be proper

Da sind sie alle einander nah, diese Herren, die aus Frankreich kommen und aus Burgund, aus den Niederlanden, aus Kärntens Tälern, von den böhmischen Burgen und vom Kaiser Leopold. Denn was der Eine erzählt, das haben auch sie erfahren und gerade so. Als ob es nur e i n e Mutter gäbe . . . [10] [11] [12]

So reitet man in den Abend hinein, in irgend einen Abend. Man schweigt wieder, aber man hat die lichten Worte mit. Da hebt der Marquis den Helm ab. Seine dunklen Haare sind weich und, wie er das Haupt senkt, dehnen sie sich frauenhaft auf seinem Nacken. Jetzt erkennt auch der von Langenau: Fern ragt etwas in den Glanz hinein, etwas Schlankes, Dunkles. Eine einsame Säule, halbverfallen. Und wie sie lange vorüber sind, später, fällt ihm ein, daß das eine Madonna war. [13]

verfallen ruined

Wachtfeuer. Man sitzt rundumher und wartet. Wartet, daß einer singt. Aber man ist so müd. Das

- 3 -

[8] Here and often Rilke portrays delicately the absorption of the young soldier in thoughts of home, childhood, and mother. To this plain truth he adds the coloring of his almost feminine imagination.
[9] **das Deutsche** *German*
[10] **(das) Burgund'** *Burgundy*—an elusive geographical entity—at this time a semi-autonomous government centered at Dijon (France)
[11] **(das) Kärnten** *Carinthia*, a part of Austria
[12] *Leopold I, Emperor of the Holy Roman Empire*
[13] Again the indefiniteness and sameness of time

[14] [15] [16] [17] [18] [19] [20]

rote Licht ist schwer. Es liegt auf den staubigen Schuhn. Es kriecht bis an die Kniee, es schaut in die gefalteten Hände hinein. Es hat keine Flügel. Die Gesichter sind dunkel. Dennoch leuchten eine Weile die Augen des kleinen Franzosen mit eigenem Licht. Er hat eine kleine Rose geküßt, und nun darf sie weiterwelken an seiner Brust. Der von Langenau hat es gesehen, weil er nicht schlafen kann. Er denkt: Ich habe keine Rose, keine.

Dann singt er. Und das ist ein altes trauriges Lied, das zu Hause die Mädchen auf den Feldern singen, im Herbst, wenn die Ernten zu Ende gehen.

Sagt der kleine Marquis: „Ihr seid sehr jung, Herr?"

Und der von Langenau, in Trauer halb und halb im Trotz: „Achtzehn." Dann schweigen sie.

Später fragt der Franzose: „Habt Ihr auch eine Braut daheim, Herr Junker?"

„Ihr?" gibt der von Langenau zurück.

„Sie ist blond wie Ihr."

Und sie schweigen wieder, bis der Deutsche ruft: „Aber zum Teufel, warum sitzt Ihr denn dann im Sattel und reitet durch dieses giftige Land den türkischen Hunden entgegen?"

Der Marquis lächelt. „Um wiederzukehren."

Und der von Langenau wird traurig. Er denkt an ein blondes Mädchen, mit dem er spielte. Wilde Spiele. Und er möchte nach Hause, für einen Augenblick nur, nur für so lange, als es braucht, um die Worte zu sagen: „Magdalena,—daß ich immer s o w a r, verzeih!"

- 4 -

der Junker, - (Jung + Herr) young nobleman, squire

[14] A striking picture of the light as a living and moving thing

[15] **eigen** *special, of their own*

[16] **Rose,** symbol of a loved woman

[17] **Herbst** recalls not only the season it must be at home (see above) but the image of fullness, harvest, and death.

[18] **zu Ende gehen** *come to an end*

[19] **zurückgeben** *return, rejoin*

[20] **um wiederzukehren** a classical soldier's reply, as valid as any: *to get back home*

W i e—war? denkt der junge Herr.—Und sie sind weit. 21

Einmal, am Morgen, ist ein Reiter da, und dann ein zweiter, vier, zehn. Ganz in Eisen, groß. Dann tausend dahinter: das Heer.

Man muß sich trennen.

„Kehrt glücklich heim, Herr Marquis.—"

„Die Maria schützt Euch, Herr Junker." 22

Und sie können nicht voneinander. 23 Sie sind Freunde auf einmal, Brüder. Haben einander mehr zu vertrauen; denn sie wissen schon so viel Einer vom Andern. Sie zögern. Und ist Hast und Hufschlag um sie. Da streift der Marquis den großen rechten Handschuh ab. Er holt die kleine Rose hervor, nimmt ihr ein Blatt. Als ob man eine Hostie bricht.

„Das wird Euch beschirmen. Lebt wohl." 24

Der von Langenau staunt. Lange schaut er dem Franzosen nach. Dann schiebt er das fremde Blatt unter den Waffenrock. Und es treibt auf und ab auf den Wellen seines Herzens. Hornruf. Er reitet zum Heer, der Junker. Er lächelt traurig: ihn schützt eine fremde Frau.

Ein Tag durch den Troß. 25 Flüche, Farben, Lachen—: davon blendet das Land. Kommen bunte Buben gelaufen. Raufen und Rufen. Kommen Dirnen mit purpurnen Hüten im flutenden Haar. Winken. Kommen Knechte, schwarzeisern wie wandernde Nacht. Packen die Dirnen heiß, daß ihnen die Kleider zerreißen. Drücken sie an den Trommelrand. Und von

- 5 -

der Handschuh, -e *here* gauntlet

die Hostie host (*in the sacrament*)

beschirmen protect, guard

treiben† (ist) *here* float; **auf und ab treiben** rise and fall

der Troß, -sse camp

raufen scuffle, brawl

die Dirne, -n girl, lass, wench

purpurn purple *or* scarlet

der Knecht, -e *here* man-at-arms

der Trommelrand edge (rim) of the drum

[21] **. . . verzeih** . . . *pardon—for being always the way I was. Was—how?*

[22] **Maria** (*the Virgin*) *Mary*

[23] **können nicht voneinander** *cannot part*

[24] **lebt wohl** *farewell*

[25] The whole passage is alive with the wild excitement of the camp—and the poetic devices multiply in harmony with the mood. Examples?

26 der wilderen Gegenwehr hastiger Hände werden die Trommeln wach, wie im Traum poltern sie, poltern—. Und abends halten sie ihm Laternen her, seltsame: Wein, leuchtend in eisernen Hauben. Wein? Oder Blut?—Wer kanns unterscheiden?

27 Endlich vor Spork. Neben seinem Schimmel ragt der Graf. Sein langes Haar hat den Glanz des Eisens.

Der von Langenau hat nicht gefragt. Er erkennt den General, schwingt sich vom Roß und verneigt sich in einer Wolke Staub. Er bringt ein Schreiben mit, das ihn empfehlen soll beim Grafen. Der aber befiehlt: „Lies mir den Wisch.“ Und seine Lippen haben sich nicht bewegt. Er braucht sie nicht dazu; sind zum Fluchen gerade gut genug. Was 28 drüber hinaus ist, redet die Rechte. Punktum. Und man sieht es ihr an. Der junge Herr ist längst 29 zu Ende. Er weiß nicht mehr, wo er steht. Der Spork ist vor Allem. Sogar der Himmel ist fort. Da sagt Spork, der große General:

30 „Cornet.“

Und das ist viel.

31 Die Kompagnie liegt jenseits der Raab. Der von Langenau reitet hin, allein. Ebene. Abend. Der Beschlag vorn am Sattel glänzt durch den Staub. Und dann steigt der Mond. Er sieht es an seinen Händen. Er träumt.

32 Aber da schreit es ihn an.
Schreit, schreit,
zerreißt ihm den Traum.

- 6 -

die Gegenwehr resistance

her-halten† hold out to

die Haube, -n (conical) helmet

der Schimmel, - white horse

der Wisch, -e scribble, scrawl

Punktum period, that's that

der Beschlag, ⸚e *here* metal knobs, studs

[26] A vivid and most most unusual image. The girls fight back against the soldiers. Their hands strike against the drums, whose muffled noise calls up memories of more serious business. The double portent is repeated, then, in the metaphor of wine and blood.

[27] **Spork** or **Sporck** (Count Johann von), a daring and unpredictable officer, commanded cavalry units in the Thirty Years War and went on to his greatest fame as leader of the victorious cavalry charge at St. Gotthard which turned back the Turks in 1664.

[28] **drüber hinaus** *beyond that*

[29] **zu Ende sein** *be finished*

[30] That is, as a result of the letter of introduction, Spork commissions the young man as cornet.

[31] **Raab,** a river which rises in Austria, crosses Hungarian territory, and empties into the Danube

[32] **es schreit ihn an** *someone* (*something*) *screams at him*

es bäumt sich something rears up (arches up)

ihn graust he shudders

Das ist keine Eule. Barmherzigkeit:
der einzige Baum
schreit ihn an: [33]
Mann!
Und er schaut: es bäumt sich. Es bäumt sich ein Leib
den Baum entlang, und ein junges Weib,
blutig und bloß,
fällt ihn an: Mach mich los!

Und er springt hinab in das schwarze Grün
und durchhaut die heißen Stricke;
und er sieht ihre Blicke glühn
und ihre Zähne beißen. [34]

Lacht sie?
Ihn graust.
Und er sitzt schon zu Roß
und jagt in die Nacht. Blutige Schnüre fest in der Faust.

Der von Langenau schreibt einen Brief, ganz in Gedanken. [35] Langsam malt er mit großen, ernsten, aufrechten Lettern:

„Meine gute Mutter,
seid stolz: Ich trage die Fahne,
seid ohne Sorge: Ich trage die Fahne,
habt mich lieb: Ich trage die Fahne—" [36]

Dann steckt er den Brief zu sich in den Waffenrock, an die heimlichste Stelle, neben das Rosenblatt. Und denkt: Er wird bald duften davon. Und denkt: Vielleicht findet ihn einmal Einer . . . Und denkt: . . . ; denn der Feind ist nah.

-7-

[33] Rilke chooses this terrifying scene for the introduction of still another poetic device, reinforcing the intensity gained by alliterations and repetitions. What is it? Is the narration now entirely poetic?
[34] **beißen:** The picture is that of clenched teeth (hence the verb) flashing in the pale light (hence the following question).
[35] **ganz in Gedanken** *absorbed in thought*
[36] A literal reading of this "letter" would miss the point. The repetitions are hardly to be taken verbatim. Rather they represent and symbolize his intense pride in his one great piece of news.

Sie reiten über einen erschlagenen Bauer. Er hat die Augen weit offen und etwas spiegelt sich drin; kein Himmel. Später heulen Hunde. Es kommt also ein Dorf, endlich. Und über den Hütten steigt steinern ein Schloß. Breit hält sich ihnen die Brücke hin.[37] Groß wird das Tor. Hoch willkommt das Horn. Horch: Poltern, Klirren und Hundegebell! Wiehern im Hof, Hufschlag und Ruf.

Rast! Gast sein einmal. Nicht immer selbst seine Wünsche bewirten mit kärglicher Kost. Nicht immer feindlich nach allem fassen; einmal sich alles geschehen lassen und wissen: Was geschieht, ist gut. Auch der Mut muß einmal sich strecken[38] und sich am Saume seidener Decken in sich selber überschlagen. Nicht immer Soldat sein. Einmal die Locken offen tragen und den weiten offenen Kragen und in seidenen Sesseln sitzen und bis in die Fingerspitzen s o:[39] nach dem Bad sein. Und wieder erst lernen, was Frauen sind. Und wie die weißen tun und wie die blauen[40] sind; was für Hände sie haben, wie sie ihr Lachen singen, wenn blonde Knaben die schönen Schalen bringen, von saftigen Früchten schwer.

Als Mahl beganns. Und ist ein Fest geworden, kaum weiß man wie. Die hohen Flammen flackten, die Stimmen schwirrten, wirre Lieder klirrten aus Glas und Glanz, und endlich aus den reifgewordnen Takten:[41] entsprang der Tanz. Und alle riß er hin. Das war ein Wellenschlagen in den Sälen, ein Sich-Begegnen und ein Sich-Erwählen, ein Abschiednehmen und ein

- 8 -

willkommt' *an unusual verb form: here with poetic effect* welcomes

wiehern neigh

die Kost fare

in sich selber überschla'gen† *see below*

saftig juicy

flacken *another unusual verb form—note the rhyme*—flare
schwirren whir, buzz

[37] **die Brücke;** in a bold image of personification the bridge extends out to them, as if in welcome.

[38] **sich strecken** *stretch out and relax* (which even courage itself must do); the picture is continued in the difficult and ambiguous phrase **in sich selber überschlagen** *fold, collapse, turn in upon itself.*

[39] **so** (*be*) *like this,* indefinite allusion to the way one feels after a bath

[40] **blau,** besides its obvious use for the rhyme, and for the color of dresses, may be significant as the Virgin Mary's color.

[41] **reifgewordene Takte** *beat* (*measure*) *now full-grown:* that is the noise gradually sorts itself out into a recognizable beat as the dance begins.

das Glanzgenießen, *coined compound,* reveling in radiance; *similarly* **das Lichterblinden** blinding of light

Wiederfinden, ein Glanzgenießen und ein Lichterblinden und ein Sich-Wiegen in den Sommerwinden, die in den Kleidern warmer Frauen sind.

Aus dunklem Wein und tausend Rosen rinnt die Stunde rauschend in den Traum der Nacht.

geartet constituted, disposed

der Staat *here* state *in the sense of* splendor

Und Einer steht und staunt in diese Pracht. Und er ist so geartet, daß er wartet, ob er erwacht. Denn nur im Schlafe schaut man solchen Staat und solche Feste solcher Frauen: ihre kleinste Geste ist eine Falte, fallend in Brokat. Sie bauen Stunden auf aus silbernen Gesprächen, und manchmal heben sie die Hände so—, und du mußt meinen, daß sie irgendwo, wo du nicht hinreichst, sanfte Rosen brächen, die du nicht siehst. Und da träumst du: Geschmückt sein mit ihnen und anders beglückt sein und dir eine Krone verdienen für deine Stirne, die leer ist.

42

Einer, der weiße Seide trägt, erkennt, daß er nicht erwachen kann; denn er ist wach und verwirrt von Wirklichkeit. So flieht er bange in den Traum und steht im Park, einsam im schwarzen Park. Und das Fest ist fern. Und das Licht lügt. Und die Nacht ist nahe um ihn und kühl. Und er fragt eine Frau, die sich zu ihm neigt:

„Bist Du die Nacht?"

Sie lächelt.

Und da schämt er sich für sein weißes Kleid.

Und möchte weit und allein und in Waffen sein.

Ganz in Waffen.

- 9 -

[42] **nicht hinreichst** *cannot reach*

Hast Du vergessen, daß Du mein Page bist für diesen Tag? Verlässest Du mich? Wo gehst Du hin? Dein weißes Kleid gibt mir Dein Recht—.“[43]

— — — — — — — — — — — — — — — —

„Sehnt es Dich nach Deinem rauhen Rock?“

— — — — — — — — — — — — — — — —

„Frierst Du?—Hast Du Heimweh?“

Die Gräfin lächelt.

Nein. Aber das ist nur, weil das Kindsein ihm von den Schultern gefallen ist, dieses sanfte dunkle Kleid. Wer hat es fortgenommen? „Du?“ fragt er mit einer Stimme, die er noch nicht gehört hat. „Du!“

Und nun ist nichts an ihm. Und er ist nackt wie ein Heiliger. Hell und schlank.

Langsam lischt das Schloß aus.[44] Alle sind schwer: müde oder verliebt oder trunken. Nach so vielen leeren, langen Feldnächten: Betten. Breite eichene Betten. Da betet sichs anders[45] als in der lumpigen Furche unterwegs, die, wenn man einschlafen will, wie ein Grab wird.

lumpig wretched, shabby

„Herrgott, wie Du willst!“

Kürzer sind die Gebete im Bett.

Aber inniger.

Die Turmstube ist dunkel.

Aber sie leuchten sich ins Gesicht mit ihrem Lächeln. Sie tasten vor sich her[46] wie Blinde und finden den Andern wie eine Tür. Fast wie Kinder, die sich vor der Nacht ängstigen, drängen sie sich in einander ein.[47] Und doch fürchten sie sich nicht. Da ist nichts,

- 10 -

[43] **gibt mir dein Recht** *gives me right to (over) you*
[44] **das Schloß lischt aus** *the castle lights go out*
[45] **da betet sichs anders** *praying is different there*
[46] **vor sich her** *before them(selves)*
[47] **sich in einander eindrängen** *press close*

was gegen sie wäre: kein Gestern, kein Morgen; denn die Zeit ist eingestürzt. Und sie blühen aus ihren Trümmern.[48]

Er fragt nicht: „Dein Gemahl?"

Sie fragt nicht: „Dein Namen?"

Sie haben sich ja gefunden, um einander ein neues Geschlecht zu sein.

Sie werden sich hundert neue Namen geben und einander alle wieder abnehmen, leise, wie man einen Ohrring abnimmt.

Handschuh *see above*

Im Vorsaal über einem Sessel hängt der Waffenrock, das Bandelier und der Mantel von dem von Langenau. Seine Handschuhe liegen auf dem Fußboden. Seine Fahne steht steil, gelehnt an das Fensterkreuz. Sie ist schwarz und schlank. Draußen jagt ein Sturm über den Himmel hin und macht Stücke aus der Nacht, weiße und schwarze. Der Mondschein geht wie ein langer Blitz vorbei, und die reglose Fahne hat unruhige Schatten. Sie träumt.

War ein Fenster offen? Ist der Sturm im Haus? Wer schlägt die Türen zu? Wer geht durch die Zimmer?—Laß.[49] Wer es auch sei. Ins Turmgemach findet er nicht.[50] Wie hinter hundert Türen ist dieser große Schlaf, den zwei Menschen gemeinsam haben; so gemeinsam wie e i n e Mutter oder e i n e n Tod.

Ist das der Morgen? Welche Sonne geht auf? Wie groß ist die Sonne? Sind das Vögel? Ihre Stimmen sind überall.

- 11 -

[48] **Trümmer,** i.e., **der Zeit** *from the ruined remains of time,* which has been shattered

[49] **laß** *let it be, no matter*

[50] **in . . . finden** *find one's way into*

Alles ist hell, aber es ist kein Tag.

Alles ist laut, aber es sind nicht Vogelstimmen.

Das sind die Balken, die leuchten. Das sind die Fenster, die schrein. Und sie schrein, rot, in die Feinde hinein, die draußen stehn im flackernden Land, schrein: Brand.

Und mit zerrissenem Schlaf im Gesicht drängen sich alle, halb Eisen, halb nackt, von Zimmer zu Zimmer, von Trakt zu Trakt und suchen die Treppe.

Und mit verschlagenem Atem stammeln Hörner im Hof:

Sammeln, sammeln!
Und bebende Trommeln.

Aber die Fahne ist nicht dabei.
Rufe: Cornet!
Rasende Pferde, Gebete, Geschrei,
Flüche: Cornet!
Eisen an Eisen, Befehl und Signal;
Stille: Cornet!
Und noch ein Mal: Cornet!
Und heraus mit der brausenden Reiterei.

— — — — — — — — — — — — — — — —

Aber die Fahne ist nicht dabei.

Er läuft um die Wette mit brennenden Gängen, durch Türen, die ihn glühend umdrängen, über Treppen, die ihn versengen, bricht er aus aus dem rasenden Bau. Auf seinen Armen trägt er die Fahne wie eine weiße, bewußtlose Frau. Und er findet ein Pferd, und es ist wie ein Schrei: über alles dahin und an allem

- 12 -

der Trakt, -e wing

mit verschlagenem Atem breathlessly

rasen *here* hurtle, dash

um die Wette laufen† run a race

vorbei, auch an den Seinen. Und da kommt auch die Fahne wieder zu sich, und niemals war sie so königlich; und jetzt sehn sie sie alle, fern voran, und erkennen den hellen, helmlosen Mann und erkennen die Fahne . . . [51] [52]

Aber da fängt sie zu scheinen an, wirft sich hinaus und wird groß und rot . . .

— — — — — — — — — — — — — — — —

Da brennt ihre Fahne mitten im Feind, und sie jagen ihr nach.

Der von Langenau ist tief im Feind, aber ganz allein. Der Schrecken hat um ihn einen runden Raum gemacht, und er hält, mitten drin, unter seiner langsam verlodernden Fahne.

Langsam, fast nachdenklich, schaut er um sich. Es ist viel Fremdes, Buntes vor ihm. Gärten—denkt er und lächelt. Aber da fühlt er, daß Augen ihn halten, und erkennt Männer und weiß, daß es die heidnischen Hunde sind—: und wirft sein Pferd mitten hinein.

Aber, als es jetzt hinter ihm zusammenschlägt, sind es doch wieder Gärten, und die sechzehn runden Säbel, die auf ihn zuspringen, Strahl um Strahl, sind ein Fest. [53]

Eine lachende Wasserkunst. [54]

Der Waffenrock ist im Schlosse verbrannt, der Brief und das Rosenblatt einer fremden Frau.—

Im nächsten Frühjahr (es kam traurig und kalt) ritt ein Kurier des Freiherrn von Pirovano langsam in Langenau ein. Dort hat er eine alte Frau weinen sehen.

- 13 -

verlodern (ist) flicker, die down (of a fire)

heidnisch heathen

[51] **über alles dahin und an allem vorbei** *over and away, past everything*
[52] **zu sich kommen** *come to (itself)* (personification)
[53] **auf . . . zuspringen** *leap upon*
[54] **Wasserkunst:** In what is perhaps the boldest and most vivid image in the whole story, Rilke brings life and death, dream-memory and terrible reality together. The bright flashing sabers of the Turks, as they leap upon the cornet, gleam like a fountain playing in a garden—and "garden" is the association he has carried from his first, brief encounter with love.

Franz Kafka

Kafka, like Rilke, was born in Prague. At the time of his birth in 1883, Prague was the capital of Bohemia, which was part of the Austro-Hungarian monarchy. His family background was Jewish, German-speaking, and middle class.

Kafka's father was a successful merchant, with no interest in literature, indeed an aversion to it. An overbearing man, he became the center of a monumental father-conflict, easily one of the most productive in literature. Kafka once told him in a letter, "Everything I have written is about you."

After a rigorous classical training in a German gymnasium, Kafka studied at the University of Prague, where he got his law degree. He worked for a time in the insurance and compensation department of the Austro-Hungarian government. Here he had his practical introduction to bureaucracy. It and the law figure in his works as two of the inexorable and incomprehensible forces which engulf the individual.

In 1912, the year he wrote *Das Urteil*, Kafka also met the girl known as "F.B." In 1914 he became engaged to her, and for three hectic years they quarreled and made up, while Kafka was tormented by anxiety and fear of marriage, and by the first serious onslaught of the disease that killed him. From now until his death in 1924, his life is a succession of lengthening visits to tuberculosis sanatoria, with intermittent periods of work and equally intermittent love affairs, only one of which rises above the level of fugitive experience.

Kafka's works are relentlessly autobiographical. In some, his name or initial marks the hero. Hero may be the wrong word for Kafka's memorable figures. (In a sense they are all the same person, and the "others" exist only as they impinge on the hero. As W. H. Auden said, one may speak of someone as "like a character from Dickens." But one can only speak of a "Kafkaesque *situation*.") Alienated, guilt-ridden, baffled and tortured, Kafka's men move across an eerie landscape like nerve-wracked victims of a nightmare. But it would be a grievous error to read his stories for their "Gothic" externals, for their surrealist visions of frustration, terror, cruelty, and anxiety. These externals, as one critic warns, are "intensified metaphysical symbol."

All but one of the works Kafka published during his lifetime appeared in the decade 1910-1920. They include the present story and *Der Heizer* (later part of *Amerika*); the famous *Verwandlung* with its traumatic opening: "One morning Gregor Samsa awoke and found himself transformed into a giant insect"; a collection of stories, *Ein Landarzt*, and the frightening story *In der Strafkolonie*—the prisoner's sentence is engraved into the flesh of his back by a monstrous machine, deeper and deeper, until he can read his own guilt in his wracked body. In 1924, the last year of his life, Kafka completed a collection of four stories called *Ein Hungerkünstler*. He was so sick that he was unable to finish proofreading it.

Kafka's three novels, *Der Prozeß*, *Das Schloß*, *Amerika*, were all published after his death, and against his last wishes, by his friend Max Brod. Brod called them "a trilogy of loneliness." Common to them is the theme of man guilty without knowing his guilt, helpless in the hands of "authorities" he can neither identify nor placate, lost in a frustrating search for meaning, justice, or—some critics add—God. There are also occasional glimpses of a complacent, diseased society capable of sustaining no one.

Kafka is unquestionably a writer of first rank. His influence in European and American letters has been prodigious. The only serious question that can be raised is whether, seen as a whole, his work is not ultimately limited by the specific, if common, neurosis which in some part engendered it. If this is *not* so, he is one of the great writers of all European literature.

Das Urteil

(1916)

Franz Kafka is a pioneer in the displacing of conventional reality as the normal environment of fiction. Like the Expressionists, he substitutes an inner reality of his own, but he goes beyond them in three important ways. His new world, his deeper reality, is not merely a recording of momentary inner states but, ultimately, an enveloping totality. It is not an extract, or formulation consistent with the ordinary world of appearances and illuminating it but a reversal which destroys it. And to describe this world he borrows the familiar features of everyday reality, and the most prosaic prose. The world of Franz Kafka is a soberly and lucidly recorded nightmare.

Das Urteil, Kafka claimed, was written from ten one evening to six the next morning, "as if I were borne on by a flood. . . . All things can be put into words, all one's ideas, even the strangest. . . ." It was his first successful work, but in it his style appears in full maturity. Here, as in all his stories, familiar reality dissolves before our eyes. The narrative line dives without warning into a submarine world, while the surface, made up of words and things, remains the same and everyone behaves temporarily as if nothing extraordinary had happened. In *Die Verwandlung* this occurs with the first sentence. In *Das Urteil* it happens by stages.

For the first several paragraphs, not a ripple disturbs the surface. Only the reader made suspicious by a long apprenticeship in Kafka will be alert to a curious remoteness between Georg and his friend, an intentional excluding of the friend from Georg's life. It is most obvious in Georg's suppression of the news of his engagement, and the compulsive "slip" it three times leads him into.

What are we to say, however, of his fiancée's sudden challenge: "If you have such friends, Georg, you shouldn't have got engaged at all"? Surely in a well-ordered world this makes no sense—what is so bad about his friend or (as far as she knows) about Georg's relation to him? In what sort of a world does it make sense? In a world where vague guilt feeling, ordinarily unexpressed and invisible to others, *becomes* reality, is *seen* by others as through a window and *is* verbalized. Or a world in which you hear other people say what you are thinking. (This still leaves open the question of the substantive reason for not getting engaged.)

The nature and meaning of the friend is curiously central to the story and offers perhaps the best avenue to a reasonably satisfying interpretation. (There is no use in seeking "the" reading of any work by Kafka.) The notion that the friend is the "artist in Georg (or Kafka)" seems dispensable. It founders on the relation of the friend to Georg's father, or of Kafka to his father. Much more tenable is the picture of the friend as a more general *alter ego*, a "Sohn nach meinem Herzen," as the father says, a better, truer Georg. Perhaps even more helpful is the notion that the friend *is* a "real person," a friend denied, as Georg in deeper truth denies all others. This gives crucial weight and sense to the father's accusation at the moment of "sentence": "Jetzt weißt du also, was es noch außer dir gab, bisher wußtest du nur von dir." In this light, Georg is really guilty—not, of course, legally or literally, in the degree urged by his father's insane advocacy in the court where he is also judge—but at heart guilty: of alienation of self from any true relationship with other human beings, of what the Existentialists call *mauvaise foi* (acting in bad faith, falsely to one's nature).

Even the uninitiated reader will soon discover the terrifying truth and power in Kafka: that he successfully transfers the cloak of reality—which in all sanity belongs to the things and words we perceive about us—to the frustration and anxiety, the complexes and neuroses of man's psyche. He will discover his trick of striking his characters down in the midst of considerable external success. (Georg is prospering.) He will discover Kafka's disconcerting penetration into the by-ways of motivation: solicitude for others as self-defense or even attack. (Georg tries to quiet his father by fussing over him. His father is in a way right when he says his son is trying to "get him down.") He will see that in Kafka what is "punished" may be guilt feeling as much as guilt, inadequacy as much as wrongdoing. (Georg is weak before his father; he is so ridden with guilt feelings he will accept any accusation, he has no inner strength to match his success. Kafka's heroes are truly the "hollow men." The shell of Georg's emptiness collapses before the mad consistency of his father's vengeful attack.)

Harder to deal with is another plane of meaning on which Kafka apparently intended to operate. The imagery of the story is our best clue. The father strikes a Jehovah-like pose—fluttering robe, hand on ceiling, the thundering accusations. He is a *Schreckbild* to which Georg must look up. All that Georg recalls from his friend's anecdotes of Russia is the picture of the clergyman cutting a cross of blood in the palm of his hand. Even his father was impressed by the story and repeated it to his friends. There is no escaping the symbolic weight of Georg's words to his father concerning his friend: "At least twice I denied him before you."

In other words, beneath the already sunken stratum of psychological meaning, there may be a plane of religious allegory. This is the most elusive part of Kafka, and what he meant to say is far less clear than the fact that he meant to say it. Of all interpretations of Kafka, those centering on a religious reading of his works are apt to be the least coherent, the most extravagant.

DAS URTEIL

Es war an einem Sonntagvormittag im schönsten Frühjahr. Georg Bendemann, ein junger Kaufmann, saß in seinem Privatzimmer im ersten Stock eines der niedrigen, leichtgebauten Häuser, die entlang des Flusses in einer langen Reihe, fast nur in der Höhe und Färbung unterschieden, sich hinzogen. Er hatte gerade einen Brief an einen sich im Ausland befindlichen Jugendfreund beendet, verschloß ihn in spielerischer Langsamkeit und sah dann, den Ellbogen auf den Schreibtisch gestützt, aus dem Fenster auf den Fluß, die Brücke und die Anhöhen am anderen Ufer mit ihrem schwachen Grün.

Er dachte darüber nach, wie dieser Freund, mit seinem Fortkommen zu Hause unzufrieden, vor Jahren schon nach Rußland sich förmlich geflüchtet hatte. Nun betrieb er ein Geschäft in Petersburg, das anfangs sich sehr gut angelassen hatte, seit langem aber schon zu stocken schien, wie der Freund bei seinen immer seltener werdenden Besuchen klagte. So arbeitete er sich in der Fremde nutzlos ab, der fremdartige Vollbart verdeckte nur schlecht das seit den Kinderjahren wohlbekannte Gesicht, dessen gelbe Hautfarbe auf eine sich entwickelnde Krankheit hinzudeuten schien. Wie er erzählte, hatte er keine rechte Verbindung mit der dortigen Kolonie seiner Landsleute, aber auch fast

-1-

förmlich as it were, in effect

sich gut an-lassen† be promising

stocken *here* stagnate, make no progress

[1] **der erste Stock** what floor?

[2] **die . . . sich hinzogen**

[3] **einen sich im Ausland befindlichen Jugendfreund** is simply the "participial" or "extended attribute" construction with an adjective where a participle usually appears. (Kafka uses many participial constructions.)

[4] **den Ellbogen . . . gestützt,** an absolute construction, (*with*) *his elbow propped . . .*

[5] **St. Petersburg,** now *Leningrad*

keinen gesellschaftlichen Verkehr mit einheimischen Familien und richtete sich so für ein endgültiges Junggesellentum ein.

Was wollte man einem solchen Manne schreiben, der sich offenbar verrannt hatte, den man bedauern, dem man aber nicht helfen konnte. Sollte man ihm vielleicht raten, wieder nach Hause zu kommen, seine Existenz hierherzuverlegen, alle die alten freundschaftlichen Beziehungen wiederaufzunehmen—wofür ja kein Hindernis bestand—und im übrigen auf die Hilfe der Freunde zu vertrauen? Das bedeutete aber nichts anderes, als daß man ihm gleichzeitig, je schonender, desto kränkender, sagte, daß seine bisherigen Versuche mißlungen seien, daß er endlich von ihnen ablassen solle, daß er zurückkehren und sich als ein für immer Zurückgekehrter von allen mit großen Augen anstaunen lassen müsse, daß nur seine Freunde etwas verstünden und daß er ein altes Kind sei, das den erfolgreichen, zu Hause gebliebenen Freunden einfach zu folgen habe. Und war es dann noch sicher, daß alle die Plage, die man ihm antun müßte, einen Zweck hätte? Vielleicht gelang es nicht einmal, ihn überhaupt nach Hause zu bringen—er sagte ja selbst, daß er die Verhältnisse in der Heimat nicht mehr verstünde—, und so bliebe er dann trotz allem in seiner Fremde, verbittert durch die Ratschläge und den Freunden noch ein Stück mehr entfremdet. Folgte er aber wirklich dem Rat und würde hier—natürlich nicht mit Absicht, aber durch die Tatsachen—niedergedrückt, fände sich nicht in seinen Freunden und nicht ohne sie zurecht, litte an Beschämung, hätte

- 2 -

das Junggesellentum bachelor's existence

sich verrennen† run into trouble, be on the wrong track

hierher′-verlegen transfer here

im übrigen for the rest

je schonender, desto kränkender *literally* the more considerately, the more insultingly; *freely:* . . . offending him more deeply, the more one tried to be considerate . . .

Ratschläge, *plural of* **Rat** *in sense of* advice

[6] **als daß man . . . sagte** than saying

[7] **daß:** a series of **daß** clauses follows.

[8] **ein für immer Zurückgekehrter** *someone who had returned for good*

[9] **bliebe** is subjunctive: *would remain*

[10] **den Freunden** goes with **entfremdet,** *alienated from*

[11] **folgte, würde, fände, litte, hätte** introduce *if*-clauses; the main clause is then the question **war es . . . nicht besser?**

es vorwärts-bringen† make progress

notdürftig scanty, inadequate

in gemeinsamer Wirtschaft keeping house together

jetzt wirklich keine Heimat und keine Freunde mehr, war es da nicht viel besser für ihn, er blieb in der Fremde, so wie er war? Konnte man denn bei solchen Umständen daran denken, daß er es hier tatsächlich vorwärtsbringen würde?

Aus diesen Gründen konnte man ihm, wenn man noch überhaupt die briefliche Verbindung aufrechterhalten wollte, keine eigentlichen Mitteilungen machen, wie man sie ohne Scheu auch den entferntesten Bekannten machen würde. Der Freund war nun schon über drei Jahre nicht in der Heimat gewesen und erklärte dies sehr notdürftig mit der Unsicherheit der politischen Verhältnisse in Rußland, die demnach also auch[12] die kürzeste Abwesenheit eines kleinen Geschäftsmannes nicht zuließen, während hunderttausende Russen ruhig in der Welt herumfuhren. Im Laufe dieser drei Jahre hatte sich aber gerade für Georg vieles verändert. Von dem Todesfall von Georgs Mutter, der vor etwa zwei Jahren erfolgt war und seit welchem Georg mit seinem alten Vater in gemeinsamer Wirtschaft lebte, hatte der Freund wohl noch erfahren und sein Beileid in einem Brief mit einer Trockenheit ausgedrückt, die ihren Grund nur darin haben konnte,[13] daß die Trauer über ein solches Ereignis in der Fremde ganz unvorstellbar wird. Nun hatte aber Georg seit jener Zeit, so wie alles andere, auch[14] sein Geschäft mit größerer Entschlossenheit angepackt. Vielleicht hatte ihn der Vater bei Lebzeiten der Mutter dadurch, daß[15] er im Geschäft nur seine Ansicht gelten lassen wollte, an einer wirklichen eigenen Tätigkeit gehindert, vielleicht war der Vater seit dem Tode der Mutter,

- 3 -

[12] **auch,** *as so often, even*

[13] **darin, daß . . .** (like **damit, daß; davon, daß;** etc.) a very common German construction, almost always clear if first rendered *in* (*with, from,* etc.) *the fact that. . . .*

[14] **so wie alles andere, auch . . .** would in English be reversed: *his business, as well as everything else.*

[15] **dadurch, daß er . . . gelten lassen wollte** (*through the fact that . . .*) *by being willing to let only his views prevail*

16

trotzdem er noch immer im Geschäft arbeitete, zurückhaltender geworden, vielleicht spielten—was sogar sehr wahrscheinlich war—glückliche Zufälle eine weit wichtigere Rolle, jedenfalls aber hatte sich das Geschäft in diesen zwei Jahren ganz unerwartet entwickelt, das Personal hatte man verdoppeln müssen, der Umsatz hatte sich verfünffacht, ein weiterer Fortschritt stand zweifellos bevor.

Der Freund aber hatte keine Ahnung von dieser Veränderung. Früher, zum letztenmal vielleicht in jenem Beileidsbrief, hatte er Georg zur Auswanderung nach Rußland überreden wollen und sich über die Aussichten verbreitet, die gerade für Georgs Geschäftszweig in Petersburg bestanden. Die Ziffern waren verschwindend gegenüber dem Umfang, den Georgs Geschäft jetzt angenommen hatte. Georg aber hatte keine Lust gehabt, dem Freund von seinen geschäftlichen Erfolgen zu schreiben, und hätte er es jetzt nachträglich getan, es hätte wirklich einen merkwürdigen Anschein gehabt.

So beschränkte sich Georg darauf, dem Freund immer nur über bedeutungslose Vorfälle zu schreiben, wie sie sich, wenn man an einem ruhigen Sonntag nachdenkt, in der Erinnerung ungeordnet aufhäufen. Er wollte nichts anderes, als die Vorstellung ungestört lassen, die sich der Freund von der Heimatstadt in der langen Zwischenzeit wohl gemacht und mit welcher er sich abgefunden hatte. So geschah es Georg, daß er dem Freund die Verlobung eines gleichgültigen Menschen mit einem ebenso gleichgültigen Mädchen dreimal in ziemlich weit auseinanderliegenden Briefen

- 4 -

der Umsatz turnover, sales

sich ab-finden† **mit** make one's peace with, become reconciled to

auseinan'derliegend separate(d)

[16] **was** is the relative with generalized antecedent: *which (was indeed quite probable)*

anzeigte, bis sich dann allerdings der Freund, ganz gegen Georgs Absicht, für diese Merkwürdigkeit zu interessieren begann.

Georg schrieb ihm aber solche Dinge viel lieber,[17] als daß er zugestanden hätte, daß er selbst vor einem Monat mit einem Fräulein Frieda Brandenfeld, einem Mädchen aus wohlhabender Familie, sich verlobt hatte. Oft sprach er mit seiner Braut über diesen Freund und das besondere Korrespondenzverhältnis, in welchem er zu ihm stand. „Er wird also gar nicht zu unserer Hochzeit kommen", sagte sie, „und ich habe doch das Recht, alle deine Freunde kennenzulernen." „Ich will ihn nicht stören", antwortete Georg, „verstehe mich recht, er würde wahrscheinlich kommen, wenigstens glaube ich es, aber er würde sich gezwungen und geschädigt fühlen, vielleicht mich beneiden und sicher unzufrieden und unfähig, diese Unzufriedenheit jemals[18] zu beseitigen, allein wieder zurückfahren. Allein— weißt du, was das ist?" „Ja, kann er denn von unserer Heirat nicht auch auf andere Weise erfahren?" „Das kann ich allerdings nicht verhindern, aber es ist bei seiner Lebensweise unwahrscheinlich." „Wenn du solche Freunde hast, Georg, hättest du dich überhaupt nicht verloben sollen." „Ja, das ist unser beider Schuld; aber ich wollte es auch jetzt nicht anders haben." Und wenn sie dann, rasch atmend unter seinen Küssen, noch vorbrachte: „Eigentlich kränkt es mich doch", hielt er es wirklich für unverfänglich, dem Freund alles zu schreiben. „So bin ich und so hat er mich hinzunehmen", sagte er sich, „ich kann nicht aus mir einen Menschen herausschneiden, der vielleicht für die

- 5 -

geschädigt *here* hurt

noch vorbrachte† managed to say, was able to say
unverfäng'lich natural enough

heraus'-schneiden† cut out; tailor

[17] **viel lieber** *much preferred* (*writing . . . to admitting . . .*)
[18] **unzufrieden** and the following explanatory phrase **unfähig . . . zu beseitigen** are predicate adjectives with **zurückfahren.**

Freundschaft mit ihm geeigneter wäre, als ich es bin."

Und tatsächlich berichtete er seinem Freunde in dem langen Brief, den er an diesem Sonntagvormittag schrieb, die erfolgte Verlobung mit folgenden Worten: „Die beste Neuigkeit habe ich mir bis zum Schluß aufgespart. Ich habe mich mit einem Fräulein Frieda Brandenfeld verlobt, einem Mädchen aus einer wohlhabenden Familie, die sich hier erst lange nach Deiner[19] Abreise angesiedelt hat, die Du also kaum kennen dürftest. Es wird sich noch Gelegenheit finden, Dir Näheres über meine Braut mitzuteilen, heute genüge[20] Dir, daß ich recht glücklich bin und daß sich in unserem gegenseitigen Verhältnis nur insofern etwas geändert hat, als Du jetzt in mir statt eines ganz gewöhnlichen Freundes einen glücklichen Freund haben wirst. Außerdem bekommst Du in meiner Braut, die Dich herzlich grüßen läßt, und die Dir nächstens selbst schreiben wird, eine aufrichtige Freundin, was für einen Junggesellen nicht ganz ohne Bedeutung ist. Ich weiß, es hält Dich vielerlei von einem Besuche bei uns zurück, wäre aber nicht gerade meine Hochzeit die richtige Gelegenheit, einmal alle Hindernisse über den Haufen zu werfen? Aber wie dies auch[21] sein mag, handle ohne alle Rücksicht und nur nach Deiner Wohlmeinung."

Mit diesem Brief in der Hand war Georg lange, das Gesicht dem Fenster zugekehrt, an seinem Schreibtisch gesessen. Einem Bekannten, der ihn im Vorübergehen von der Gasse aus gegrüßt hatte, hatte er kaum mit einem abwesenden Lächeln geantwortet.

- 6 -

grüßen lassen† send greetings

der Junggeselle, -n, -n bachelor

über den Haufen werfen† cast aside, throw overboard

ohne alle Rücksicht without regard to anything else

nach deiner Wohlmeinung according to what you think is best

[19] **Deiner** is capitalized, like all other forms of **du,** in letters.

[20] **genüge,** present subjunctive, literally *let it suffice*

[21] **auch** again in concessive function: *however this may be*

Endlich steckte er den Brief in die Tasche und ging aus seinem Zimmer quer durch einen kleinen Gang in das Zimmer seines Vaters, in dem er schon seit Monaten nicht gewesen war. Es bestand auch sonst keine Nötigung dazu, denn er verkehrte mit seinem Vater ständig im Geschäft, das Mittagessen nahmen sie gleichzeitig in einem Speisehaus ein, abends versorgte sich zwar jeder nach Belieben, doch saßen sie dann meistens, wenn nicht Georg, wie es am häufigsten geschah, mit Freunden beisammen war oder jetzt seine Braut besuchte, noch ein Weilchen, jeder mit seiner Zeitung, im gemeinsamen Wohnzimmer. Georg staunte darüber, wie dunkel das Zimmer des Vaters selbst an diesem sonnigen Vormittag war. Einen solchen Schatten warf also die hohe Mauer, die sich jenseits des schmalen Hofes erhob. Der Vater saß beim Fenster in einer Ecke, die mit verschiedenen Andenken an die selige Mutter ausgeschmückt war, und las die Zeitung, die er seitlich vor die Augen hielt, wodurch er irgendeine Augenschwäche auszugleichen suchte. Auf dem Tisch standen die Reste des Frühstücks, von dem nicht viel verzehrt zu sein schien.

22 23 24 25

„Ah, Georg!“ sagte der Vater und ging ihm gleich entgegen. Sein schwerer Schlafrock öffnete sich im Gehen, die Enden umflatterten ihn— ‚Mein Vater ist noch immer ein Riese‘, sagte sich Georg.

26

„Hier ist es ja unerträglich dunkel“, sagte er dann.

„Ja, dunkel ist es schon“, antwortete der Vater.

„Das Fenster hast du auch geschlossen?“

„Ich habe es lieber so.“

nach Belieben to one's own taste

selig late

[22] **seit Monaten,** a degree of "distance" ordinarily unlikely, in spite of the succeeding rationalization, for people living **in gemeinsamer Wirtschaft;** it sets up a remoteness both as artificial and as significant as the remoteness from his St. Petersburg friend.

[23] **wenn nicht Georg . . . besuchte** is a sort of parenthetical subordinate clause; here as usual it will help if one breaks Kafka's sentences down into their simpler components.

[24] **Mauer,** often with Kafka a symbol of the shutting off of life, especially when (as here) it precludes light or a view. Remember its symbolic function in the Thomas Mann story.

[25] **seitlich,** it turns out later, provides a significant hint that all is not as it seems to be in this scene. In general the picture is a curious one, yet it is hard to say exactly why.

[26] **Riese,** too, concludes a significant picture, the father as not only giant but judge (the robe fluttering about him).

„Es ist ja ganz warm draußen", sagte Georg, wie im Nachhang zu dem Früheren, und setzte sich.

Der Vater räumte das Frühstücksgeschirr ab und stellte es auf einen Kasten.

„Ich wollte dir eigentlich nur sagen", fuhr Georg fort, der den Bewegungen des alten Mannes ganz verloren folgte, „daß ich nun doch nach Petersburg meine Verlobung angezeigt habe." Er zog den Brief ein wenig aus der Tasche und ließ ihn wieder zurückfallen.

„Nach Petersburg?" fragte der Vater.

„Meinem Freunde doch", sagte Georg und suchte des Vaters Augen.—Im Geschäft ist er doch ganz anders, dachte er, wie er hier breit sitzt und die Arme über der Brust kreuzt.

„Ja. Deinem Freunde", sagte der Vater mit Betonung.

„Du weißt doch, Vater, daß ich ihm meine Verlobung zuerst verschweigen wollte. Aus Rücksichtnahme, aus keinem anderen Grunde sonst. Du weißt selbst, er ist ein schwieriger Mensch. Ich sagte mir, von anderer Seite kann er von meiner Verlobung wohl erfahren, wenn das auch bei seiner einsamen Lebensweise kaum wahrscheinlich ist—das kann ich nicht hindern—, aber von mir selbst soll er es nun einmal nicht erfahren."

„Und jetzt hast du es dir wieder anders überlegt?" fragte der Vater, legte die große Zeitung auf den Fensterbord und auf die Zeitung die Brille, die er mit der Hand bedeckte.

„Ja, jetzt habe ich es mir wieder überlegt. Wenn

-8-

das Geschirr dishes, "things"

verloren absorbed

breit sitzen† sit stretched out and relaxed

von anderer Seite from some other quarter

es sich anders überle'gen change one's mind

in die Breite ziehen† open wide

bei einer Sache halten† concern oneself with a matter, talk about a thing

er mein guter Freund ist, sagte ich mir, dann ist meine glückliche Verlobung auch für ihn ein Glück. Und deshalb habe ich nicht mehr gezögert, es ihm anzuzeigen. Ehe ich jedoch den Brief einwarf, wollte ich es dir sagen."

„Georg", sagte der Vater und zog den zahnlosen Mund in die Breite, „hör einmal! Du bist wegen dieser Sache zu mir gekommen, um dich mit mir zu beraten. Das ehrt dich ohne Zweifel. Aber es ist nichts, es ist ärger als nichts, wenn du mir jetzt nicht die volle Wahrheit sagst. Ich will nicht Dinge aufrühren, die nicht hierher gehören. Seit dem Tode unserer teueren Mutter sind gewisse unschöne Dinge vorgegangen. Vielleicht kommt auch für sie die Zeit, und vielleicht kommt sie früher, als wir denken. Im Geschäft entgeht mir manches, es wird mir vielleicht nicht verborgen— ich will jetzt gar nicht die Annahme machen, daß es mir verborgen wird—, ich bin nicht mehr kräftig genug, mein Gedächtnis läßt nach, ich habe nicht mehr den Blick für alle die vielen Sachen. Das ist erstens der Ablauf der Natur, und zweitens hat mich der Tod unseres Mütterchens viel mehr niedergeschlagen als dich.—Aber weil wir gerade bei dieser Sache halten, bei diesem Brief, so bitte ich dich, Georg, täusche mich nicht. Es ist eine Kleinigkeit, es ist nicht des Atems wert, also täusche mich nicht. Hast du wirklich diesen Freund in Petersburg?"

27 28 29

Georg stand verlegen auf. „Lassen wir meine Freunde sein. Tausend Freunde ersetzen mir nicht meinen Vater. Weißt du, was ich glaube? Du schonst dich nicht genug. Aber das Alter verlangt seine Rechte.

- 9 -

[27] **zahnlos,** *etc.*: Note the continuing contrast of senile characteristics and characteristics of overwhelming power in the picture of Georg's father.

[28] **verborgen,** i.e., perhaps others in the firm are not concealing things from him (but it looks that way).

[29] **Freund in Petersburg:** Here reality—or Georg's grasp of it—is called starkly into question. Note that Georg immediately tries to placate his father.

Du bist mir im Geschäft unentbehrlich, das weißt du ja sehr genau, aber wenn das Geschäft deine Gesundheit bedrohen sollte, sperre ich es noch morgen für immer. Das geht nicht. Wir müssen da eine andere Lebensweise für dich einführen. Aber von Grund aus. Du sitzt hier im Dunkeln und im Wohnzimmer hättest du schönes Licht. Du nippst vom Frühstück, statt dich ordentlich zu stärken. Du sitzt bei geschlossenem Fenster, und die Luft würde dir so gut tun. Nein, mein Vater! Ich werde den Arzt holen, und seinen Vorschriften werden wir folgen. Die Zimmer werden wir wechseln, du wirst ins Vorderzimmer ziehen, ich hierher. Es wird keine Veränderung für dich sein, alles wird mit übertragen werden. Aber das alles hat Zeit, jetzt lege dich noch ein wenig ins Bett, du brauchst unbedingt Ruhe. Komm, ich werde dir beim Ausziehn helfen, du wirst sehn, ich kann es. Oder willst du gleich ins Vorderzimmer gehn, dann legst du dich vorläufig in mein Bett. Das wäre übrigens sehr vernünftig."

von Grund aus completely, from top to bottom

nippen nibble

Georg stand knapp neben seinem Vater, der den Kopf mit dem struppigen weißen Haar auf die Brust hatte sinken lassen.

knapp *here* close, right

„Georg", sagte der Vater leise, ohne Bewegung.

Georg kniete sofort neben dem Vater nieder, er sah die Pupillen in dem müden Gesicht des Vaters übergroß in den Winkeln der Augen auf sich gerichtet.

„Du hast keinen Freund in Petersburg. Du bist immer ein Spaßmacher gewesen und hast dich auch mir gegenüber nicht zurückgehalten. Wie sollst du denn gerade dort einen Freund haben! Das kann ich gar nicht glauben."

gegenü'ber *here* in relation to

- 10 -

[30] **mit** here *at the same time*

[31] **das hat Zeit** *there is time for that*

„Denk doch einmal nach, Vater", sagte Georg, hob den Vater vom Sessel und zog ihm, wie er nun doch recht schwach dastand, den Schlafrock aus, „jetzt wird es bald drei Jahre her sein, da war mein Freund bei uns zu Besuch. Ich erinnere mich noch, daß du ihn nicht besonders gern hattest. Wenigstens zweimal habe ich ihn vor dir verleugnet, trotzdem er gerade bei mir im Zimmer saß. Ich konnte ja deine Abneigung gegen ihn ganz gut verstehn, mein Freund hat seine Eigentümlichkeiten. Aber dann hast du dich doch auch wieder ganz gut mit ihm unterhalten. Ich war damals noch so stolz darauf, daß du ihm zuhörtest, nicktest und fragtest. Wenn du nachdenkst, mußt du dich erinnern. Er erzählte damals unglaubliche Geschichten von der Russischen Revolution. Wie er zum Beispiel auf einer Geschäftsreise in Kiew bei einem Tumult einen Geistlichen auf einem Balkon gesehen hatte, der sich ein breites Blutkreuz in die flache Hand schnitt, diese Hand erhob und die Menge anrief. Du hast ja selbst diese Geschichte hier und da wiedererzählt." [32]

Währenddessen war es Georg gelungen, den Vater wieder niederzusetzen und ihm die Trikothose, die er über den Leinenunterhosen trug, sowie die Socken vorsichtig auszuziehn. Beim Anblick der nicht besonders reinen Wäsche machte er sich Vorwürfe, den Vater vernachlässigt zu haben. Es wäre sicherlich auch seine Pflicht gewesen, über den Wäschewechsel seines Vaters zu wachen. Er hatte mit seiner Braut darüber, wie sie die Zukunft des Vaters einrichten wollten, noch nicht ausdrücklich gesprochen, denn sie hatten still- [33] [34]

- 11 -

die flache Hand the palm of the hand

die Trikot'hose, -n knitted tights (underwear)
die Leinenunterhose, -n linen shorts; *see below*

[32] **Kiew,** our spelling *Kiev,* Russian city, capital of the Ukraine

[33] **Leinenunterhosen** may also be long. In any case, they are usually worn instead of, not with, **Trikothosen.** The precise nature of the situation is not clear, but there is no question as to what it implies. Georg's father is odd in this respect, too.

[34] **darüber . . . gesprochen** ("save" the **wie** clause for the end in English)

schweigend vorausgesetzt, daß der Vater allein in der alten Wohnung bleiben würde. Doch jetzt entschloß er sich kurz mit aller Bestimmtheit, den Vater in seinen künftigen Haushalt mitzunehmen. Es schien ja fast, wenn man genauer zusah, daß die Pflege, die dort dem Vater bereitet werden sollte, zu spät kommen könnte.

Auf seinen Armen trug er den Vater ins Bett. Ein schreckliches Gefühl hatte er, als er während der paar Schritte zum Bett hin merkte, daß an seiner Brust der Vater mit seiner Uhrkette spielte. Er konnte ihn nicht gleich ins Bett legen, so fest hielt er sich an dieser Uhrkette.

Kaum war er aber im Bett, schien alles gut. Er deckte sich selbst zu und zog dann die Bettdecke noch besonders weit über die Schulter. Er sah nicht unfreundlich zu Georg hinauf.

„Nicht wahr, du erinnerst dich schon an ihn?" fragte Georg und nickte ihm aufmunternd zu.

„Bin ich jetzt gut zugedeckt?" fragte der Vater, als könne er nicht nachschauen, ob die Füße genug bedeckt seien.

„Es gefällt dir also schon im Bett", sagte Georg und legte das Deckzeug besser um ihn.

„Bin ich gut zugedeckt?" fragte der Vater noch einmal und schien auf die Antwort besonders aufzupassen.

„Sei nur ruhig, du bist gut zugedeckt."

„Nein!" rief der Vater, daß die Antwort an die Frage stieß, warf die Decke zurück mit einer Kraft, daß sie einen Augenblick im Fluge sich ganz entfaltete, und stand aufrecht im Bett. Nur eine Hand hielt er leicht

35

- 12 -

stoßen† an *here* impinge on, come directly on the heels of

[35] **mit einer Kraft** *with such strength*

der Plafond', -s ceiling
das Früchtchen rascal of a son

an den Plafond. „Du wolltest mich zudecken, das weiß ich, mein Früchtchen, aber zugedeckt bin ich noch nicht. Und ist es auch die letzte Kraft, genug für dich, zuviel für dich. Wohl kenne ich deinen Freund. Er wäre ein Sohn nach meinem Herzen. Darum hast du ihn auch betrogen die ganzen Jahre lang. Warum sonst? Glaubst du, ich habe nicht um ihn geweint? Darum doch sperrst du dich in dein Büro, niemand soll stören, der Chef ist beschäftigt—nur damit du deine falschen Briefchen nach Rußland schreiben kannst. Aber den Vater muß glücklicherweise niemand lehren, den Sohn zu durchschauen. Wie du jetzt geglaubt hast, du hättest ihn untergekriegt, so untergekriegt, daß du dich mit deinem Hintern auf ihn setzen kannst und er rührt sich nicht, da hat sich mein Herr Sohn zum Heiraten entschlossen!"

36

37

mein Herr Sohn, *sarcastic imitation of combinations like* **(mein) Herr General;** *render* my fine upstanding son

Georg sah zum Schreckbild seines Vaters auf. Der Petersburger Freund, den der Vater plötzlich so gut kannte, ergriff ihn wie noch nie. Verloren im weiten Rußland sah er ihn. An der Türe des leeren, ausgeraubten Geschäftes sah er ihn. Zwischen den Trümmern der Regale, den zerfetzten Waren, den fallenden Gasarmen stand er gerade noch. Warum hatte er so weit wegfahren müssen!

das Regal', -e show-case, shelf (in store)

„Aber schau mich an!" rief der Vater, und Georg lief, fast zerstreut, zum Bett, um alles zu fassen, stockte aber in der Mitte des Weges.

„Weil sie die Röcke gehoben hat", fing der Vater zu flöten an, „weil sie die Röcke so gehoben hat, die widerliche Gans", und er hob, um das darzustellen, sein Hemd so hoch, daß man auf seinem Oberschenkel

flöten (die Flöte flute) pipe
die Gans, ⸚e goose, *frequently used in derogatory sense of women, implying witlessness;* simpleton, ninny
das Hemd, -en *here* nightshirt
der Oberschenkel, - thigh

- 13 -

[36] **ist es auch:** note verb first and **auch**—what kind of construction is this?

[37] **muß** here *has to*

die Narbe aus seinen Kriegsjahren sah, „weil sie die Röcke so und so und so gehoben hat, hast du dich an sie herangemacht, und damit du an ihr ohne Störung [38] dich befriedigen kannst, hast du unserer Mutter Andenken geschändet, den Freund verraten und deinen Vater ins Bett gesteckt, damit er sich nicht rühren kann. Aber kann er sich rühren oder nicht?" Und er stand vollkommen frei und warf die Beine. Er strahlte vor Einsicht.

Georg stand in einem Winkel, möglichst weit vom [39] Vater. Vor einer langen Weile hatte er sich fest entschlossen, alles vollkommen genau zu beobachten, damit er nicht irgendwie auf Umwegen, von hinten her, von oben herab überrascht werden könne. Jetzt erinnerte er sich wieder an den längst vergessenen Entschluß und vergaß ihn, wie man einen kurzen Faden durch ein Nadelöhr zieht.

„Aber der Freund ist nun doch nicht verraten!" rief der Vater, und sein hin und her bewegter Zeigefinger bekräftigte es. „Ich war sein Vertreter hier am Ort."

„Komödiant!" konnte sich Georg zu rufen nicht [40] enthalten, erkannte sofort den Schaden und biß, nur zu spät—die Augen erstarrt—, in seine Zunge, daß er vor Schmerz einknickte.

„Ja, freilich habe ich Komödie gespielt! Komödie! Gutes Wort! Welcher andere Trost blieb dem alten verwitweten Vater? Sag—und für den Augenblick der Antwort sei du noch mein lebender Sohn—, was blieb mir übrig, in meinem Hinterzimmer, verfolgt vom [41] ungetreuen Personal, alt bis in die Knochen? Und

- 14 -

sich befriedigen an have one's pleasure with

die Beine werfen† kick one's legs

er strahlte vor Einsicht he glowed with insight, he was radiant with insight

der Komödiant', -en, -en actor, comedian

ein-knicken (bend) double

die Komö'die, -n comedy, play; **Komö'die spielen** act (a part)

[38] Georg's father appends to his angry and evil accusation a virtual "bill of particulars" against his son—and in a real sense these may be taken as the measure of Georg's vast feelings of guilt. They may in fact be baseless, but they are "true" because Georg accepts them. (Note: **Bett** = *grave?*)

[39] Here, as clearly as anywhere, we can see how Kafka selects his plane of reality. Georg's terrified inferiority is the true reality. It is made "visible" in this posture of the trapped animal—whether to be taken literally or not. (Similarly, his father's superiority—or Georg's admission of it—was reflected in **Er strahlte vor Einsicht.**) Portraying such states as reality gives to Kafka's descriptions the mode of a surrealist landscape.

[40] Had Georg been able to take his father as an "actor," he might have escaped his terrible fate, but he immediately withdraws his one overt attempt to fight back.

[41] The father is portrayed as at once senile, overpowering, and paranoid—a shocking yet enormously effective combination.

sich überpur'zeln turn somersaults

von dem du ausgingst† *render* who were my flesh and blood

durchzi'schen (zischen = hiss, *etc.*) shoot through

die Kundschaft clientele

Hemd *see above*

sich ein-hängen† in take someone's arm

mein Sohn ging im Jubel durch die Welt, schloß Geschäfte ab, die ich vorbereitet hatte, überpurzelte sich vor Vergnügen und ging vor seinem Vater mit dem verschlossenen Gesicht eines Ehrenmannes davon! Glaubst du, ich hätte dich nicht geliebt, ich, von dem du ausgingst?"

Jetzt wird er sich vorbeugen, dachte Georg, wenn er fiele und zerschmetterte! Dieses Wort durchzischte seinen Kopf. [42]

Der Vater beugte sich vor, fiel aber nicht. Da Georg sich nicht näherte, wie er erwartet hatte, erhob er sich wieder. [43]

„Bleib, wo du bist, ich brauche dich nicht! Du denkst, du hast noch die Kraft, hierherzukommen, und hältst dich bloß zurück, weil du so willst. Daß du dich nicht irrst! Ich bin noch immer der viel Stärkere. Allein hätte ich vielleicht zurückweichen müssen, aber so hat mir die Mutter ihre Kraft abgegeben, mit deinem Freund habe ich mich herrlich verbunden, deine Kundschaft habe ich hier in der Tasche!" [44]

‚Sogar im Hemd hat er Taschen!' sagte sich Georg und glaubte, er könnte ihn mit dieser Bemerkung in der ganzen Welt unmöglich machen. Nur einen Augenblick dachte er das, denn immerfort vergaß er alles.

„Häng dich nur in deine Braut ein und komm mir entgegen! Ich fege sie dir von der Seite weg, du weißt nicht, wie!"

Georg machte Grimassen, als glaube er das nicht. Der Vater nickte bloß, die Wahrheit dessen, was er sagte, beteuernd, in Georgs Ecke hin.

- 15 -

[42] **wenn er fiele . . .** *what if he fell . . .* —a last, irrational hope

[43] What is implied in the phrase **wie er erwartet hatte?**

[44] **daß du nicht . . .** *see that you don't . . .*

„Wie hast du mich doch heute unterhalten, als du kamst und fragtest, ob du deinem Freund von der Verlobung schreiben sollst. Er weiß doch alles, dummer Junge, er weiß doch alles! Ich schrieb ihm doch, weil du vergessen hast, mir das Schreibzeug wegzunehmen. Darum kommt er schon seit Jahren nicht, er weiß ja alles hundertmal besser als du selbst, deine Briefe zerknüllt er ungelesen in der linken Hand, während er in der rechten meine Briefe zum Lesen sich vorhält!"

Seinen Arm schwang er vor Begeisterung über dem Kopf. „Er weiß alles tausendmal besser!" rief er.

„Zehntausendmal!" sagte Georg, um den Vater zu verlachen, aber noch in seinem Munde bekam das Wort einen todernsten Klang.

„Seit Jahren passe ich schon auf, daß du mit dieser Frage kämest! Glaubst du, mich kümmert etwas anderes? Glaubst du, ich lese Zeitungen? Da!" und er warf Georg ein Zeitungsblatt, das irgendwie mit ins Bett getragen worden war, zu. Eine alte Zeitung, mit einem Georg schon ganz unbekannten Namen. [45]

„Wie lange hast du gezögert, ehe du reif geworden bist! Die Mutter mußte sterben, sie konnte den Freudentag nicht erleben, der Freund geht zugrunde in seinem Rußland, schon vor drei Jahren war er gelb zum Wegwerfen, und ich, du siehst ja, wie es mit mir steht. Dafür hast du doch Augen!"

„Du hast mir also aufgelauert!" rief Georg.

Mitleidig sagte der Vater nebenbei: „Das wolltest du wahrscheinlich früher sagen. Jetzt paßt es ja gar nicht mehr."

Und lauter: „Jetzt weißt du also, was es noch

- 16 -

zerknüllen crumple

reif *may have two planes of meaning;* mature; ripe (for condemnation)

gelb zum Wegwerfen yellow enough to throw away (*remember the friend's ominous complexion*)

auf-lauern lie in wait (ambush) for, spy on

[45] **Georg** is dative, but not with **einem.** What does **einem** modify?

eigentlich . . . noch eigentlicher it is true . . . what is closer to the truth

überrum'peln run into, take by surprise

die Schürze, -n apron

es trieb† ihn he was driven (by forces within him)

der Turner, - gymnast

die Stange, -n bar

außer dir gab, bisher wußtest du nur von dir! Ein unschuldiges Kind warst du ja eigentlich, aber noch eigentlicher warst du ein teuflischer Mensch!—Und darum wisse: Ich verurteile dich jetzt zum Tode des Ertrinkens!" [46]

Georg fühlte sich aus dem Zimmer gejagt, den Schlag, mit dem der Vater hinter ihm aufs Bett stürzte, trug er noch in den Ohren davon. Auf der Treppe, über deren Stufen er wie über eine schiefe Fläche eilte, überrumpelte er seine Bedienerin, die im Begriffe war, hinaufzugehen, um die Wohnung nach der Nacht aufzuräumen. „Jesus!" rief sie und verdeckte mit der Schürze das Gesicht, aber er war schon davon. [47] Aus dem Tor sprang er, über die Fahrbahn zum Wasser trieb es ihn. Schon hielt er das Geländer fest, wie ein Hungriger die Nahrung. Er schwang sich über, als der ausgezeichnete Turner, der er in seinen Jugendjahren zum Stolz seiner Eltern gewesen war. Noch hielt er sich mit schwächer werdenden Händen fest, erspähte zwischen den Geländerstangen einen Autoomnibus, der mit Leichtigkeit seinen Fall übertönen würde, rief leise: „Liebe Eltern, ich habe euch doch immer geliebt", und ließ sich hinabfallen.

In diesem Augenblick ging über die Brücke ein geradezu unendlicher Verkehr. [48]

- 17 -

[46] What significance could be attached to the form of death to which Georg is condemned?

[47] The exclamation is not as profane as it would be in English.

[48] Of what might the **geradezu unendlicher Verkehr** be symbolic?

Paul Ernst

If one were to look for a single writer who encompassed within his career most of the intellectual and literary currents of Germany from 1900 to Hitler, that writer might well be Paul Ernst. At one time or the other, sometimes concurrently, he was a Nietzschean, a Marxist, an anti-Marxist, and a saved Christian—and the Nazis thought he was one of them. He was a critic, a political and social worker, an editor, a public speaker, a drama critic, and a literary man. He was a Naturalist, a Neo-Romanticist, a Neo-Classicist—in fact, the most important Neo-Classicist.

His output was prodigious and varied. He wrote hundreds of essays and speeches, a score or more of dramas in all forms (including one he considered specifically his own), several autobiographical works, philosophical treatises, works on political economy, *Novellen* by the hundreds, half a dozen novels, and a German epic six times as long as the *Iliad*.

Ernst was born at Elbingerode in the Harz in 1866. He was the son of a mine foreman. He studied at the universities of Göttingen, Tübingen, Berlin and Bern—first for the ministry and then economics and sociology, since he could see no social conscience in the theology he was taught. He wrote, spoke, and edited a paper for the Social Democratic (i.e., Marxist) party. Like many later intellectuals in their experience with Communism (Orwell, Malraux, Fast, Koestler), Ernst underwent a profound break with his Marxist past. One of his major economic and social works is *Der Zusammenbruch des Marxismus* (1918).

Great Germans seem inevitably to have their *italienische Reise*—not merely a trip, but a deep cultural experience. Ernst is a notable example. In Italy at the turn of the century he clarified his view of aesthetics and literary form and turned to classical modes of writing—simple, strict, compact, and restrained. In particular, he sharpened his concept of the *Novelle*, developing the ideas which made him one of the greatest theoreticians of the genre.

There is an undeniable element of confusion or inconsistency in Ernst's philosophical writings. He denied the historical Jesus, for example, but claimed to have experienced the "grace of faith" in Christ. There is none of this in his stories. In some the background is Italian, perfectly rendered, though with German psychological overtones. In some it is German, often with implied or explicit praise of the old ways. But always the line of the plot is tightly drawn, almost skeletal. A *Novelle* by Ernst may sound like the digest of a longer work. Anything conceivably unessential in action or atmosphere is left out. Concentration is upon the essential ethical issue, as a man intervenes in the fate of another, or takes final stock of himself, or encounters inevitability in any of its forms.

The end of Ernst's life is clouded with the homage paid him by the Nazis. Their regard for him was based largely on his *Grundlagen der neuen Gesellschaft* (1930; a reworking of *Zusammenbruch des Marxismus*, with a good deal of "leader" theory added) and on his proclamation of the breakdown of German liberalism and idealism. His literary works cannot be tarred with the same brush, as the Nazis found when they tried to produce his uncompromising plays.

Mercifully, before this unhappy recognition had gone too far, Ernst died at his home in Styria in 1933.

Der geraubte Brief

(1929)

To Paul Ernst, the *Novelle* is an ideal vehicle for the portrayal of the tightly knit ethical relationships in the light of which he saw and evaluated life. A brief view of some of his principles may help to explain our story.

True character he found in the willingness to intervene in the course of events, to give orders, and to bear responsibility. To Ernst, the first important thing about an action is that it be decisively taken. Steps taken for mixed motives or in the sentimental hope that things will turn out well he condemns. It is not that Ernst ignores good and bad. He simply gives greater weight to the undiluted quality of an act, even a bad one, than does conventional ethics.

Ernst's characters are apt to draw drastic consequences from a judgment of their own position. The hero comes to a sudden and clear awareness that he is "out of joint" with the times, that his future as an honest man is closed. At this point, typically, he commits suicide. The suddenness of the deed may shock us, but it is clear that Ernst believes his death to be a rigorously logical and warranted step.

Ernst is interested in acts of impulse or steps taken under stress, because they reveal whether we are "whole" in our ethical make-up. He is willing to concede that two persons may act each in accord with his particular occupation or class or ethic, and thus come into irreconcilable conflict.

Ernst is also interested in the complicated chain of right-or-wrong decisions, of true or specious interpretations of duty (a concept which is closely allied, for Ernst, to a person's position in society). This chain can be considerably extended and highly complicated, until a vigorous exercise of Ernstian dialectics is required before one can be sure who is right and who is wrong, and which is the better person.

Ernst's *Novellen* are among the shortest in the history of the genre. Atmosphere and detailed characterization are at a minimum. To get to the main business, he will state baldly what others would motivate carefully. (We are simply asked to accept the fact that Manfred loves Marie.) Once he is there, however, he will take great pains to develop his pattern of decision, action, and consequences.

This seems like a long preamble for a very short *Novelle*. But it may serve to warn us that the story is more complicated—and therefore more interesting—than it seems at first glance.

The story has a happy ending; it is thus a comedy. It can not carry the theories of the author to their ultimate and often remorseless end. But the essential relationships are there. Had Ernst decided to work the same incident into a tragedy, it is likely that some one of his three main characters would have done something very drastic.

The crucial ethical decision is Melanie's stopping of the letter. Typically it is made in haste and urgency. Melanie corresponds to the higher types in Ernst's hierarchy, those who decide and act. Her intervention affects both Manfred and Marie.

This is of course not her only intervention into Manfred's fate. Her father was obviously prepared to discard him as a candidate for the professorship. Melanie's intercession causes him to reconsider. We do not actually know for what precise reasons he changes his mind, whether on the basis of academic merits or the interests of Melanie.

Manfred is low in the same hierarchy of forcefulness and self-determination. (This being a comedy, he will not have to pay the consequences.) He is invited in the first place for reasons other than he thinks. He owes his continued candidacy to Melanie. And he owes to her the presence of Marie at the decisive dinner party.

Clearly we are meant to see Manfred in an ironically humorous light. He theorizes grandly, condemning his fellow men who think life is only a confusion of chance and accident. He says Melanie thinks so too—whereas she thinks nothing of the kind, or at least acts on no such premise. As for him, he believes that God wills all that happens to him. "Everything is fated." This is not only pompous, but inaccurate. His whole fate at the moment of the story hinges on Melanie. Or so it seems.

There may even be irony behind this irony. The most important question about *Der geraubte Brief* has not yet been asked. With it we should end this introduction, for it poses the captivating ambiguity which raises the story so far above the trivial. For what purpose did Melanie really stop the letter, to bring Marie to the party, or to keep her away?

DER GERAUBTE BRIEF

Ein junger Mann, er heiße[1] Manfred, war zu Besuch bei Verwandten in der Hauptstadt, welche eine einzige Tochter hatten namens Melanie.

Manfred war ein junger Gelehrter. Er war als Helfer einem seiner früheren Lehrer an der Universität beigegeben, und hielt bereits selber Vorlesungen; aller Wahrscheinlichkeit nach hatte er noch viele Jahre vor sich, in denen er sich recht ärmlich durchdrücken mußte. Der Oheim, bei welchem er zu Besuch weilte, war vortragender Rat im Unterrichtsministerium, von ihm hing seine Beförderung ab.

Es war die Zeit im Winter, wo die großen Gesellschaften sind. Auf einer solchen Gesellschaft hatte Manfred ein junges Mädchen kennengelernt, wir wollen ihr den Namen Marie geben, an welche er am andern Tag folgenden Brief richtete: ,,Es ist ungehörig, daß ich Ihnen als fast Fremder schreibe; aber ich weiß keine andere Möglichkeit, mich Ihnen zu nähern, und übermorgen muß ich wieder abreisen. Ich habe Ihre Anschrift durch Melanie erfahren. Sie sagte mir, daß Sie ein armes Mädchen sind. Ich selber bin auch arm, und es kann lange dauern, bis ich daran denken darf, zu heiraten. Aber ich liebe Sie. Sie haben für heute Abend mit Ihren Eltern eine Einladung; auch ich soll in der Gesellschaft sein. Wenn ich eine Hoffnung haben

- 1 -

sich durch-drücken get (squeeze) by

vortragender Rat im Unterrichtsministe'rium Advisory Counselor to the Ministry of Education

ungehörig improper, unseemly

[1] **er heiße** (*subjunctive*) let us call him

darf, so bitte ich Sie, zu kommen." Marie las den Brief langsam, sie drehte das Blatt um und betrachtete die leere Rückseite. Sie seufzte, dann faltete sie das Blatt und legte es in ein kleines Kästchen, dessen Schlüssel sie beständig bei sich trug. Sie sagte ihrer Mutter, sie habe Kopfschmerzen und könne am Abend die Gesellschaft nicht besuchen.

2 Am Abend erwartete Manfred Marien. Sie kam nicht. Es wurde getanzt. Er tanzte und sprach viel mit Melanie.

Er sagte: „Den heutigen Menschen erscheint das Leben als eine Reihe von wirren Zufällen. Auch Ihnen erscheint es so. Ich weiß nicht, wie die Leute mit einer solchen Ansicht leben können. Unsere Vorfahren glaubten, daß unser Leben von Gott geleitet wird. Der Glaube ist kindlich; aber was er meint, das ist richtig; und man kann ihn nicht anders ausdrücken, als kindlich, denn unser Vater ist es ja, der uns leitet, und wie könnte ein Kind seinen Vater anders verstehen als kindlich? Ohne den Willen Gottes fällt nicht ein Haar von meinem Haupt—"

Melanie sagte: „Für die Frau ist die Liebe Schicksal. Für den Mann nicht."

„Es ist Alles Schicksal", sagte Manfred, „und Alles ist eine Verbindung von göttlichem Führen und menschlichem Gehen."

Am andern Morgen erhielt Manfred einen Brief seines Lehrers. Er durfte noch drei Tage länger in seinen Ferien verweilen. Er war der erste in der Familie, der wach war. Er hatte eine Besorgung zu

-2-

[2] **Marien** is accusative of **Marie.** The old feminine singular **-n** ending (common to the oblique cases of certain noun classes) is not infrequent in proper names.

machen und ging fort; am Frühstückstisch war Melanie mit ihren Eltern allein.

Ihr Vater sagte: „Ich habe Manfred zu Besuch kommen lassen, um ihn näher kennen zu lernen. Eine Professur ist zu verleihen, für welche er an sich geeignet wäre, trotz seiner Jugend, durch seine wissenschaftlichen Leistungen und die Empfehlungen der Fakultät. Ich habe aber meine Bedenken. Mir sind diese übermäßig frommen Menschen nicht angenehm. Ich vermute Strebertum und Liebedienerei.“ [3]

Melanie wurde rot. „Du hast eine ganz falsche Vorstellung von ihm“, sagte sie. „Ich glaube fast, er ist gar nicht kirchlich. Er ist ein ganz freier Mensch.“

Der Vater sah das Mädchen erstaunt an. „Du nimmst ja seine Partei mit großer Lebhaftigkeit“, sagte er.

„Einem jungen Mädchen gibt er sich wohl natürlicher, als er sich dir gibt“, sagte sie, „und seine Gedanken über die religiösen Dinge sind auch nicht leicht mitzuteilen. Ich versichere dich, ihm liegt nichts ferner als Strebertum.“ [4]

„Du bist ja ein kluges Mädchen“, erwiderte nachdenklich der Vater. „Vielleicht habe ich mich geirrt. Ich müßte ihn mir noch einmal vornehmen. Möglich, daß ich zu ungeduldig war. Man macht unwillkürlich seine Abteilungen und ordnet dann gedankenlos jede neue Erscheinung einer solchen Abteilung zu.“

Vor dem Hause war ein Briefkasten. Pünktlich elf Uhr kam jeden Tag ein Postbote und leerte ihn. Als der Postbote kam, seinen Ledersack mit dem eisernen

- 3 -

an sich per se

das Strebertum excessive ambition, pushiness

die Lie'bedienerei' toadying

sich geben† show oneself in a . . . light

zu-ordnen assign, consign

[3] **. . . ist zu verleihen** *there is (a professorship) open (to be assigned)*

[4] **ihm liegt nichts ferner** *there is nothing more unlike him*

Bügel unter den Kasten schob und den Kasten in ihn entleerte, da stand plötzlich Melanie neben ihm. Sie sagte: „Ich habe eine große Bitte an Sie. Ich habe einen Brief an meine Freundin Marie in den Kasten gesteckt, der nicht abgehen darf. Ich muß ihn zurückhaben. Bitte, geben Sie ihn mir."

der Bügel, - ring, hoop

Der Postbote sagte: „Das darf ich nicht. Das ist verboten." Er zog seinen Ledersack aufgeklappt unter[5] dem Briefkasten hervor. Melanie sah hinein, der Brief an Marie lag oben auf.[6] Sie griff zu und nahm ihn heraus.

aufgeklappt (with the top) open

„Die Anschrift ist ja von einer Männerhand", rief der Postbote. Aber Melanie hörte nicht auf ihn hin.[7] Sie schwang den Brief hoch und eilte mit ihm ins Haus zurück. Verdutzt sah ihr der Postbote nach, stand unschlüssig einen Augenblick da, ob er hinter dem jungen Mädchen herlaufen sollte; aber sie hatte die Haustür hinter sich zugeschlagen, er hätte klingeln müssen. Ärgerlich klappte er seinen Sack zusammen und ging fort. Indessen ging Manfred unruhig in seinem Zimmer auf und ab. „Ich habe ihr noch einmal geschrieben", dachte er bei sich. „Ich habe dringlicher geschrieben. Ich habe ihr gesagt, daß ich noch länger hier sein darf und sie diesen Abend treffen kann. Vielleicht war mein erster Brief zu nüchtern. Wie konnte sie denn auch auf diese ungefühlten Worte hin[8] kommen! Ich war zu nüchtern, ich wagte nicht, ihr mein Gefühl zu schreiben. Aber dieses Mal ist es mir geglückt, auszudrücken, was ich fühle. Wenn sie kommt, wenn sie kommt—das ist ein Zeichen, dann ist alles gut."

- 4 -

[5] **unter . . . hervor** *out from under*
[6] **oben auf** *on top*
[7] **auf . . . hin-hören** *listen, pay attention to*
[8] **auf . . . hin** *on the basis of*

Marie kam mit ihren Eltern am Abend in die Gesellschaft. Manfred sah sie gleich und eilte auf sie zu. Sie wurde rot und verlegen. „Ich habe von der Frau des Hauses schon gehört, daß Ihre Eltern zugesagt hatten", sagte er. „Ich habe gebeten, mich Ihnen als Tischnachbar zu bestimmen." Marie konnte nichts erwidern, sie nickte nur mit dem Kopf. Er ergriff ihre Hand, sie fühlte einen warmen Druck, sie war wie gelähmt.

Er führte Marien zu Tisch. Es fiel ihm auf, wie bleich Melanie war, er sagte das Marien, und sie wurde verlegen. Nun saß er mit ihr zusammen, zu seiner Linken saß eine ältere Dame, die einen mütterlichen Blick lächelnd über die Beiden gleiten ließ.[9] Ein hoher Tafelaufsatz stand da, aus Kristall und Silber, der verdeckte die Beiden fast dem Gegenüber. Es war das Rauschen, Summen und Sprechen, in welchem die Einzelnen sich fast unbeobachtet wähnen können.

der Tafelaufsatz, =e centerpiece

„Wie danke ich Ihnen, daß Sie gekommen sind, wie danke ich Ihnen", sagte Manfred. „Und denken Sie, wie Glück immer zusammenkommt, es ist mir eine Professur zugesagt; nun ist die lange Brautzeit nicht nötig, Liebste, Liebste, nun liegt das Leben vor uns!"

Marie errötete tief und blickte auf ihren Teller. Eine Träne blitzte in ihrem Auge.

Er sagte erschreckt: „Habe ich Sie beleidigt?"

Sie schüttelte den Kopf, lächelte und sah ihn liebevoll an.

- 5 -

[9] **gleiten lassen** *cast*

Ernst Wiechert

Ernst Wiechert was born in 1887, in East Prussia. The region in which he spent his early years is now part of Poland, and little remains of its German population. His father was a forester near Sensburg, in the area of the Masurian Lakes. The moors and the vast forests dominated his childhood, and they became the constant refuge of his later life and thought.

Wiechert went to the *Realschule* and the university in Königsberg. With a broad background in sciences, philosophy, English and German, he became a master in secondary schools—first in Königsberg (1911-30), then in Berlin until 1933. He was a quiet and lonely person, inclined to introspection and melancholy. Teaching did not entirely satisfy him, though he gathered about him a circle of devoted students, almost disciples. The hero of his first novel, *Die Flucht*, was a teacher, disillusioned in his profession, who fled to the forests and ultimately shot himself. (The somber note of suicide appears often. His mother and his first wife took their own lives, and Wiechert himself was for a time close to the edge of despair.)

Wiechert served the whole of World War I in active duty, most of it at the front. The immense futility of the war, the deadening sameness of the soldier's life depressed him as much as did war's violence. The period immediately after 1918 he spent, not in teaching, but in seclusion, surrounded by his East Prussian forests. In this isolation he wrote, and his troubled state of mind is reflected in works of revolt, filled with brutality and hatred, and marked by a strong tendency to blame Christianity for Germany's wretchedness. This time of trial and discontent lasted for many years. By 1927, however, he speaks of a breaking of the old mold and the beginning of a new life. He never abandons his close attachment to nature, nor his seeking of refuge there, but from this time on he faces suffering and death with two other resources: religious faith and the satisfaction of service to one's fellow man.

Wiechert resigned his teaching position in 1933. Concern about political developments was the immediate cause of his resignation. With the increasing popularity of his work, he was in a position to make a modest living as a writer. His *Novelle*, *Der Hauptmann von Kapernaum*, had won an international award. He was also the first recipient of the Raabe Prize. He moved to the Starnberger See, then to a pleasant house in Wolfratshausen, in Upper Bavaria.

The Nazis—who seized upon any promising threads of resemblance to their patchwork doctrine—attached themselves to Wiechert's love of the land, his praise of peasant life, and his earlier hate-rattling, anti-Christian Germanness. They had reckoned without their host, so to speak. Wiechert felt free to question the rulers of the Third Reich in speeches and open letters. In 1936 he told students at the University of Munich, "Aber die Wage ist schon aufgehoben über solch ein Volk, und an jeder Wand wird die Hand erscheinen, die die Buchstaben von Feuer schreibt." By 1938 the Nazis finally found it necessary to throw him into the notorious concentration camp of Buchenwald. He had protested too vigorously their treatment of Martin Niemöller, the controversial submarine commander turned preacher. He was released in two months but remained under Gestapo surveillance.

After the war he went to Switzerland, partly for his health but also because people in postwar Germany (who had at first acclaimed his *Jeromin-Kinder*) no longer seemed to understand him, nor he them. In 1949, the year before his death, he came to the United States to lecture, at the invitation of Stanford University. He died near Zürich.

Though Wiechert's work passes through many stages, there are certain constant elements in it. His view of nature as the proper home and ultimate retreat never left him. He spoke of "return to the great forests." Man's world is a chaotic and transitory interruption of the "great orderliness." A note of melancholy, a lyric tone of deep suffering, is the most common characteristic of his style. His emotionality is obviously profound. It attracts some and repels others. Always he is the moralist, though here the only common denominator of his several stages is his intensity. He called himself a fanatic.

Der Todeskandidat

(1933)

The environment of the war, for all of Wiechert's long years of military service, is accidental to *Der Todeskandidat*. It serves primarily to intensify the moral concern which is basic to Wiechert's story, a concern with guilt and atonement. More relevant in the scheme of Wiechert's writing is the fact that the central figure is a teacher, and an unhappy and victimized one besides. In this literary likeness he often saw himself. The relationship of a teacher or a preacher to others is a dominant theme in Wiechert's creative imagination.

The balancing of guilt, forgiveness, and expiation, and the power and symmetry of the motifs which support these themes, lend *Der Todeskandidat* its undeniable appeal. There is no question—there never is in Wiechert—of the intensity and passion with which he views the moral issue. The opposing forces in the school are vividly described. Their two collisions, the first a defeat, the second a disaster, are excellent drama. The cruelty of the students is ingeniously sadistic. Georgesohn is pathetic in his utter shyness and desperate ineffectuality. The sequence of his discomfiture, demoralization, and collapse is expertly characterized. The encounter between the hopelessly uneven forces results in a rout, and the most serious possible consequences ensue for the teacher and his career. In an expertly crafted scene weighted with personal emotion and religious symbol, the restored Georgesohn forgives the criminal indignity done him. When he dies it recalls his figurative death years before. It is again an act of sacrifice, and the beneficiaries are his former tormenters. This time, however, the sacrifice of Georgesohn is meaningful because it is voluntary. Before, it was a slaughter; now it is an act of redemption for those who survive. Repeatedly in Wiechert's later work, men who have erred or been weak find a new reserve of spiritual strength. In their strength they sacrifice themselves for the good of their souls or the salvation of others. The Christian intent is clear, whether it is latent or explicit.

In technique and structure, the merit of *Der Todeskandidat* is beyond question. The double death of the *Todeskandidat*, as teacher and as soldier, is paralleled by the double use of the prayer. The first death is disgrace, the first prayer a mockery; the second death redeems, the second prayer consoles. Jonas is twice "crippled," the first time is feigned, the second is real and a part of his atonement. The relating and harmonizing of these elements is a literary achievement of high order.

Balance of another kind—or the absence of it—*may* be the most vulnerable aspect of the story and of Wiechert's work as a whole. Some writers, including many whose dedication and intensity of concern we admire, allow themselves and their stories to swing too far in opposite directions. They draw one situation with isolated intensity, for strong effect, and the next one the same way, without adequate regard for the necessity of reconciling them. They go to extremes in their anxiousness to prove a deeply felt point. The attendant risk is that inconsistency and instability will creep into their work, and that emotion will become sentimentality. Does Wiechert err in this direction? The question is raised with no foregone answer in mind, but as an open issue in the literary criticism of a specific work. The story is substantial enough to bear such examination.

DER TODESKANDIDAT

die Gymnasial'aula, -aulen auditorium or lecture-hall of a *Gymnasium* (secondary school)
die Or'gelempo're, -n organ loft

der Marmor, -e marble

gotische Buchstaben Gothic letters (*the older and more ornate script*)

gefallen killed in action

das Plättchen, - flake, leaf

In der Gymnasialaula einer kleinen östlichen Stadt hängt unter der Orgelempore eine Ehrentafel für die Toten des Großen Krieges. Sie hängt dort im Schatten, wie es sich für Tote gebührt, aber so, daß jeder, der den Raum betritt oder verläßt, genötigt ist, sie anzublicken. Sie ist aus weißem Marmor, und aus der breiten Schattenwand, hinter den alten Holzpfeilern, leuchtet das weiße Viereck so deutlich und mahnend heraus wie ein Wegweiser oder ein Meilenstein aus einem dämmernden Walde.

Die Namen sind mit gotischen Buchstaben in die weiße Fläche eingegraben, und ihre verschlungenen Furchen—sehr viele Furchen—sind mit einer lichtblauen Farbe getönt, so daß über dem kalten Weiß ein gleichsam tröstlicher Schimmer schwebt. Am unteren Rande aber, wo die Namen der gefallenen Lehrer stehen, ist seit dem Morgen nach der Einweihung des Totenmals etwas Seltsames zu sehen: ein goldener Namenszug. Das Gold ist nicht mit dünnen Plättchen hineingefügt in den Stein, nicht fest und starr, sondern gleichsam hineingehaucht, wie in die Furchen der Walnüsse, die Kinder unter den Weihnachtsbaum hängen.[1] Es hat etwas Mattes und Zerbrechliches, und davon kommt es, daß dieser Name über den andern zu schweben scheint.[2] Daß es ist, als sei er nicht einge-

- 1 -

[1] Refers to the custom of hanging lightly gilded nuts as ornaments on the Christmas tree.

[2] **davon kommt es, daß** *that is why* (continued by next **Daß . . .** *Why . . .*)

graben in den harten Stein, sondern als hebe er sich auf aus ihm als aus einem fremden Element.

Der Name des Toten ist Georgesohn, Oberleutnant Heinrich Georgesohn, gefallen am 17. 10. 1918 vor Le Cateau, und fünfzehn Jahre vor dem Großen Kriege nannten wir ihn den Todeskandidaten. Wir waren Tertianer, grausam wie alle Kinder, und in einer harten Landschaft allen lyrischen Umschreibungen abgeneigt. Georgesohn kam als Probekandidat an unsere Schule, und auf das noch Ungesicherte einer solchen Existenz, wurzellos zwischen Staatsexamen und Anstellung schwebend, stürzte sich die Klasse wie ein Rudel junger Hyänen.

Auch waren wir nicht ohne Erfahrungen in dem Kampf gegen schwache Könige. Wir hatten ein System der gewaltsamen Erkundung ausgebildet, das nicht ungefährlich, aber von unbedingter Zuverlässigkeit war. Da haben wir Jonas, eines Niederungsbauern Sohn, zum vierten Male sitzengeblieben, breit und stämmig wie ein Memelkahn, mit Stimmbruch und deutlichen Anzeichen eines Schnurrbartes. Wir stehen auf, wenn ein Probekandidat zur ersten Stunde bei uns erscheint, langsam, grinsend, lauernd, aber noch ohne Anzeichen von Meuterei. Wir studieren sein Gesicht, seinen Gang, die Bewegung seiner Hände, seine Augen, und bevor er das Katheder erreicht hat, sehen wir einander schon an: wir wissen, was ein Richter zu wissen hat. „Setzt euch!" sagt der Kandidat, oder „Bitte, setzt euch!" oder „Hinsetzen!" auch das wissen wir vorher. Aber dann bleibt Jonas stehen. Er steht in der vordersten Bank am Fenster, breit und gefährlich,

-2-

der Tertia'ner, - fourth or fifth year student (*in a Gymnasium*): *see below*

der Pro'bekandidat', -en, -en probationary teacher

das Rudel, - pack

die Erkundung reconnaissance, information gathering

die Niederung, -en low land; *here a place name, an area near the river Memel*

sitzen-bleiben† *here* fail, be held back (*i.e., not promoted*)

stämmig sturdy

grinsen *here* smirk

das Kathe'der, - teacher's desk, lectern

[3] **17.10.1918** *am siebzehnten Oktober 1918*

[4] **Le Cateau** city in northeastern France, not far from the Netherlands

[5] **Kandidat'** is a common academic term, usually for a person working toward a higher degree or (as in **Probekandidat** below) for a permanent position.

[6] **Tertianer** comes from **die Tertia, -ien,** the fourth (**Untertertia**) and fifth (**Obertertia**) years of the Gymnasium. **Sekun'da** (*below*) is the next grade or form, likewise divided into lower and upper forms. **Unter-** and **Oberprima** are the last grades.

[7] Having taken his state examination, Georgesohn has a temporary position until he proves himself worthy of an **Anstellung** or permanent appointment.

[8] The Memel River, formerly the boundary of East Prussia and Lithuania, is now entirely in Soviet territory.

[9] **hinsetzen!** is the most peremptory form of the command to sit down, something like our saying "Seats!"

[10] **breit** here does not mean simply broad but a combination of big and thick-set.

und starrt den Kandidaten an. „Auch du darfst dich setzen", sagt dieser freundlich, mit einem mißlingenden Versuch der Ironie, während seine Augen schon unruhig über die feindlichen Gesichter fliegen. Aber Jonas bleibt stehen. „Ich bin gelähmt in den Knien", sagt er mit einer erschreckend tiefen Stimme, „von Kindesbeinen an . . . ich muß immer stehen . . . den ganzen Vormittag". [11]

von Kindesbeinen an from early childhood (*see below*)

Dies ist der Augenblick der Entscheidung. Niemand atmet in der Klasse, und alle wissen, daß nun der Würfel fällt. Auch der Kandidat. Er begreift es am schnellsten. Da steht das Schicksal, nicht nur dieser Stunde, sondern aller kommenden, ja, vielleicht des ganzen Lebens. Ein breites und stämmiges Schicksal, mit gelähmten Knien und kalten Augen, die furchtlos zur Entscheidung auffordern.

der Würfel fällt† the die is (being) cast

Fast alle scheitern schon an diesem Augenblick. „Wie heißt du?" fragen sie. „Ich werde mich erkundigen, ob sich das so verhält. Wenn nicht, dann mußt du bestraft werden . . ." Ein Hohngeheul bricht auf ihn nieder, und Jonas, die Mundwinkel verächtlich herabgezogen, wendet sich langsam zur Klasse, hebt die Hand mit zur Erde gekehrtem Daumen und läßt sich nachlässig in seiner Bank nieder. Das Urteil ist gefällt.

es verhält† **sich so** that is the case

Nur ein einziges Mal in den vier Jahren der Tertien und Sekunden erlebten wir eine Niederlage. Mit einem Doktor der Theologie, einem schmalen, blassen Männlein mit einer blauen Brille vor seinen unsichtbaren Augen. „Von Kindesbeinen an?" wiederholte er lächelnd. „Sieh mal an . . ." Und er ging zu

die Tertien (*pl. of* **die Tertia**); **die Sekun'den** (*pl. of* **die Sekunda**) *see note 6; use the German terms.*

sieh mal an *as exclamation* well, what do you know

- 3 -

[11] The latent double meaning in **von Kindesbeinen an** is apparent when the noun is used alone (*below*).

Jonas hinunter, hob ihn aus der Bank heraus, trug den nun wirklich Gelähmten durch die Klasse und warf ihn gegen die Tür, daß der Kalk von den Pfosten rieselte. Und als Jonas, taumelnd und betäubt, sich aufzurichten versuchte, empfing er ein paar Maulschellen, die sich weit über unsren Erfahrungskreis erhoben. „Geheilt!" sagte das Männlein ruhig. „Hinsetzen!" Erst in der Pause kam Jonas völlig zu sich, „Allerhand . . ." sagte er, als das Männlein gegangen war. „Allerhand . . ."

Aber Georgesohn trug keine blaue Brille. Er war lang und hager, und seine großen Füße stießen überall an. Sein Gesicht erschrak bei jedem Laut, und in der ersten Stunde entdeckten wir, daß er unter dem Katheder seine Hände faltete. Er errötete, als Jonas von seinen „Kindesbeinen" erzählte, suchte hilflos und vergeblich eine Wohnung in unsren kalten Augen und sagte dann leise: „Ja . . . ein schweres Schicksal . . . so bleib also stehen, mein Kind . . ."

„Mein Kind" entschied den Fall. „Guten Morgen, mein Kind", riefen wir zu Beginn der nächsten Stunde, auf den Treppen, im Hof, auf der Straße. Er lächelte, demütig, verloren, und auch wir lächelten, aber es gereichte ihm nicht zum Troste.

Nun wären wir vielleicht dieses gefährlichen Spiels müde geworden, wenn nicht von Zeit zu Zeit die Menschenwürde in dem Kandidaten sich empört hätte. Dann war es, als zerrisse sein Gesicht und aus den Spalten bräche die Verzweiflung des Tieres heraus. Er schlug in uns hinein, blind und rasend, mit ver-

-4-

der Kalk *here* plaster
rieseln *here* shower
taumeln reel, stagger
die Maulschelle, -n slap in the face
sich erheben† **über** *here* exceed, transcend
allerhand' *as exclamation*, imagine that! *or* I'll be darned!
an-stoßen† *here* bump into things
Kindesbeine *see above*
die Wohnung *here* place of refuge
hinein-schlagen† **in** hit out at

die Peitsche, -n whip

sich ballen be clenched

die Saite, -n string (*of a violin, etc.*), chord
ruchlos wicked, infamous

hängen bleiben† get caught

störten Augen, und für eine Stunde beugten wir uns wie Sklaven unter der Peitsche.

Bis Jonas auch dieses bändigte. Beim nächsten Ausbruch, als der kleine Adomeit das erste und fast unschuldige Opfer war, sank dieser unter Georgesohns Schlägen zusammen, stürzte aus der Bank und lag regungslos auf der Erde. Seine Hände ballten sich, die Füße streckten sich aus, und unter den halbgeschlossenen Lidern erschien, sorgsam geübt, das Weiße des Augapfels. In der Totenstille des Raumes erhob sich Jonas mit den gelähmten Knien, beugte sich zu dem Liegenden nieder und sagte, ohne die Blicke zu heben: „Sie haben ihn getötet, Herr Kandidat". Dann drückte er dem Toten die Augen zu, legte ihm die Hände über der Brust zusammen und sprach mit seiner erschreckend tiefen Stimme: „Lasset uns beten!"

Wir sahen Georgesohn an. Ganz tief in unserm Innern erbebte eine verborgene Saite bei diesem ruchlosen Spiel, und es hätte nur eines Wortes von ihm bedurft, um ihn zu unserm geliebten Herrn zu machen. Aber er sprach es nicht. Er starrte auf die Gruppe zu seinen Füßen, und keiner von uns wußte, ob er das Spiel durchschaue. Dann plötzlich, mit einem zerbrochenen Laut in seiner Stimme, stürzte er aus der Klasse, und da seine Füße an der letzten Bank hängen blieben, wischte dieser Unfall auch die Verzweiflung aus seinem Bild, und ein brüllendes Gelächter geleitete ihn auf den Gang, über die Treppen, bis in den unbekannten Schlupfwinkel, in dem seine Verstörung sich verbarg. [12]

Von dieser Stunde an hieß er der Todeskandidat.

- 5 -

[12] That is, Georgesohn's stumbling causes the student's image or picture (**Bild**) of him to change; they no longer see in him the desperation which they momentarily understood, but once again only the hopeless awkwardness which made him the butt of their mockery.

Die Szene wiederholte sich, nicht nur bei uns, sondern in jeder Klasse, in der seine Beherrschung ihn verließ. Mit Variationen gleichsam, aber unverändert im „Gerüst der Handlung". Solange bis eines Tages der Direktor die Tür öffnete und vor seinen Füßen ein „Toter" lag. Der Tote wurde erweckt, auf eine unangenehm eindringliche Weise, aber Georgesohn kam nicht wieder. Es hieß, er sei aus dem Amt geschieden, habe die Stadt verlassen und in seinen vorgerückten Jahren das Studium der Theologie begonnen. Seltsam war, daß wir von dem so plötzlich Verschollenen zu sprechen vermieden und daß Jonas' Stellung in der Klasse für lange Zeit erschüttert war, ohne daß ein zureichender Grund angegeben werden konnte.

Ein paar Jahre später verloren wir alle einander schnell aus den Augen, schneller noch aus den Herzen, und der Tag der Einweihung des Ehrenmals war auch der erste, an dem wir uns in der alten Aula wieder zusammenfanden. Die Zeitungen unsrer Provinz hatten viele Aufrufe gebracht, um die ehemaligen Lehrer und Schüler zu versammeln, und so sahen wir einander vor der weißen Tafel wieder, soweit der Krieg uns übrig gelassen hatte, suchten die alten Namen zusammen, erinnerten uns der Toten und standen dann lange Zeit schweigend, die Augen auf den Namen am unteren Rand der Tafel gerichtet, indes Scham und Bitterkeit uns leise und verstohlen zu erfüllen begannen.

Nach dieser Feier geschah es auch, daß Jonas, mit einem leeren Ärmel an seinem grauen Rock, uns aufforderte, am Abend zusammenzukommen, da er

- 6 -

das Gerüst der Handlung, *a term of literary criticism, hence in quotes,* framework (structure) of the plot
der Direk'tor, -s, -en principal, headmaster
aus dem Amt scheiden† resign
der Verschollene, -n, -n the vanished man
übrig lassen† spare
verstohlen furtive, secret

uns von dem Toten etwas zu sagen habe. Und so verwandelt hatte sich sein Gesicht seit seinen Kindertagen, daß niemand sich seiner Bitte entzog.

Es war eine kleine Weinstube, und wir hatten einen Raum für uns allein. Sechzehn von sechsundvierzig. Als niemand mehr kam, wandte Jonas, an der Schmalseite des Tisches, seine grauen Augen von der Tür zu uns. „Dreißig haben es also wieder gutgemacht . . ." sagte er leise, „und den andern will ich es nun erzählen . . . Wir kamen 1916 zu ihm, an die Somme,[13] Hotop, Jürgen, Adomeit und ich. Von diesem Ersatzbataillon aus, so daß es nicht einmal ein wunderbarer Zufall war. Wir waren Unteroffiziere, alle vier, und wir brachten ihm einen Transport von fünfzig Mann. Wir kamen am Abend an, in der Ruhestellung, und der Feldwebel baute uns auf. Wir standen vor der Front, und es war nicht leicht, dort zu stehen, als er kam. Wir erkannten ihn sofort, alle vier, aber in seinem Gesicht veränderte sich nichts. Siebzehn Jahre sind ja eine lange Zeit, aber ich glaube, daß man ein gutes Gedächtnis für seine Henker hat. ‚Die Namen, bitte', sagte er ruhig, als er vor uns stand. Sein Gesicht war ganz anders geworden, gewandelt und geformt und geläutert, ein ganz schmales, ja, ein unerschütterliches Gesicht. ‚Jonas?' wiederholte er. ‚Aus welcher Landschaft? . . . So . . . ja . . . dort oben hat man noch biblische Namen . . .'

Das war alles. Wir zitterten noch lange nachher, und Hotop wollte um unsre Versetzung bitten. Aber dann blieben wir doch. Fremd waren wir, schrecklich fremd. Die alten Leute in der Kompagnie wurden

- 7 -

der Transport', -e detachment
die Ruhestellung inactive duty
der Feldwebel, - sergeant
auf-bauen reorganize into an active formation
vor der Front in the front row

[13] **Somme,** river in northeastern France, scene of some of the fiercest fighting of World War I

nicht müde, von ihm zu erzählen, und wenn sie gewußt hätten, wer wir waren, so hätten sie uns mit ihren Spaten erschlagen . . . Wir machten vieles zusammen mit ihm durch, aber niemals fiel ein Wort, weder des Tadels, noch des Lobes, noch der Erinnerung.

14

Bis es Hotop traf. Wir waren zurückgegangen, um eine Aufnahmestellung zu erkunden, er und wir vier. Er hatte uns beim Namen aufgerufen. In einer Mulde traf uns der Feuerüberfall, und Hotop bekam das Sprengstück in die Brust. Er lag da, und Georgesohn kniete neben ihm und hielt ihm den Kopf. ‚Nicht verlassen . . .', flüsterte Hotop, ‚Herr Kandidat, bitte nicht verlassen . . .' Die Erde brüllte in dem engen Tal, aber jeder von uns hörte die ruhige Stimme ihm Antwort sagen: ‚Niemand wird dich verlassen . . . im dunklen Tal . . .' Und während seine Hand über die Stirn des Sterbenden strich, immer auf und ab, waren seine Augen über uns hinaus in das glühende und schreiende Feld gerichtet, ruhige, traurige, unerschütterliche Augen, vor denen wir uns zur Erde warfen, die Stirn in das versengte Gras gepreßt.

15

Und dann starb Hotop . . . und dann . . . ja, dann drückte er ihm die Augen zu und legte ihm die Hände über der zerrissenen Brust zusammen und sah uns an. Wir hatten die Gesichter gehoben, als der Atem still geworden war, und empfingen nun seinen Blick. Einen Blick ohne Frage, ohne Anklage, ohne Erinnerung, einen Blick, der uns zerteilte und durch das Zerteilte bis zu unsren Kindesbeinen fiel.

‚Lasset uns beten . . .', sagte er leise, sprach das Vaterunser, stand auf und ging davon, ohne uns

-8-

es traf† Hotop Hotop got it

die Aufnahmestellung, -en covering position

der Feuerüberfall artillery barrage

das Sprengstück, -e shell fragment, shrapnel

zerteilte . . . das Zerteilte . . . fiel *translate* rent asunder . . . the rent . . . penetrated.

das Vaterun'ser Lord's Prayer

[14] **niemals fiel ein Wort** *never a word was passed* more emphatic than **kein Wort fiel** *not a word was passed (spoken)*

[15] **im dunklen Tal** is reminiscent of what Biblical phrase?

anzusehen, durch das Feuer hindurch, nach der Stellung zurück.

16

Er wurde am gleichen Abend verwundet und kam nicht wieder. Auch Jürgen ist gefallen, und nur Adomeit ist noch da. Er kann es euch bestätigen. Mehr können wir nicht . . . keiner von uns . . .“

Und Jonas stand auf, nickte uns zu und verließ den Raum.

Am nächsten Morgen war das geschehen, was zu Beginn erzählt worden ist: die Vergoldung des toten Namens. Es ist viel darüber gesprochen und geraten und gekämpft worden. Das Kollegium und ein Teil der kleinen Stadt haben auf eine Entfernung der Willkür gedrungen, aber der Direktor hat sich geweigert. Es stehe allen denen zu, hat er gesagt, die auf dieser Tafel stünden, und wenn nur ein einzelner Name von dem Gold des Ruhmes bedeckt worden sei, so könne niemand wissen, ob ihm nicht ein Vielfaches des Erleidens und Sterbens bereitet gewesen sei, sicherlich aber sei ein Vielfaches der Liebe an ihn gewendet worden. Und mit der Liebe sei es so, daß auch das Vielfache noch immer hinter dem zurückbliebe, was wir den Toten schuldeten.

17

das Kolle′gium, -ien staff

die Willkür *here* arbitrary action, offense

ein Vielfaches a multitude, a great deal, a large measure
bereiten *here* allot

zurück′-bleiben† *here* fall short

- 9 -

[16] What is the significance of the way this scene is described? That is, of what is it reminiscent in the story itself?

[17] **es ist viel . . . worden** *there was a great deal of . . . ing*

Wolfgang Borchert

The life of Wolfgang Borchert is compressed with tragic intensity into the period of the second World War and its immediate aftermath. The violent fate, the anguish and the occasional hope of his generation have found in Borchert an eloquent voice. It was a voice of great courage, with a warning made doubly urgent by its brevity.

He was born in 1921, first began to write seriously around 1939, first published in 1946, and died in 1947. He died one day before the première of his play *Draußen vor der Tür*, which is a story "von denen, die nach Hause kommen und die dann doch nicht nach Hause kommen, weil für sie kein Zuhause mehr da ist."

Hamburg was the city of his birth, and he bore a deep affection for it in all its aspects, high and low. He first worked as a bookseller, then briefly as an actor. By the time he was twenty, he was in the German army, and the incredibly rapid course of his tragedy begins. Borchert was in trouble before he had left training camp. He did not hesitate to say in his letters what he thought about the Nazis and about war. Before he could be jailed on the censor's information, however, he was at the Russian front. He was seriously wounded and hospitalized. Jaundice and diphtheria complicated his case, his liver was seriously affected. For much of the rest of his life he ran a fever. He was taken from the hospital to be put in prison, taken out of prison to stand trial for the error of his ways. He was condemned to death, and the sentence was left hanging over him for six weeks. For six months he was in a cell. Then, in a curious gesture of magnanimity, his sentence was commuted and he was sent back to Russia. By this time he was so sick that he was unfit for further active duty, and he was sent back to garrison. There he was offered a chance to join an independent theater group entertaining soldiers along the Russian front. The day before he was to leave he was denounced by one of his associates—this time for jokes contrary to the spirit of Nazi Germany. He was again arrested and sent to a Berlin prison for nine months. By the spring of 1945 he was in southwest Germany, where he was released by the Americans, into whose hands he had fallen. He walked most of the way back to Hamburg, with all of Germany going to pieces on both sides of him.

Borchert found his parents again, and his beloved Hamburg, rubble though it was. But his health had been completely and finally ruined. In spite of the pain he was in, he managed to work briefly on the staff of the State Theater. Soon, however, he was unable to stand without someone's help. He was outwardly active and spirited, always ready to welcome friends or to argue about literature, unsparing in his work. The courage of these months is eloquently described by his friend Bernhard Meyer-Marwitz in the epilogue to Borchert's *Gesamtwerk*.

Early in 1946 there was an evening of readings from his work, the early poems and some of the stories. Borchert was himself slightly amused and skeptical, but the program was a success. During 1946 he also wrote the leading piece in an anthology dedicated to Hamburg and had his poems published. In 1947, in the space of eight days, he wrote *Draußen vor der Tür*, and its tremendous success as a radio broadcast opened the way for the publication of his stories. Borchert was unable to hear the program because the electric current in his district was temporarily shut off.

In 1947, friends joined in an effort to get him to Switzerland, where he could have better care and where there was an adequate supply of medicines. Hardship and disease, however, had done their work. In Basel he had to be hospitalized immediately. Two months later, after extreme suffering, he died.

Die lange lange Straße lang

(1947)

Postwar literature in Germany was not as radically experimental as many had expected or hoped. In 1945 it had become possible for German writers to write freely once again, and a revolution seemed in order. In form and style, at least, it did not come, despite the prompt and vigorous resurgence of literary activity. The late forties and the fifties have little to rival the formal innovations of the Expressionists earlier in the century. The boldest venture of the decade was probably the radio play (*Hörspiel*).

Perhaps this relative absence of literary risk-taking was to be expected. A world in upheaval does not necessarily produce an upheaval in art. When all the forms of society have disintegrated, artists may not be inclined to afford massive experimentation, lest there be no firm point whatever in the chaos. This is especially true when an influential segment of the literary and critical world subscribes to the doctrine that the only thing of permanent value is form itself (the view of Gottfried Benn).

One of the most distinctive (if not drastically experimental) styles to emerge in these years was Wolfgang Borchert's. Had he lived longer he might have sought new avenues of expression, in narrative prose particularly. There are signs of this in the little he was able to publish in his lifetime, and in the small volume of posthumous works, *Traurige Geranien*, published in 1962. He used language in fresh and sometimes startling ways, in an attempt to convey a message of desperate intensity and urgency. His most notable achievements are the radio play *Draußen vor der Tür* and the present story.

The unifying external or surface reality which gives coherence to *Die lange lange Straße lang* is reasonably clear: a man walks down a street in Germany, hurrying to catch a streetcar; he is a man just returned from a terrible war, torn by responsibility and guilt, wanting to live but barely able to do so, alienated, burdened by memory and pity, but himself remembered and pitied by no one—except perhaps one "buddy" and one girl. The vehicle of narration is a series of hallucinatory visions of the past and the present. His "walk" thus traverses three spatial and temporal levels: Russia and the war, the return home, the "actual" present. It is also an allegorical journey through contemporary society and human existence at a dozen levels. The whole narrative structure is one of singular power and diversity.

The reproduction in prose fiction of the inner workings of a man's mind is not in any sense strikingly new. Yet Borchert's deployment of familiar devices will appear more subtle and more impressive the more one tries to analyze it. On the one hand it clearly resembles the stream-of-consciousness outpouring in which Schnitzler's Leutnant Gustl reveals himself and his fate, or Faulkner's Benjy his picture of the past. Yet Fischer is less an individualized figure, the fevered visions are less specifically or consistently those of his own mind. At the other end of the spectrum lie, after all, certain sections of the narrative which seem to emanate from the consciousness and point of view of Borchert rather than Fischer: the nails and their Christian echo; the skat game and the commentary that rounds it off. Even if all of them be interpreted as "his," Fischer's hallucinations are also those of many men, indeed of a whole generation. He is, in the phrase from *Draußen*, "einer von denen, die nach Hause kommen." In yet another facet, this disordered nightmare constitutes the author's systematic exploration of an entire society, in allegorical scope and intent. The affinity with Expressionism is clear.

Borchert's resources of language are extraordinary—and also reminiscent of Expressionism. Of the writers represented in this book, only Rilke uses words as he does. Repetition and variation of words or phrases carry each motif through the story and relate it to other motifs. Borchert makes brilliant use of accumulation and intensification (57, 57 million; "Wand Wand Tür Laterne Wand Wand Fenster Wand Wand"), groupings and clusters ("Wankt von der Hungerwelt. Wankt so welthungrig und straßenbahngelb"), crossing of motifs ("*begraben* ist die *Infantrie* unterm *Fußballplatz*"). Motifs are gathered together by shared cues; see note 12 on *pink, pank*. Alliteration is almost as prominent as in the *Cornet:* "Hütten aus Holz und aus Hoffnung." Word compounding is luxuriant: *bierflaschengrün; mädchenheimlicher Mondrausch*. All these aspects of language are poetic and, as such, elements of beauty and order. They exist largely in ironic and painful contrast to the content of guilt, devastation, despair, and cynicism, serving further to underscore that content. Yet in some degree, true beauty is undeniably there, if only vestigially or in muted potential—Borchert's tribute to life in the midst of death.

There is perhaps some danger of overstatement in Borchert. Each reader will decide where he stands on that issue. There is perhaps a more serious danger in us, namely that our revulsion for war will fade—and as a minor corollary our regard for Borchert lessen. That would be a double pity. Borchert is a great talent. He also had his answer to the problem of war, which obsessed him. It was in general a love of life in all its aspects and, in political action, pacifism to the point of civil disobedience. The word motif of one of his eloquent short pieces is "Sag NEIN!" This is the answer of a radical young man, rebellious and perhaps irresponsible. The problem to which it is addressed, however, awaits its full and definitive answer.

DIE LANGE LANGE STRASSE LANG

Links zwei drei vier links zwei drei vier links zwei weiter, Fischer! drei vier links zwei vorwärts, Fischer! schneidig, Fischer! drei vier atme, Fischer! weiter, Fischer, immer weiter zickezacke zwei drei vier schneidig ist die Infantrie zickezackejuppheidi schneidig ist die Infantrie die Infantrie---- [1]

Ich bin unterwegs. Zweimal hab ich schon gelegen. Ich will zur Straßenbahn. Ich muß mit. Zweimal hab ich schon gelegen. Ich hab Hunger. Aber mit muß ich. Muß. Ich muß zur Straßenbahn. Ich muß mit. Zweimal hab ich schon drei vier links zwei drei vier aber mit muß ich drei vier zickezacke zacke drei vier juppheidi ist die Infantrie die Infantrie fantrie fantrie--- 57 haben sie bei Woronesch begraben. 57, die hatten keine Ahnung, vorher nicht und nachher nicht. Vorher haben sie noch gesungen. Zickezackejuppheidi. Und einer hat nach Hause geschrieben: --- dann kaufen wir uns ein Grammophon. Aber dann haben viertausend Meter weiter ab die Andern auf Befehl auf einen Knopf gedrückt. Da hat es gerumpelt wie ein alter Lastwagen mit leeren Tonnen über Kopfsteinpflaster: Kanonenorgel. Dann haben sie 57 bei Woronesch begraben. Vorher haben sie noch gesungen. Hinterher haben sie nichts mehr gesagt. 9 Autoschlosser, 2 Gärtner, 5

[2] [3] [4]

- 1 -

rumpeln rumble, rattle
die Tonne, -n keg, barrel

[1] **zickezacke** is roughly the equivalent of *rah, rah,* esp. at soccer games, etc.; **juppheidi;** a familiar refrain-like repetition from folk songs, like our *tra-la-la.*

[2] **zweimal hab ich schon** complete: **gelegen.** Disjointed repetitions characterize the working of Fischer's exhausted and hallucinating mind. They appear frequently, like bits of musical motifs, and can always be completed, as here, by reference to what went before.

[3] **Woro'nesch** *Woronezh,* city south of Moscow, levelled (much as Borchert's Hamburg was) in WWII.

[4] **das Kopfsteinpflaster** means *cobblestone pavement,* but Borchert later plays with the components of the word, in a sort of savage pun. **Kano'nenorgel (Kano'ne + die Orgel, -n** *organ*) is typical of Borchert's many startling and seemingly arbitrary word combinations, for ironic or pathetic effect. In general, the vocabulary or marginal glosses will provide the basic words only.

Beamte, 6 Verkäufer, 1 Friseur, 17 Bauern, 2 Lehrer, 1 Pastor, 6 Arbeiter, 1 Musiker, 7 Schuljungen. 7 Schuljungen. Die haben sie bei Woronesch begraben. Sie hatten keine Ahnung. 57.

Und mich haben sie vergessen. Ich war noch nicht ganz tot. Juppheidi. Ich war noch ein bißchen lebendig. Aber die andern, die haben sie bei Woronesch begraben. 57. 57. Mach noch ne Null dran. 570. Noch ne Null und noch ne Null. 57 000. Und noch und noch und noch. 57 000 000. Die haben sie bei Woronesch begraben. Sie hatten keine Ahnung. Sie wollten nicht. Das hatten sie gar nicht gewollt. Und vorher haben sie noch gesungen. Juppheidi. Nachher haben sie nichts mehr gesagt. Und der eine hat das Grammophon nicht gekauft. Sie haben ihn bei Woronesch und die andern 56 auch begraben. 57 Stück.[5] Nur ich. Ich, ich war noch nicht ganz tot. Ich muß zur Straßenbahn. Die Straße ist grau. Aber die Straßenbahn ist gelb. Ganz wunderhübsch gelb. Da muß ich mit. Nur daß die Straße so grau ist. So grau und so grau. Zweimal habe ich schon zickezacke vorwärts, Fischer! drei vier links zwei links zwei gelegen drei vier weiter, Fischer! Zickezacke juppheidi schneidig ist die Infantrie schneidig, Fischer! weiter, Fischer! links zwei drei vier wenn nur der Hunger der elende Hunger immer der elende links zwei drei vier links zwei links zwei links zwei---

Wenn bloß die Nächte nicht wärn. Wenn bloß die Nächte nicht wärn. Jedes Geräusch ist ein Tier. Jeder Schatten ist ein schwarzer Mann. Nie wird man die Angst vor den schwarzen Männern los. Auf dem Kopfkissen grummeln die ganze Nacht die Kanonen: Der

-2-

[5] **Stück** is used here as a numerator for things: "*pieces*," "*items*."

Puls. Du hättest mich nie allein lassen sollen, Mutter. Jetzt finden wir uns nicht wieder. Nie wieder. Nie hättest du das tun sollen. Du hast doch die Nächte gekannt. Du hast doch gewußt von den Nächten. Aber du hast mich von dir geschrien. Aus dir heraus und in diese Welt mit den Nächten hineingeschrien. Und seitdem ist jedes Geräusch ein Tier in der Nacht. Und in den blaudunklen Ecken warten die schwarzen Männer. Mutter Mutter! in allen Ecken stehn die schwarzen Männer. Und jedes Geräusch ist ein Tier. Jedes Geräusch ist ein Tier. Und das Kopfkissen ist so heiß. Die ganze Nacht grummeln die Kanonen dadrauf. Und dann haben sie 57 bei Woronesch begraben. Und die Uhr schlurft wie ein altes Weib auf Latschen davon davon davon. Sie schlurft und schlurft und schlurft und keiner keiner hält sie auf. Und die Wände kommen immer näher. Und die Decke kommt immer tiefer. Und der Boden der Boden der wankt von der Welle Welt. Mutter Mutter! warum hast du mich allein gelassen, warum? Wankt von der Welle. Wankt von der Welt. 57. Rums. Und ich will zur Straßenbahn. Die Kanonen haben gegrummelt. Der Boden wankt. Rums. 57. Und ich bin noch ein bißchen lebendig. Und ich will zur Straßenbahn. Die ist gelb in der grauen Straße. Wunderhübsch gelb in der grauen. Aber ich komm ja nicht hin. Zweimal hab ich schon gelegen. Denn ich hab Hunger. Und davon wankt der Boden. Wankt so wunderhübsch gelb von der Welle Welt. Wankt von der Hungerwelt. Wankt so welthungrig und straßenbahngelb.

Eben hat einer zu mir gesagt: Guten Tag, Herr

6

die Latsche, -n (old) slipper

rums boom

[6] **blaudunkel** is an intentional "inversion."

Fischer. Bin ich Herr Fischer? Kann ich Herr Fischer sein, einfach wieder Herr Fischer? Ich war doch Leutnant Fischer. Kann ich denn wieder Herr Fischer sein? Bin ich Herr Fischer? Guten Tag, hat er gesagt. Aber der weiß nicht, daß ich Leutnant Fischer war. Einen guten Tag hat er gewünscht – für Leutnant Fischer gibt es keine guten Tage mehr. Das hat er nicht gewußt.

Und Herr Fischer geht die Straße lang. Die lange Straße lang. Die ist grau. Er will zur Straßenbahn. Die ist gelb. So wunderhübsch gelb. Links zwei, Herr Fischer. Links zwei drei vier. Herr Fischer hat Hunger. Er hält nicht mehr Schritt. Er will doch noch mit, denn die Straßenbahn ist so wunderhübsch gelb in dem Grau. Zweimal hat Herr Fischer schon gelegen. Aber Leutnant Fischer kommandiert: Links zwei drei vier vorwärts, Herr Fischer! Weiter, Herr Fischer! Schneidig, Herr Fischer, kommandiert Leutnant Fischer. Und Herr Fischer marschiert die graue Straße lang, die graue graue lange Straße lang. Die Mülleimerallee.[7] Das Aschkastenspalier. Das Rinnsteinglacis. Die Champs-Ruinés. Den Muttschuttschlaginduttbroadway. Die Trümmerparade. Und Leutnant Fischer kommandiert. Links zwei links zwei. Und Herr Fischer Herr Fischer marschiert, links zwei links zwei links zwei links vorbei vorbei vorbei – – – –

Das kleine Mädchen hat Beine, die sind wie Finger so dünn. Wie Finger im Winter. So dünn und so rot und so blau und so dünn. Links zwei drei vier machen die Beine. Das kleine Mädchen sagt immerzu und Herr Fischer marschiert nebenan das sagt immerzu: Lieber

Schritt' halten† stay in step; keep up

[7] **Mülleimerallee'** (**der Mülleimer** *garbage-can* + **die Allee'** *avenue*), and the rest, combine in a bitter yet amusing fashion elements of desperately ordinary, battered reality and high-sounding, aristocratic words for "street," etc. Behind the mockery lies, of course, the reduction of beautiful avenues to rubble. The combination is something like Tin Pan Alley, except that our "alley" is not as fancy as *Allee*. Skid Row is analogous. Other compounding elements: **der Aschkasten** *ash-can;* **das Spalier'** *lane;* **der Rinnstein** *gutter;* **das Glacis** (glasi') *glacis* (actually part of a fort; here roughly *Heights*); **Champs-Ruinés** is a play on Paris' *Champs-Elysées.* **Muttschuttschlagindutt** is impossible to render: **der Mutt** *mud,* **der Schutt** *rubble,* **schlagindutt** perhaps = *schlag ihn tot* (or **der Dutt** *pile, heap*). But the sound-play is at least as important, e.g. *bled-red-knockumdead.* **Trümmer** (pl.) *ruins;* **die Para'de** *parade* (*grounds*).

Gott, gib mir Suppe. Lieber Gott, gib mir Suppe. Ein Löffelchen nur. Ein Löffelchen nur. Ein Löffelchen nur. Die Mutter hat Haare, die sind schon tot. Lange schon tot. Die Mutter sagt: Der liebe Gott kann dir keine Suppe geben, er kann es doch nicht. Warum kann der liebe Gott mir keine Suppe geben? Er hat doch keinen Löffel. Den hat er nicht. Das kleine Mädchen geht auf seinen Fingerbeinen, den dünnen blauen Winterbeinen, neben der Mutter. Herr Fischer geht nebenan. Von der Mutter sind die Haare schon tot. Sie sind schon ganz fremd um den Kopf. Und das kleine Mädchen tanzt rundherum um die Mutter herum um Herrn Fischer herum rundherum: Er hat ja keinen Löffel. Er hat ja keinen Löffel. Er hat ja keinen nicht mal einen hat ja keinen Löffel. So tanzt das kleine Mädchen rundherum. Und Herr Fischer marschiert hinteran. Wankt nebenan auf der Welle Welt. Wankt von der Welle Welt. Aber Leutnant Fischer kommandiert: Links zwei juppvorbei[8] schneidig, Herr Fischer, links zwei und das kleine Mädchen singt dabei: Er hat ja keinen Löffel. Er hat ja keinen Löffel. Und zweimal hat Herr Fischer schon gelegen. Vor Hunger gelegen. Er hat ja keinen Löffel. Und der andere kommandiert: Juppheidi juppheidi die Infantrie die Infantrie die Infantrie----

57 haben sie bei Woronesch begraben. Ich bin Leutnant Fischer. Mich haben sie vergessen. Ich war noch nicht ganz tot. Zweimal hab ich schon gelegen. Jetzt bin ich Herr Fischer. Ich bin 25 Jahre alt. 25 mal 57. Und die haben sie bei Woronesch begraben. Nur ich, ich, ich bin noch unterwegs. Ich muß die

[8] **juppvorbei** is another of Borchert's word combinations (see p. 1), here, from the song refrain (see note 1) an abbreviated **juppheidi,** plus **vorbei** *gone, past.*

Straßenbahn noch kriegen. Hunger hab ich. Aber der liebe Gott hat keinen Löffel. Er hat ja keinen Löffel. Ich bin 25 mal 57. Mein Vater hat mich verraten und meine Mutter hat mich ausgestoßen aus sich. Sie hat mich allein geschrien. So furchtbar allein. So allein. Jetzt gehe ich die lange Straße lang. Die wankt von der Welle Welt. Aber immer spielt einer Klavier. Immer spielt einer Klavier. Als mein Vater meine Mutter sah – spielte einer Klavier. Als ich Geburtstag hatte – spielte einer Klavier. Bei der Heldengedenkfeier in der Schule – spielte einer Klavier. Als wir dann selbst Helden werden durften, als es den Krieg gab – spielte einer Klavier. Im Lazarett – spielte dann einer Klavier. Als der Krieg aus war – spielte immer noch einer Klavier. Immer spielt einer. Immer spielt einer Klavier. Die ganze lange Straße lang.

Die Lokomotive tutet. Timm sagt, sie weint. Wenn man hochkuckt, zittern die Sterne. Immerzu tutet die Lokomotive. Aber Timm sagt, sie weint. Immerzu. Die ganze Nacht. Die ganze lange Nacht nun schon. Sie weint, das tut einem im Magen weh, wenn sie so weint, sagt Timm. Sie weint wie Kinder, sagt er. Wir haben einen Wagen mit Holz. Das riecht wie Wald. Unser Wagen hat kein Dach. Die Sterne zittern, wenn man hochkuckt. Da tutet sie wieder. Hörst du? sagt Timm, sie weint wieder. Ich versteh nicht, warum die Lokomotive weint. Timm sagt es. Wie Kinder, sagt er. Timm sagt, ich hätte den Alten nicht vom Wagen schubsen sollen. Ich hab den Alten nicht vom Wagen geschubst. Du hättest es nicht tun sollen, sagt Timm. Ich habe es nicht getan. Sie weint, hörst du, wie sie

- 6 -

weint, sagt Timm, du hättest es nicht tun sollen. Ich hab den Alten nicht vom Wagen geschubst. Sie weint nicht. Sie tutet. Lokomotiven tuten. Sie weint, sagt Timm. Er ist von selbst vom Wagen gefallen. Ganz von selbst, der Alte. Er hat gepennt, Timm, gepennt hat er, sag ich dir. Da ist er von selbst vom Wagen gefallen. Du hättest es nicht tun sollen. Sie weint. Die ganze Nacht nun schon. Timm sagt, man soll keine alten Männer vom Wagen schubsen. Ich hab es nicht getan. Er hat gepennt. Du hättest es nicht tun sollen, sagt Timm. Timm sagt, er hat in Rußland mal einen Alten in den Hintern getreten. Weil er so langsam war. Und er nahm immer so wenig auf einmal. Sie waren beim Munitionsschleppen. Da hat Timm den Alten in den Hintern getreten. Da hat der Alte sich umgedreht. Ganz langsam, sagt Timm, und er hat ihn ganz traurig angekuckt. Gar nichts weiter. Aber er hat ein Gesicht gehabt wie sein Vater. Genau wie sein Vater. Das sagt Timm. Die Lokomotive tutet. Manchmal hört es sich an, als ob sie schreit. Timm meint sogar, sie weint. Vielleicht hat Timm recht. Aber ich hab den Alten nicht vom Wagen geschubst. Er hat gepennt. Da ist er von selbst.[9] Es rüttelt ja ziemlich auf den Schienen. Wenn man hochkuckt, zittern die Sterne. Der Wagen wankt von der Welle Welt. Sie tutet. Schrein tut sie. Schrein, daß die Sterne zittern. Von der Welle Welt.

Aber ich bin noch unterwegs. Zwei drei vier. Zur Straßenbahn. Zweimal hab ich schon gelegen. Der Boden wankt von der Welle Welt. Wegen dem Hunger. Aber ich bin unterwegs. Ich bin schon so lange so lange unterwegs. Die lange Straße lang. Die Straße.

- 7 -

von selbst all by himself
pennen (*colloq.*) sleep, snooze

an-kucken look at (*colloq.*)

rütteln shake, bump
die Schiene, -n rail

[9] **von selbst** implies the same completion as above (**gefallen**).

10

Der kleine Junge hält die Hände auf. Ich soll die Nägel holen. Der Schmied zählt die Nägel. Drei Mann? fragt er.

Vati sagt, für drei Mann.

Die Nägel fallen in die Hände. Der Schmied hat dicke breite Finger. Der kleine Junge ganz dünne, die sich biegen von den großen Nägeln.

Ist der, der sagt, er ist Gottes Sohn, auch dabei?

Der kleine Junge nickt.

Sagt er immer noch, daß er Gottes Sohn ist?

Der kleine Junge nickt. Der Schmied nimmt die Nägel noch mal. Dann läßt er sie wieder in die Hände fallen. Die kleinen Hände biegen sich davon. Dann sagt der Schmied: Na ja.

na ja oh well

Der kleine Junge geht weg. Die Nägel sind schön blank. Der kleine Junge läuft. Da machen die Nägel ein Geräusch. Der Schmied nimmt den Hammer. Na ja, sagt der Schmied. Dann hört der kleine Junge hinter sich: Pink Pank Pink Pank. Er schlägt wieder, denkt der kleine Junge. Nägel macht er, viele blanke Nägel.

pink pank bing bang

11

57 haben sie bei Woronesch begraben. Ich bin über. Aber ich hab Hunger. Mein Reich ist von dieser dieser Welt. Und der Schmied hat die Nägel umsonst gemacht, juppheidi, umsonst gemacht, die Infantrie, umsonst die schönen blanken Nägel. Denn 57 haben sie bei Woronesch begraben. Pink Pank macht der Schmied. Pink Pank bei Woronesch. Pink Pank. 57 mal Pink Pank. Pink Pank macht der Schmied. Pink Pank macht die Infantrie. Pink Pank machen die Ka-

- 8 -

[10] The nails introduce a new and complex motif. **"Drei Mann"** gives a first clue, later fully developed. **"Gottes Sohn"** identifies the one reference of the motif. The notion of burial, "*no use, they buried them, all 57, at Woronezh,*" adds to the meaning of the nails.

[11] What "kingdom" lies behind this allusion?

nonen. Und das Klavier spielt immerzu Pink Pank Pink Pank Pink Pank---- [12]

57 kommen jede Nacht nach Deutschland. 9 Autoschlosser, 2 Gärtner, 5 Beamte, 6 Verkäufer, 1 Friseur, 17 Bauern, 2 Lehrer, 1 Pastor, 6 Arbeiter, 1 Musiker, 7 Schuljungen. 57 kommen jede Nacht an mein Bett, 57 fragen jede Nacht: Wo ist deine Kompanie? Bei Woronesch, sag ich dann. Begraben, sag ich dann. Bei Woronesch begraben. 57 fragen Mann für Mann: Warum? Und 57mal bleib ich stumm.

57 gehen nachts zu ihrem Vater. 57 und Leutnant Fischer. Leutnant Fischer bin ich. 57 fragen nachts ihren Vater: Vater, warum? Und der Vater bleibt 57mal stumm. Und er friert in seinem Hemd. Aber er kommt mit.

der Ortsvorsteher, - mayor

57 gehen nachts zum Ortsvorsteher. 57 und der Vater und ich. 57 fragen nachts den Ortsvorsteher: Ortsvorsteher, warum? Und der Ortsvorsteher bleibt 57mal stumm. Und er friert in seinem Hemd. Aber er kommt mit. [13]

57 gehen nachts zum Pfarrer. 57 und der Vater und der Ortsvorsteher und ich. 57 fragen nachts den Pfarrer: Pfarrer, warum? Und der Pfarrer bleibt 57mal stumm. Und er friert in seinem Hemd. Aber er kommt mit.

57 gehen nachts zum Schulmeister. 57 und der Vater und der Ortsvorsteher und der Pfarrer und ich. 57 fragen nachts den Schulmeister: Schulmeister, warum? Und der Schulmeister bleibt 57mal stumm. Und er friert in seinem Hemd. Aber er kommt mit.

- 9 -

[12] Note how **pink pank** gathers together no fewer than four or five separate motifs.

[13] **das Hemd** may also mean *nightshirt* (as in the Kafka story; v.s.) or *undershirt*.

57 gehen nachts zum General. 57 und der Vater und der Ortsvorsteher und der Pfarrer und der Schulmeister und ich. 57 fragen nachts den General: General, warum? Und der General – der General dreht sich nicht einmal rum. Da bringt der Vater ihn um. Und der Pfarrer? Der Pfarrer bleibt stumm.

57 gehen nachts zum Minister. 57 und der Vater und der Ortsvorsteher und der Pfarrer und der Schulmeister und ich. 57 fragen nachts den Minister: Minister, warum? Da hat der Minister sich sehr erschreckt. Er hatte sich so schön hinterm Sektkorb versteckt, hinterm Sekt. Und da hebt er sein Glas und prostet nach Süden und Norden und Westen und Osten. Und dann sagt er: Deutschland, Kameraden, Deutschland! Darum! Da sehen die 57 sich um. Stumm. So lange und stumm. Und sie sehen nach Süden und Norden und Westen und Osten. Und dann fragen sie leise: Deutschland? Darum? Dann drehen die 57 sich rum. Und sehen sich niemals mehr um. 57 legen sich bei Woronesch wieder ins Grab. Sie haben alte arme Gesichter. Wie Frauen. Wie Mütter. Und sie sagen die Ewigkeit durch: Darum? Darum? Darum? 57 haben sie bei Woronesch begraben. Ich bin über. Ich bin Leutnant Fischer. Ich bin 25. Ich will noch zur Straßenbahn. Ich will mit. Ich bin schon lange lange unterwegs. Nur Hunger hab ich. Aber ich muß. 57 fragen: Warum? Und ich bin über. Und ich bin schon so lange die lange lange Straße unterwegs.

Unterwegs. Ein Mann. Herr Fischer. Ich bin es. Leutnant steht drüben und kommandiert: Links zwei drei vier links zwei drei vier zickezacke juppheidi zwei

- 10 -

der Sektkorb, ⸚e champagne basket
der Sekt champagne
prosten toast

[14] Their looking around may have a very literal force: *was it this (devastated) Germany we fought and died for?*

drei vier links zwei drei vier die Infantrie die Infantrie pink pank pink pank drei vier pink pank drei vier pink pank pink pank die lange Straße lang pink pank immer lang immer rum warum warum warum pink pank pink pank bei Woronesch darum bei Woronesch darum pink pank die lange lange Straße lang. Ein Mensch. 25. Ich. Die Straße. Die lange lange. Ich. Haus Haus Haus Wand Wand Milchgeschäft Vorgarten Kuhgeruch Haustür.

Zahnarzt
Sonnabends nur nach Vereinbarung

Wand Wand Wand

Hilde Bauer ist doof

Leutnant Fischer ist dumm. 57 fragen: warum. Wand Wand Tür Fenster Glas Glas Glas Laterne alte Frau rote rote Augen Bratkartoffelgeruch Haus Haus Klavierunterricht pink pank die ganze Straße lang die Nägel sind so blank Kanonen sind so lang pink pank die ganze Straße lang Kind Kind Hund Ball Auto Pflasterstein Pflasterstein Kopfsteinköpfe Köpfe pink pank Stein Stein grau grau violett Benzinfleck grau grau die lange lange Straße lang Stein Stein grau blau flau flau so grau Wand Wand grüne Emaille

Schlechte Augen schnell behoben
Optiker Terboben[15]
Im 2. Stockwerk oben

Wand Wand Wand Stein Hund Hund hebt Bein Baum Seele Hundetraum Auto hupt noch Hund pupt doch Pflaster rot Hund tot Hund tot Hund tot Wand Wand Wand die lange Straße lang Fenster Wand Fenster Fenster Fenster Lampen Leute Licht Männer

- 11 -

nach Verein'barung by appointment

doof (*adj.; slang*) a dope

flau weak, flat, faint
die Email'le enamel
beheben† correct

pupen (*vulgar*) poop, break wind

[15] **Terboben** is a proper name.

immer noch Männer blanke Gesichter wie Nägel so blank so wunderhübsch blank----

[16] Vor hundert Jahren spielten sie Skat. Vor hundert Jahren spielten sie schon. Und jetzt jetzt spielen sie noch. Und in hundert Jahren dann spielen sie auch immer noch. Immer noch Skat. Die drei Männer. [17] Mit blanken biederen Gesichtern.

Passe.

Karl, sag mehr.

Ich passe auch.

Also dann--ihr habt gemauert, meine Herren.

Du hättest ja auch passen können, dann hätten wir einen schönen Ramsch gehabt.

Man los. Man los. Wie heißt er?

Das Kreuz ist heilig. Wer spielt aus?

[18] Immer der fragt.

Einmal hat es die Mutter erlaubt. Und noch mal Trumpf!

Was, Karl, du hast kein Kreuz mehr?

Diesmal nicht.

Na, dann wollen wir mal auf die Dörfer gehen. Ein Herz hat jeder.

[19] Trumpf! Nun wimmel, Karl, was du bei der Seele hast. Achtundzwanzig.

Und noch einmal Trumpf!

Vor hundert Jahren spielten sie schon. Spielten sie Skat. Und in hundert Jahren, dann spielen sie noch. Spielen sie immer noch Skat mit blanken biederen Gesichtern. Und wenn sie ihre Fäuste auf den Tisch donnern lassen, dann donnert es. Wie Kanonen. Wie 57 Kanonen.

- 12 -

mauern "chicken" (*play a no-risk game*)

der Ramsch throw-in, passed hand

man = nur

auf die Dörfer gehen† go fishing, draw (other players out)

wimmeln play high

[16] The skat game becomes an extended metaphor, with built-in puns or double meanings for ironic effect, constituting a bitter commentary on man's stubbornly opaque dedication to trivial pleasure even in surroundings of crisis and tragedy.

[17] **bieder** *honorable, upright* has an overtone of the naive or commonplace.

[18] **der = der, der**

[19] **was du bei der Seele hast** roughly *everything you've got*

Aber ein Fenster weiter sitzt eine Mutter. Die hat drei Bilder vor sich. Drei Männer in Uniform. Links steht ihr Mann. Rechts steht ihr Sohn. Und in der Mitte steht der General. Der General von ihrem Mann und ihrem Sohn. Und wenn die Mutter abends zu Bett geht, dann stellt sie die Bilder, daß sie sie sieht, wenn sie liegt. Den Sohn. Und den Mann. Und in der Mitte den General. Und dann liest sie die Briefe, die der General schrieb. 1917. Für Deutschland. – steht auf dem einen. 1940. Für Deutschland. – steht auf dem anderen. Mehr liest die Mutter nicht. Ihre Augen sind ganz rot. Sind so rot.

Aber ich bin über. Juppheidi. Für Deutschland. Ich bin noch unterwegs. Zur Straßenbahn. Zweimal hab ich schon gelegen. Wegen dem Hunger. Juppheidi. Aber ich muß hin. Der Leutnant kommandiert. Ich bin schon unterwegs. Schon lange lange unterwegs.

Da steht ein Mann in einer dunklen Ecke. Immer stehen Männer in den dunklen Ecken. Immer stehn dunkle Männer in den Ecken. Einer steht da und hält einen Kasten und einen Hut. Pyramidon! bellt der Mann. Pyramidon! 20 Tabletten genügen. Der Mann grinst, denn das Geschäft geht gut. Das Geschäft geht so gut. 57 Frauen, rotäugige Frauen, die kaufen Pyramidon. Mach eine Null dran. 570. Noch eine und noch eine. 57 000. Und noch und noch und noch. 57 000 000. Das Geschäft geht gut. Der Mann bellt: Pyramidon. Er grinst, der Laden floriert: 57 Frauen, rotäugige Frauen, die kaufen Pyramidon. Der Kasten wird leer. Und der Hut wird voll. Und der Mann grinst. Er kann gut grinsen. Er hat keine Augen. Er

[20] [21]

florie'ren prosper, thrive

- 13 -

[20] **Pyramidon'** is a patented pain-reliever; as if one wrote in English *Anacin.* What are 20 tablets "enough" for?

[21] **er kann gut . . .** *he can afford to . . .*

ist glücklich: Er hat keine Augen. Er sieht die Frauen nicht. Sieht die 57 Frauen nicht. Die 57 rotäugigen Frauen.

Nur ich bin über. Aber ich bin schon unterwegs. Und die Straße ist lang. So fürchterlich lang. Aber ich will zur Straßenbahn. Ich bin schon unterwegs. Schon lange lange unterwegs.

In einem Zimmer sitzt ein Mann. Der Mann schreibt mit Tinte auf weißem Papier. Und er sagt in das Zimmer hinein:

Auf dem Braun der Ackerkrume
weht hellgrün ein Gras.
Eine blaue Blume[22]
ist vom Morgen naß.

die Ackerkrume topsoil

Er schreibt es auf das weiße Papier. Er liest es ins leere Zimmer hinein. Er streicht es mit Tinte wieder durch. Er sagt in das Zimmer hinein:

Auf dem Braun der Ackerkrume
weht hellgrün ein Gras.
Eine blaue Blume
lindert allen Haß.

Der Mann schreibt es hin. Er liest es in das leere Zimmer hinein. Er streicht es wieder durch. Dann sagt er in das Zimmer hinein:

Auf dem Braun der Ackerkrume
weht hellgrün ein Gras.
Eine blaue Blume–
Eine blaue Blume–
Eine blaue–

Der Mann steht auf. Er geht um den Tisch herum. Immer um den Tisch herum. Er bleibt stehen:

- 14 -

[22] The blue flower has special connotations for Germans, it was the Romanticists' symbol of infinite longing. The association here is ludicrously discordant.

Eine blaue–
Eine blaue–
Auf dem Braun der Ackerkrume–

Der Mann geht immer um den Tisch herum.

57 haben sie bei Woronesch begraben. Aber die Erde war grau. Und wie Stein. Und da weht kein hellgrünes Gras. Schnee war da. Und der war wie Glas. Und ohne blaue Blume. Millionenmal Schnee. Und keine blaue Blume. Aber der Mann in dem Zimmer weiß das nicht. Er weiß es nie. Er sieht immer die blaue Blume. Überall die blaue Blume. Und dabei haben sie 57 bei Woronesch begraben. Unter glasigem Schnee. Im grauen gräulichen Sand. Ohne Grün. Und ohne Blau. Der Sand war eisig und grau. Und der Schnee war wie Glas. Und der Schnee lindert keinen Haß. Denn 57 haben sie bei Woronesch begraben. 57 begraben. Bei Woronesch begraben.

Das ist noch gar nichts, das ist ja noch gar nichts! sagt der Obergefreite mit der Krücke. Und er legt die Krücke über seine Fußspitze und zielt. Er kneift das eine Auge klein und zielt mit der Krücke über die Fußspitze. Das ist noch gar nichts, sagt er. 86 Iwans[23] haben wir die eine Nacht geschafft. 86 Iwans. Mit einem MG, mein Lieber, mit einem einzigen MG in einer Nacht. Am andern Morgen haben wir sie gezählt. Übereinander lagen sie. 86 Iwans. Einige hatten das Maul noch offen. Viele auch die Augen. Ja, viele hatten die Augen noch offen. In einer Nacht, mein Lieber. Der Obergefreite zielt mit seiner Krücke auf die alte Frau, die ihm auf der Bank gegenübersitzt. Er zielt auf die eine alte Frau und er trifft 86 alte Frauen.

- 15 -

klein kneifen† squint

das MG = Maschi′nengewehr machine gun

[23] **Iwan,** one of the commonest of Russian first names, became the popular designation of a Russian soldier. Cf. *Tommy;* also (*G.I.*) *Joe* and *Mac* as forms of address.

Aber die wohnen in Rußland. Davon weiß er nichts. Es ist gut, daß er das nicht weiß. Was sollte er sonst wohl machen? Jetzt, wo es Abend wird?

Nur ich weiß es. Ich bin Leutnant Fischer. 57 haben sie bei Woronesch begraben. Aber ich war nicht ganz tot. Ich bin noch unterwegs. Zweimal hab ich schon gelegen. Vom Hunger. Denn der liebe Gott hat ja keinen Löffel. Aber ich will auf jeden Fall zur Straßenbahn. Wenn nur die Straße nicht so voller Mütter wäre. 57 haben sie bei Woronesch begraben. Und der Obergefreite hat am anderen Morgen 86 Iwans gezählt. Und 86 Mütter schießt er mit seiner Krücke tot. Aber er weiß es nicht, das ist gut. Wo sollte er sonst wohl hin. Denn der liebe Gott hat ja keinen Löffel. Es ist gut, wenn die Dichter die blauen Blumen blühen lassen. Es ist gut, wenn immer einer Klavier spielt. Es ist gut, wenn sie Skat spielen. Immer spielen sie Skat. Wo sollten sie sonst wohl hin, die alte Frau mit den drei Bildern am Bett, der Obergefreite mit den Krücken und den 86 toten Iwans, die Mutter mit dem kleinen Mädchen, das Suppe haben will, und Timm, der den alten Mann getreten hat? Wo sollten sie sonst wohl hin?

Aber ich muß die lange lange Straße lang. Lang. Wand Wand Tür Laterne Wand Wand Fenster Wand Wand und buntes Papier buntes bedrucktes Papier.

Sind Sie schon versichert?
Sie machen sich und Ihrer Familie
eine Weihnachtsfreude
mit einer Eintrittserklärung in die
URANIA LEBENSVERSICHERUNG [24]

- 16 -

[24] **mit einer Eintrittserklärung in die Urania Lebensversicherung** *by taking out a policy with Urania Life Insurance.* Urania is a real company, but the name also has "heavenly" associations.

57 haben ihr Leben nicht richtig versichert. Und die 86 toten Iwans auch nicht. Und sie haben ihren Familien keine Weihnachtsfreude gemacht. Rote Augen haben sie ihren Familien gemacht. Weiter nichts, rote Augen. Warum waren sie auch nicht in der Urania Lebensversicherung? Und ich kann mich nun mit den roten Augen herumschlagen. Überall die roten rotgeweinten rotgeschluchzten Augen. Die Mutteraugen, die Frauenaugen. Überall die roten rotgeweinten Augen. Warum haben sich die 57 nicht versichern lassen? Nein, sie haben ihren Familien keine Weihnachtsfreude gemacht. Rote Augen. Nur rote Augen. Und dabei steht es doch auf tausend bunten Plakaten: Urania Lebensversicherung Urania Lebensversicherung--

sich herum′-schlagen† fight it out

25

Evelyn steht in der Sonne und singt. Die Sonne ist bei Evelyn. Man sieht durch das Kleid die Beine und alles. Und Evelyn singt. Durch die Nase singt sie ein wenig und heiser singt sie bißchen. Sie hat heute nacht zu lange im Regen gestanden. Und sie singt, daß mir heiß wird, wenn ich die Augen zumach. Und wenn ich sie aufmach, dann seh ich die Beine bis oben und alles. Und Evelyn singt, daß mir die Augen verschwimmen. Sie singt den süßen Weltuntergang. Die Nacht singt sie und Schnaps, den gefährlich kratzenden Schnaps voll wundem Weltgestöhn. Das Ende singt Evelyn, das Weltende, süß und zwischen nackten schmalen Mädchenbeinen: heiliger himmlischer heißer Weltuntergang. Ach, Evelyn singt wie nasses Gras, so schwer von Geruch und Wollust und so grün. So dunkelgrün, so grün wie leere Bierflaschen neben den

26

die Wollust voluptuousness, desire

- 17 -

[25] **rot + geweint (weinen); rot + geschluchzt (schluchzen** *sob***)**

[26] **der Schnaps, ⸗e** strictly speaking means *brandy* or *eau de vie*, generically however *hard liquor*, as we use *whiskey;* later used in typical Borchert compounds **schnapsgrün, schnapssüß.**

Bänken, auf denen Evelyns Knie abends mondblaß aus dem Kleid raussehen, daß mir heiß wird.

Sing, Evelyn, sing mich tot. Sing den süßen Weltuntergang, sing einen kratzenden Schnaps, sing einen grasgrünen Rausch. Und Evelyn drückt meine graskalte Hand zwischen die mondblassen Knie, daß mir heiß wird.

Und Evelyn singt. Komm lieber Mai und mache, singt Evelyn und hält meine graskalte Hand mit den Knien. Komm lieber Mai und mache die Gräber wieder grün. Das singt Evelyn. Komm lieber Mai und mache die Schlachtfelder bierflaschengrün und mache den Schutt, den riesigen Schuttacker grün wie mein Lied, wie mein schnapssüßes Untergangslied.[27] Und Evelyn singt auf der Bank ein heiseres hektisches Lied, daß mir kalt wird. Komm lieber Mai und mache die Augen wieder blank, singt Evelyn und hält meine Hand mit den Knien. Sing, Evelyn, sing mich zurück unters bierflaschengrüne Gras, wo ich Sand war und Lehm war und Land war. Sing, Evelyn, sing und sing mich über die Schuttäcker und über die Schlachtfelder und über das Massengrab rüber in deinen süßen heißen mädchenheimlichen Mondrausch. Sing, Evelyn, sing, wenn die tausend Kompanien durch die Nächte marschieren, dann sing, wenn die tausend Kanonen die Äcker pflügen und düngen mit Blut. Sing, Evelyn, sing, wenn die Wände die Uhren und Bilder verlieren, dann sing mich in schnapsgrünen Rausch und in deinen süßen Weltuntergang. Sing, Evelyn, sing mich in dein Mädchendasein hinein, in dein heimliches, nächtliches Mädchengefühl, das so süß ist, daß mir heiß wird,

- 18 -

tot-singen† sing . . . to death

der Mondrausch moonlight ecstasy

düngen fertilize

[27] **der Untergang** in **Untergangslied** is related to **Weltuntergang** below: *decline and fall, end of the world.*

wieder heiß wird von Leben. Komm lieber Mai und mache das Gras wieder grün, so bierflaschengrün, so evelyngrün. Sing, Evelyn! 28

Aber das Mädchen, das singt nicht. Das Mädchen, das zählt, denn das Mädchen hat einen runden Bauch. Ihr Bauch ist etwas zu rund. Und nun muß sie die ganze Nacht am Bahnsteig stehen, weil einer von den 57 nicht versichert war. Und nun zählt sie die ganze Nacht die Waggons. Eine Lokomotive hat 18 Räder. Ein Personenwagen 8. Ein Güterwagen 4. Das Mädchen mit dem runden Bauch zählt die Waggons und die Räder – die Räder die Räder die Räder –––– 78, sagt sie einmal, das ist schon ganz schön. 62, sagt sie dann, das reicht womöglich nicht. 110, sagt sie, das reicht. Dann läßt sie sich fallen und fällt vor den Zug. Der Zug hat eine Lokomotive, 6 Personenwagen und fünf Güterwagen. Das sind 86 Räder. Das reicht. Das Mädchen mit dem runden Bauch ist nicht mehr da, als der Zug mit seinen 86 Rädern vorbei ist. Sie ist einfach nicht mehr da. Kein bißchen. Kein einziges kleines bißchen ist mehr von ihr da. Sie hatte keine blaue Blume und keiner spielte für sie Klavier und keiner mit ihr Skat. Und der liebe Gott hatte keinen Löffel für sie. Aber die Eisenbahn hatte die vielen schönen Räder. Wo sollte sie sonst auch hin! Was sollte sie sonst wohl tun? Denn der liebe Gott hatte nicht mal einen Löffel. Und nun ist von ihr nichts mehr über, gar nichts mehr über. 29 30

Nur ich. Ich bin noch unterwegs. Noch immer unterwegs. Schon lange, so lang schon lang schon unterwegs. Die Straße ist lang. Ich komm die Straße

- 19 -

der Waggon', -s railroad car

schon ganz schön pretty good

[28] **evelyngrün = Evelyn + grün**

[29] Note the number as motif. What does it recall?

[30] Again a gathering together of earlier motifs.

und den Hunger nicht entlang. Sie sind beide so lang.

Hin und wieder schrein sie los. Links auf dem Fußballplatz. Rechts in dem großen Haus. Da schrein sie manchmal los. Und die Straße geht da mitten durch, Auf der Straße geh ich. Ich bin Leutnant Fischer. Ich bin 25. Ich hab Hunger. Ich komm schon von Woronesch. Ich bin schon lange unterwegs. Links ist der Fußballplatz. Und rechts das große Haus. Da sitzen sie drin. 1000. 2000. 3000. Und keiner sagt ein Wort. Vorne machen sie Musik. Und einige singen. Und die 3000 sagen kein Wort. Sie sind sauber gewaschen. Sie haben ihre Haare geordnet und reine Hemden haben sie an. So sitzen sie da in dem großen Haus und lassen sich erschüttern. Oder erbauen. Oder unterhalten. Das kann man nicht unterscheiden. Sie sitzen und lassen sich sauber gewaschen erschüttern. Aber sie wissen nicht, daß ich Hunger hab. Das wissen sie nicht. Und daß ich hier an der Mauer steh – ich, der von Woronesch, der auf der langen Straße mit dem langen Hunger unterwegs ist, schon so lange unterwegs ist – daß ich hier an der Mauer steh, weil ich vor Hunger vor Hunger nicht weiter kann. Aber das können sie ja nicht wissen. Die Wand, die dicke dumme Wand ist ja dazwischen. Und davor steh ich mit wackligen Knien – und dahinter sind sie in sauberer Wäsche und lassen sich Sonntag für Sonntag erschüttern. Für zehn Mark lassen sie sich die Seele umwühlen und den Magen umdrehen und die Nerven betäuben. Zehn Mark, das ist so furchtbar viel Geld. Für meinen Bauch ist das furchtbar viel Geld. Aber dafür steht

entlang' *here* all the way to the end

wacklig shaky

auch das Wort PASSION auf den Karten, die sie für zehn Mark bekommen. MATTHÄUS-PASSION.[31] Aber wenn der große Chor dann BARABBAS schreit, BARABBAS blutdurstig blutrünstig schreit, dann fallen sie nicht von den Bänken, die Tausend in sauberen Hemden. Nein und sie weinen auch nicht und beten auch nicht und man sieht ihren Gesichtern, sieht ihren Seelen eigentlich gar nicht viel an, wenn der große Chor BARABBAS schreit. Auf den Billetts steht für zehn Mark MATTHÄUS-PASSION. Man kann bei der Passion ganz vorne sitzen, wo die Passion recht laut erlitten wird, oder etwas weiter hinten, wo nur noch gedämpft gelitten wird. Aber das ist egal. Ihren Gesichtern sieht man nichts an, wenn der große Chor BARABBAS schreit. Alle beherrschen sich gut bei der Passion. Keine Frisur geht in Unordnung vor Not und vor Qual. Nein, Not und Qual, die werden ja nur da vorne gesungen und gegeigt, für zehn Mark vormusiziert. Und die BARABBAS-Schreier die tun ja nur so, die werden ja schließlich fürs Schreien bezahlt. Und der große Chor schreit BARABBAS. MUTTER! schreit Leutnant Fischer auf der endlosen Straße. Leutnant Fischer bin ich. BARABBAS! schreit der große Chor der Saubergewaschenen. HUNGER! bellt der Bauch von Leutnant Fischer. Leutnant Fischer bin ich. TOR! schreien die Tausend auf dem Fußballplatz. BARABBAS! schreien sie links von der Straße. TOR! schreien sie rechts von der Straße. WORONESCH! schrei ich dazwischen. Aber die Tausend schrein gegenan. BARABBAS! schrein sie rechts. TOR! schrein sie links. PASSION spielen sie rechts. FUSSBALL

- 21 -

gedämpft quiet, muffled
das ist egal' it doesn't make any difference

geigen fiddle
vor-musizie'ren play music, give a musical performance

gegenan' against me

[31] **die Matthäus-Passion** (*Bach's*) "*St. Matthew's Passion.*" **Barrabas** (either spelling possible) was to have been crucified with Jesus, but the people cried out for his release and Pilate assented. What previous allusion is picked up here?

spielen sie links. Ich steh dazwischen. Ich. Leutnant Fischer. 25 Jahre jung. 57 Millionen Jahre alt. Woronesch-Jahre. Mütter-Jahre. 57 Millionen Straßen-Jahre alt. Woronesch-Jahre. Und rechts schrein sie BARABBAS. Und links schrein sie TOR. Und dazwischen steh ich ohne Mutter allein. Auf der wankenden Welle Welt ohne Mutter allein. Ich bin 25. Ich kenne die 57, die sie bei Woronesch begraben haben, die 57, die nichts wußten, die nicht wollten, die kenn ich Tag und Nacht. Und ich kenne die 86 Iwans, die morgens mit offenen Augen und Mäulern vor dem Maschinengewehr lagen. Ich kenne das kleine Mädchen, das keine Suppe hat und ich kenne den Obergefreiten mit den Krücken. BARABBAS schrein sie rechts für zehn Mark den Saubergewaschenen ins Ohr. Aber ich kenne die alte Frau mit den drei Bildern am Bett und das Mädchen mit dem runden Bauch, das unter die Eisenbahn sprang. TOR! schrein sie links, tausendmal TOR! Aber ich kenne Timm, der nicht schlafen kann, weil er den alten Mann getreten hat und ich kenne die 57 rotäugigen Frauen, die bei dem blinden Mann Pyramidon einkaufen. PYRAMIDON steht für 2 Mark auf der kleinen Schachtel. PASSION steht auf den Eintrittskarten rechts von der Straße, für 10 Mark PASSION. POKALSPIEL steht auf den blauen, den blumenblauen Billetts für 4 Mark auf der linken Seite der Straße. BARABBAS! schrein sie rechts. TOR! schrein sie links. Und immer bellt der blinde Mann: PYRAMIDON! Dazwischen steh ich ganz allein, ohne Mutter allein, auf der Welle, der wankenden Welle Welt allein. Mit meinem bellenden Hunger!

das Pokal'spiel, -e cup match

- 22 -

Und ich kenne die 57 von Woronesch. Ich bin Leutnant Fischer. Ich bin 25. Die anderen schrein TOR und BARABBAS im großen Chor. Nur ich bin über. Bin so furchtbar über. Aber es ist gut, daß die Saubergewaschenen die 57 von Woronesch nicht kennen. Wie sollten sie es sonst wohl aushalten bei Passion und Pokalspiel. Nur ich bin noch unterwegs. Von Woronesch her. Mit Hunger schon lange lange unterwegs. Denn ich bin über. Die andern haben sie bei Woronesch begraben. 57. Nur mich haben sie vergessen. Warum haben sie mich bloß vergessen? Nun hab ich nur noch die Wand. Die hält mich. Da muß ich entlang. TOR! schrein sie hinter mir her. BARABBAS! schrein sie hinter mir her. Die lange lange Straße entlang. Und ich kann schon lange nicht mehr. Ich kann schon so lange nicht mehr. Und ich hab nur noch die Wand, denn meine Mutter ist nicht da. Nur die 57 sind da. Die 57 Millionen rotäugigen Mütter, die sind so furchtbar hinter mir her. Die Straße entlang. Aber Leutnant Fischer kommandiert: Links zwei drei vier links zwei drei vier zickezacke BARABBAS die blaue Blume ist so naß von Tränen und von Blut zickezacke juppheidi begraben ist die Infantrie unterm Fußballplatz unterm Fußballplatz. [32]

Ich kann schon lange nicht mehr, aber der alte Leierkastenmann macht so schneidige Musik. Freut euch des Lebens, singt der alte Mann die Straße lang. Freut euch, ihr bei Woronesch, juppheidi, so freut euch doch solange noch die blaue Blume blüht freut euch des Lebens solange noch der Leierkasten läuft---- [33]

Der alte Mann singt wie ein Sarg. So leise. Freut

- 23 -

der Sarg, ⸚e coffin

[32] **ich kann schon lange nicht mehr** *all my strength was gone long ago*

[33] **„Freut euch des Lebens, solange noch das Lämpchen glüht“** are words in a familiar old German song, here used as a basis for a bitter and extended parody. The refrain is soon reduced to **„freut euch solange noch,“** roughly “*enjoy things while you still (can)*.”

euch! singt er, solange noch, singt er, so leise, so nach Grab, so wurmig, so erdig, so nach Woronesch singt er, freut euch solange noch das Lämpchen Schwindel glüht! Solange noch die Windel blüht!

die Windel, -n diaper

Ich bin Leutnant Fischer! schrei ich. Ich bin über. Ich bin schon lange die lange Straße unterwegs. Und 57 haben sie bei Woronesch begraben. Die kenn ich.

Freut euch, singt der Leierkastenmann.

Ich bin 25, schrei ich.

Freut euch, singt der Leierkastenmann.

Ich hab Hunger, schrei ich.

34 Freut euch singt er und die bunten Hampelmänner an seiner Orgel schaukeln. Schöne bunte Hampelmänner hat der Leierkastenmann. Viele schöne hampelige Männer. Einen Boxer hat der Leierkastenmann. Der Boxer schwenkt die dicken dummen Fäuste und ruft: Ich boxe! Und er bewegt sich meisterlich. Einen fetten Mann hat der Leierkastenmann. Mit einem dicken dummen Sack voll Geld. Ich regiere, ruft der fette Mann und er bewegt sich meisterlich. Einen General hat der Leierkastenmann. Mit einer dicken dummen Uniform. Ich kommandiere, ruft er immerzu, ich kommandiere! Und er bewegt sich meisterlich. 35 Und einen Dr. Faust hat der Leierkastenmann mit einem weißen weißen Kittel und einer schwarzen Brille. Und der ruft nicht und schreit nicht. Aber er bewegt sich fürchterlich so fürchterlich.

hampelig dangling

Freut euch, singt der Leierkastenmann und seine Hampelmänner schaukeln. Schaukeln fürchterlich. Schöne Hampelmänner hast du, Leierkastenmann, sag ich. Freut euch, singt der Leierkastenmann. Aber was

- 24 -

[34] **der Hampelmann, ⸗er** a hanging, marionette-like wooden or cardboard figure, made to move like a jumping-jack.

[35] **Dr. Faust** *Faust* the alchemist, **der Kittel, -** *lab coat*, later **der Brillenmann,** *man with glasses*, constitute a complex of motifs connected with science in the service of destruction and the blind, amoral use of scientific knowledge which horrified Borchert.

macht der Brillenmann, der Brillenmann im weißen Kittel? frag ich. Er ruft nicht, er boxt nicht, er regiert nicht und er kommandiert nicht. Was macht der Mann im weißen Kittel, er bewegt sich, bewegt sich so fürchterlich! Freut euch, singt der Leierkastenmann, er denkt, singt der Leierkastenmann, er denkt und forscht und findet. Was findet er denn, der Brillenmann, denn er bewegt sich so fürchterlich. Freut euch, singt der Leierkastenmann, er erfindet ein Pulver, ein grünes Pulver, ein hoffnungsgrünes Pulver.[36] Was kann man mit dem grünen Pulver machen, Leierkastenmann, denn er bewegt sich fürchterfürchterlich.[37] Freut euch, singt der Leierkastenmann, mit dem hoffnungsgrünen Pulver kann man mit einem Löffelchen voll 100 Millionen Menschen totmachen, wenn man pustet, wenn man hoffnungsvoll pustet. Und der Brillenmann erfindet und erfindet. Freut euch doch solange noch, singt der Leierkastenmann. Er erfindet! schrei ich. Freut euch solange noch, singt der Leierkastenmann, freut euch doch solange noch.

pusten blow, puff

Ich bin Leutnant Fischer. Ich bin 25. Ich hab dem Leierkastenmann den Mann im weißen Kittel weggenommen. Freut euch doch solange noch. Ich hab dem Mann, dem Brillenmann im weißen Kittel, den Kopf abgerissen! Freut euch doch solange noch. Ich hab dem weißen Kittelbrillenmann, dem Grünpulvermann, die Arme abgedreht. Freut euch doch solange noch. Ich hab den Hoffnungsgrünenerfindermann mittendurchgebrochen. Ich hab ihn mittendurchgebrochen. Nun kann er kein Pulver mehr mi-

- 25 -

[36] Borchert twists the conventional meaning of the compounding form **hoffnungs-** *hopeful, hope-(green,* etc.) into a parody of its usual sentimental meaning.

[37] **fürchterfürchterlich** is an intensified modifier formed by repeating the stem syllables of **fürchterlich,** in a parody of, for example, repeated word elements in popular songs.

schen, nun kann er kein Pulver mehr erfinden. Ich hab ihn mittenmittendurchgebrochen.

Warum hast du meinen schönen Hampelmann kaputt gemacht, ruft der Leierkastenmann, er war so klug, er war so weise, er war so faustisch klug und weise und erfinderisch. Warum hast du den Brillenmann kaputt gemacht, warum? fragt mich der Leierkastenmann.

Ich bin 25, schrei ich. Ich bin noch unterwegs, schrei ich. Ich hab Angst, schrei ich. Darum hab ich den Kittelmann kaputt gemacht. Wir wohnen in Hütten aus Holz und aus Hoffnung, schrei ich, aber wir wohnen. Und vor unsern Hütten da wachsen noch Rüben und Rhabarber. Vor unsern Hütten da wachsen Tomaten und Tabak. Wir haben Angst! schrei ich. Wir wollen leben! schrei ich. In Hütten aus Holz und aus Hoffnung! Denn die Tomaten und Tabak, die wachsen doch noch. Die wachsen doch noch. Ich bin 25, schrei ich, darum hab ich den Brillenmann im weißen Kittel umgebracht. Darum hab ich den Pulvermann kaputt gemacht. Darum darum darum--- Freut euch, singt da der Leierkastenmann, so freut euch doch solange noch solange noch solange noch freut euch, singt der Leierkastenmann und nimmt aus seinem furchtbar großen Kasten einen neuen Hampelmann mit einer Brille und mit einem weißen Kittel und mit einem Löffelchen ja Löffelchen voll hoffnungsgrünem Pulver. Freut euch, singt der Leierkastenmann, freut euch solange noch ich hab doch noch so viele viele weiße Männer so furchtbarfurchtbar viele. Aber die bewegen sich so fürchterfürchterlich, schrei

- 26 -

faustisch Faustian, like Faust

die Rübe, -n carrot; beet
der Rhabar'ber rhubarb

ich, und ich bin 25 und ich hab Angst und ich wohne in einer Hütte aus Holz und aus Hoffnung. Und Tomaten und Tabak, die wachsen doch noch.

Freut euch doch solange noch, singt der Leierkastenmann.

Aber der bewegt sich doch so fürchterlich, schrei ich.

Nein, er bewegt sich nicht, er wird er wird doch nur bewegt.

Und wer bewegt ihn denn, wer wer bewegt ihn denn?

Ich, sagt da der Leierkastenmann so fürchterlich, ich!

Ich hab Angst, schrei ich und mach aus meiner Hand eine Faust und schlag sie dem Leierkastenmann dem fürchterlichen Leierkastenmann in das Gesicht. Nein, ich schlag ihn nicht, denn ich kann sein Gesicht das fürchterliche Gesicht nicht finden. Das Gesicht ist so hoch am Hals. Ich kann mit der Faust nicht heran. Und der Leierkastenmann der lacht so fürchterfürchterlich. Doch ich find es nicht ich find es nicht. Denn das Gesicht ist ganz weit weg und lacht so lacht so fürchterlich. Es lacht so fürchterlich!

Durch die Straße läuft ein Mensch. Er hat Angst. Seine Mutter hat ihn allein gelassen. Nun schrein sie so fürchterlich hinter ihm her. Warum? schrein 57 von Woronesch her. Warum? Deutschland, schreit der Minister. Barabbas, schreit der Chor. Pyramidon, ruft der blinde Mann. Und die andern schrein: Tor. Schrein 57mal Tor. Und der Kittelmann, der weiße Brillenkittelmann, bewegt sich so fürchterlich. Und

- 27 -

erfindet und erfindet und erfindet. Und das kleine Mädchen hat keinen Löffel. Aber der weiße Mann mit der Brille hat einen. Der reicht gleich für 100 Millionen. Freut euch, singt der Leierkastenmann.

Ein Mensch läuft durch die Straße. Die lange lange Straße lang. Er hat Angst. Er läuft mit seiner Angst durch die Welt. Durch die wankende Welle Welt. Der Mensch bin ich. Ich bin 25. Und ich bin unterwegs. Bin lange schon und immer noch unterwegs. Ich will zur Straßenbahn. Ich muß mit der Straßenbahn, denn alle sind hinter mir her. Sind furchtbar hinter mir her. Ein Mensch läuft mit seiner Angst durch die Straße. Der Mensch bin ich. Ein Mensch läuft vor dem Schreien davon. Der Mensch bin ich. Ein Mensch glaubt an Tomaten und Tabak. Der Mensch bin ich. Ein Mensch springt auf die Straßenbahn, die gelbe gute Straßenbahn. Der Mensch bin ich. Ich fahre mit der Straßenbahn, der guten gelben Straßenbahn.

Wo fahren wir hin? frag ich die andern. Zum Fußballplatz? Zur Matthäus-Passion? Zu den Hütten aus Holz und aus Hoffnung mit Tomaten und Tabak? Wo fahren wir hin? frag ich die andern. Da sagt keiner ein Wort. Aber da sitzt eine Frau, die hat drei Bilder im Schoß. Und da sitzen drei Männer beim Skat nebendran. Und da sitzt auch der Krückenmann und das kleine Mädchen ohne Suppe und das Mädchen mit dem runden Bauch. Und einer macht Gedichte. Und einer spielt Klavier. Und 57 marschieren neben der Straßenbahn her. Zickezackejuppheidi schneidig war die Infantrie bei Woronesch heijuppheidi. An der

der Schoß, ⸗e lap

- 28 -

Spitze marschiert Leutnant Fischer. Leutnant Fischer bin ich. Und meine Mutter marschiert hinterher. Marschiert 57millionenmal hinter mir her. Wohin fahren wir denn? frag ich den Schaffner. Da gibt er mir ein hoffnungsgrünes Billett. Matthäus – Pyramidon steht da drauf. [38] Bezahlen müssen wir alle, sagt er und hält seine Hand auf. Und ich gebe ihm 57 Mann. Aber wohin fahren wir denn? frag ich die andern. Wir müssen doch wissen: wohin? Da sagt Timm: Das wissen wir auch nicht. Das weiß keine Sau. [39] Und alle nicken mit dem Kopf und grummeln: Das weiß keine Sau. Aber wir fahren. Tingeltangel, macht die Klingel der Straßenbahn und keiner weiß wohin. Aber alle fahren mit. Und der Schaffner macht ein unbegreifliches Gesicht. Es ist ein uralter Schaffner mit zehntausend Falten. Man kann nicht erkennen, ob es ein böser oder ein guter Schaffner ist. Aber alle bezahlen bei ihm. Und alle fahren mit. Und keiner weiß: ein guter oder böser. Und keiner weiß: wohin. Tingeltangel, macht die Klingel der Straßenbahn. Und keiner weiß: wohin? Und alle fahren: mit. Und keiner weiß ---- und keiner weiß ---- und keiner weiß ----

tingeltangel ding-dong, ding-a-ling

- 29 -

[38] **Matthäus** *Matthew* refers back to **Matthäus-Passion.**

[39] **die Sau, ⸗e** *pig, sow;* **keine Sau** is slang for *niemand.*

Gerd Gaiser

Gerd Gaiser did not appear as a writer until after the second World War. His first book of stories, *Zwischenland*, came out in 1949, to be followed by his novel *Eine Stimme hebt an*—which caused much excitement in critical and literary circles. In 1951 he received the Fontane Prize of the city of Berlin. His vivid novel of the flyer's war, *Die sterbende Jagd*, was published in 1953. He has written a great deal since then, including the volume of stories, *Einmal und oft* (1956) from which the present one is taken. Three other collections of stories appeared in the years 1959-1960 alone. His list of honors continues to grow. In 1955 he received the prize award of the Bavarian Academy of Fine Arts, and in the following year he became a member of the Berlin Academy of Arts. In 1959 he was awarded the Immermann Prize, in 1960 the Raabe Prize. Few modern prose writers have been so frequently honored. His war novel, which the famous critic Hans Egon Holthusen called the best in German, has appeared in English as *The Last Squadron*, and he was one of four writers to be represented with stories in the *Atlantic Monthly* Supplement "Perspective of Germany" (March, 1957). His novel *Schlußball* (1958), structurally one of the most significant in modern German literature, is also one of the most trenchant commentaries on the *Wirtschaftswunder*. It too was translated into English and eight other languages.

Gaiser was born at Oberriexingen in Württemberg in 1908. His father was a minister, and Gaiser's first field of study was theology. He soon turned to art and painting, attended art academies in Stuttgart and Königsberg, as well as the University of Tübingen, and took his degree in art history.

During the war he was a pursuit pilot. He was captured by the British and spent years in prisoner-of-war camps in Italy—an experience which figures almost as widely in the background of his writing as does his service in the Luftwaffe.

Back in Germany after the war he cut wood for a living and continued his painting. Some of his stories deal with painters or use the language of the palette for striking effects. His principal career, however, has lain in teaching (art) and, of course, in writing. He lives in Reutlingen, where in 1949 he became instructor and *Studienrat* in the *Gymnasium*, and is now on the faculty of the *Pädagogische Hochschule*.

Gaiser's work has passed through several distinct and important phases. The common thread that runs through them is the problem of life in a disintegrating world, or in a world of false values. For the flyers of *Die sterbende Jagd* it is how to fight when there is no longer any reason for it, no longer any meaning to their tradition of "chivalry." What keeps them going is mere courage, the consciousness that it would be cowardly and false to quit. For those who return there is not even the shadow of glory. Gaiser paints the wretched existence of chaotic cities in the days of the black markets; he records the triumph of crude and unscrupulous men, the silent defeat of decency and restraint. But his characters do not give up. They explore the source of strength that Gaiser himself first found: Nature. They also discover in themselves the elemental will to stick it out. In his most recent work, less Naturalistic, more "surreal," he still discovers viable meaning and reality behind the façade of life.

Gaiser is a controversial figure, as great writers usually are until their reputation is fully established. His technical skill is acknowledged, the richness of his pictures and colors and images. The same is true of his power of imagination. But he has been criticized because his characters, especially in earlier books, evince a distrust of the traditions and works of European culture. He has been accused of reviving an outworn nature myth. Because his description of flyers and of air battles is real and not subjectively weighted he has been accused of viewing war as Homeric adventure. He has been called a profound pessimist. Some of this may be true, but much of it misses the point. His writing is a long tribute to the durability of man in the midst of violence and crisis (which have been and always will be with us), and to his ability ultimately to find some meaning in life. The restoration of bonds of affection with other men is no message of pessimism. Of this, *Fehleisen* is sufficient testimony.

Fehleisen

(1956)

The men who fought were the protagonists of the human drama in Germany in the years before the catastrophe of 1945. Return from war is the long and bitter denouement that ends that part of the drama and prepares for the next. In every country this was a difficult time, and for every man at least a risk. In Germany it was of searing impact, because the Germans, having lost, had not even the temporary elation of victory to blind them therapeutically to devastation and change. They had lost, as a physical nation, more than others—or felt they had. They were occupied, and they had leisure to reflect on the genesis of the destruction they saw everywhere. They had to find new terms on which to live their lives, for the old ones were discredited. In *Fehleisen*, Gaiser gives the concentrated psychological history of such a return.

The dangerous mood of this restless man is clear enough. He is neither an "important person" nor an abstract thinker. The issues of his return he must work out on the plane of his own small life. The prospect is grim. Cut off from his occupation, he is in further danger of cutting himself off from all human contact. Disillusioned because he had been "used for a bad war," he can find no impelling motive to rise out of his lethargy. He cannot give himself to any project or person. He takes the frequent step of disillusioned men, distrust not only of illusion but of any ideal or commitment.

The plain, straightforward language of *Fehleisen* will not cause the reader to overlook its symbolism, which runs clear and deep. (Indeed, the principal aesthetic question to be raised about the story is whether the symbolism is excessively clear.) The ring is plainly the uniting symbolic element. It extends from the beginning of the story to the end, and its appearance in any given scene helps greatly in an understanding of the scene and its meaning. Anyone who takes the trouble to gather the evidence will have the key to the story, and considerable insight into the craft of writing.

The ring is his mother's gift, out of her impulse to do something for Fehleisen. It is made of the gold of two old family rings. This was important enough to send his mother back up the stairs to the woman who made it. Fehleisen, who received the ring along with an explanation of its origin, is not grateful but profoundly irritated. (Why is he so upset?) The ring is the point of comparison for the initial annoyance Brack's letter causes him. And so on. What, then, does the ring symbolize?

In analyzing a story so carefully constructed, it is dangerous to call anything accidental. This applies to the snake, as we shall see. Even Fehleisen's return from the forest to the "traveled road" is significant. The forest, for all of Gaiser's earlier preoccupation with it as a place of refuge and asylum (which it was for Wiechert too), is a place of aloneness. Is the traveled road the way of life among one's fellow beings?

Clearly paramount is the nature of the parables Brack (the painter in the story) is illustrating. They are parables of the lost and the found. And this whole story is a parable of the lost and the found—of the ring and what it stands for.

Finally, the peculiar optimism of Gaiser's tale, couched in an unusual metaphor: the irrational forces of life, chance and coincidence, not only "make sense," they operate in our favor if we give them a chance. We cannot fathom them rationally —we cannot expect to "balance the books." But, contrary to the Existentialist axiom, human life is neither meaningless nor absurd.

FEHLEISEN

Ein ungeduldiger Mensch hieß Fehleisen; der war Soldat gewesen und mit dem Leben herausgekommen so, daß er jetzt hätte anfangen können, wenn auch nur mit dem, was er auf dem Leib trug.[1] Allerdings fiel er unter eine Ziffer des Statuts, das die Kampfhandlungen beendete, und diese Ziffer untersagte ihm, in seiner erlernten Beschäftigung tätig zu sein. Niemand hatte auf ihn gewartet als seine Mutter, die in Witwenschaft lebte; so konnte sie ihm auch nicht viel helfen außer dem, daß sie eben seine Mutter war.[2] Dies alles war nicht, um[3] einen Menschen zum Erliegen zu bringen, denn Ungezählte trafen es[4] weit schlimmer, und ein Mann allein schlägt sich überall durch. Doch Fehleisen wartete vergeblich, daß ihm die Lust kommen sollte, sich selbst oder irgend etwas anderes zu erhalten und zu verteidigen, so ließ er sich treiben und wollte aus diesem Treiben auch nicht heraus. Er litt und schämte sich, weil er sich für einen schlechten Krieg hatte brauchen lassen müssen; so nahm er sich vor, es nur noch mit den Tatsachen zu halten, vor allen Dingen aber, nie und nirgends mehr zu vertrauen.[5] Das Vergangene sah er nackt und vergeblich, die Gegenwart feindselig, und wie viele seinesgleichen sah er die Zukunft für eine Vokabel an.

Seine Mutter sah ihm zu und sorgte sich um ihn,

- 1 -

die Ziffer, -n *here* paragraph
untersa′gen forbid
erliegen† (ist) succumb, give up
die Voka′bel, -n word

[1] **auf dem Leib** *on his back*
[2] **außer dem, daß . . . war** *except for being . . .*
[3] **war nicht, um** *was not enough to*
[4] **trafen es** *were hit, had it*
[5] **nie und nirgends mehr zu vertrauen** roughly *not to put his faith in anything any more; never to trust anybody or anything again*

und ob sie dabei nun bestimmte Gedanken hegte oder nicht, ihre Regung war einfach und mütterlich: es verlangte sie danach,[6] diesem Sohn etwas zu schenken. Zu kaufen hätte sie damals, auch wenn sie reicher gewesen wäre, nichts gefunden;[7] so sann sie auf einen Gegenstand, der dauern konnte und dem Sohn etwas bedeuten.[8] Sie kramte in ihrem Kästchen und fand zwei bescheidene Ringe, die von ihrer Mutter und Großmutter stammten, auch kannte sie eine Goldschmiedin, die bereit war, einen Auftrag auszuführen für das damals fast wertlose Geld. Ein hochedler Stein war nicht aufzutreiben, doch fand auch die Goldschmiedin noch etwas in ihrem Vorrat, einen sogenannten Sarder, der für einen Ring taugen mochte. Als alles beraten war, fiel der Mutter, schon auf der Straße, noch etwas ein. Sie kehrte um, stieg die Treppe noch einmal hinauf, entschuldigte sich und ließ sich versprechen,[9] daß die Meisterin nicht eben Gold für Gold nehmen wolle. Der Ring müsse alt und neu sein und eben aus jenem Gold, das sie gebracht habe. Sie kenne solche Wünsche, sagte die Meisterin und versprach es so.

Der Ring wurde fertig, und die Mutter kam damit in ihrer Freude zu ihrem Sohn. Da kränkte Fehleisen sie mit einem seltsamen Ausbruch. Denn er wandte sich brüsk um, kaum daß er das Geschenk gesehen und erklärt bekommen[10] hatte, woher das Gold stammte. Das sei kein Ding mehr für ihn, sagte er zu der erschrockenen Frau, und der Übermut fehle ihm, seine Arbeiterhände mit Zierden zu behängen; was aber die Leute angehe, die dieses Gold nachgelassen hätten, so

- 2 -

hegen cherish, have
die Regung, -en impulse
kramen rummage, (dig) around
hochedel precious
der Sarder sard *or* carnelian
beraten (*p.p.*) discussed and settled
die Meisterin, -nen (*fem.*) craftsman; *or translate simply* lady

[6] **es verlangte sie danach** *she felt the desire, she longed*

[7] People were unwilling to sell things of any worth for money of uncertain or depressed value. As is pointed out below, and later in the story, craftsmen and artists did take the inflated money and hence were at least busy.

[8] **bedeuten,** as well as **dauern,** is to be taken with **konnte.**

[9] **ließ sich versprechen, daß die Meisterin** *made the lady promise her*

[10] **erklärt bekommen** *have it explained to one:* a frequent conversational pattern: **geschenkt bekommen, zugeschickt bekommen,** etc. (The source of the ring—who it is from, of what it is made—and Fehleisen's reaction to it are the first of many clues to the symbolism involved.)

fänden sie schwerlich an ihm etwas gutzuheißen noch er an ihnen etwas zu verstehen; und wer verspielt habe, der habe auch ausgespielt und brauche keinen neuen Ring mehr zu seinem alten Rock, in dem ihm übrigens nichts fehle. Nach einigen Sätzen dieser Art schämte er sich plötzlich, als die alte Frau verstummt blieb und er im Umwenden ihr verhofftes Gesicht sah, er faßte nach ihrer Hand, küßte sie und bat sie, ihm zu verzeihen. Von da an trug er den Ring ein paar Tage. Fiel aber sein Blick auf ihn, so schien ihm, als habe er sich einfangen lassen; und er wußte nicht recht, sollte er nachgeben oder sich widersetzen.

Vom Krieg her besann sich Fehleisen auf einen Mann ungefähr seines Alters, der Brack geheißen hatte und ein Maler gewesen war.[11] Von dieser Eigenschaft hatte Brack kein Aufheben gemacht, die Rede kam darauf fast zufällig, denn natürlich erzählte man sich ja einmal von seinen bürgerlichen Beschäftigungen. Sie hatten über Kunst nicht viel miteinander zu reden gehabt, denn Fehleisen verstand davon wenig, doch freundeten sie sich während einiger ruhigen Wochen ein wenig an, worauf sie sich aber ganz aus den Augen verloren. Jetzt meldete Brack sich plötzlich, und zwar zur Verwunderung Fehleisens aus ziemlicher Nähe. Fehleisen kannte das Dorf, aus dem der Brief kam. Brack hatte, so schrieb er, das Ende des Kriegs als Schwerverwundeter erlebt, und dann nahm ihn, da er eine Heimat nicht mehr besaß, ein Mädchen auf, das mit ihm entlassen wurde und das in seinem Lazarett Schwester gewesen war. Sogleich schien aus diesem Entschluß den beiden ihr Heil zu entstehen. Erst besaß

- 3 -

wer verspielt habe . . . anyone who had lost his money was out of the game

verhofft drained of hope, forlorn

(ein) Aufheben machen make a fuss

[11] **Brack** is not an uncommon name, but here it is obviously to be associated with the French artist Braque, for whom Gaiser has high regard.

12 auch sie nichts, auf das sie ihr Leben hätte begründen können, und stand dafür einiges gegen sie, denn die Verwandtschaft billigte die Wahl des Mädchens nicht. Aber der jungen Frau kam etwas Unerwartetes zu Hilfe: von einer Tante, die sie einmal gepflegt hatte, erbte sie ein Grundstück. Dieses Stück war nicht eben eine Pracht, aber immerhin hatte darauf eine Art von Ferienhäuschen gestanden, das feste Mauern hatte, wenn es auch erbrochen, geplündert, und das Dach teilweise abgetragen war. Der Boden konnte, wenn er geschickt bestellt wurde, einen großen Teil Nahrung bringen. Bauen war damals ein Hexenwerk, aber sie waren geduldig und zäh und verrichteten das meiste selber; der Maler, der sich eine Zeitlang für ein Wrack angesehen hatte, erholte sich und vermochte zu leisten, was notwendig war. So waren sie unter Dach 13 gelangt und mochten fürs erste nicht mehr verlangen; 14 doch schrieb Brack, daß er auch soeben wieder anfange zu malen. Er nehme dabei übrigens wahr, fügte Brack hinzu, daß die Zeit dazwischen nicht tot geblieben sei, 15 sondern ihn gefördert habe auch in der scheinbaren Unterbrechung. Denn er stehe jetzt ganz woanders als da, wo er aufgehört habe, und manchen Ballast habe er abgestoßen. Noch etwas, meldete Brack, ein Kuriosum: sie hätten eine Hausnatter. 16 Sie sahen das Tier nie, doch verriet sich sein Schlupf unter der Hausstaffel. Eine zarte Spur führte dorthin, wenn ein Morgenregen Schlamm auf die Platten geschwemmt hatte. Sie versuchten es auch und setzten ein Schälchen Milch aus; das Tier nahm davon. 17 Dies alles berichtete Brack leichthin und nicht als Wichtigkeiten, zum

-4-

eine Pracht *here* anything wonderful

das Hexenwerk, -e fiendish job

zäh persistent, tenacious

woan'ders stehen† be at a different point (stage of development)

die Hausnatter, -n ring-snake *or* house-snake (*see below*)

die Hausstaffel, -n house-steps

der Schlamm mud

die Platte, -n flagstone

schwemmen wash (up)

[12] **stand . . . einiges** is, in a conventional grammatical view, an irregular bit of word order, but this position of the verb is common in both present colloquial and ancient usage.

[13] **unter Dach gelangen (ist)** get a roof over one's head

[14] **mochten fürs erste nicht mehr verlangen** *had for the time being no other needs* (*desires*)

[15] **tot** here *useless*

[16] **Hausnatter:** In European folk beliefs the snake has a markedly dual role. Here it is obviously not a symbol of evil but a *spiritus familiaris,* a bringer of good luck, a guardian against illness, etc. It is often suggested that this function of the house-snake may be related to the widespread belief that snakes contain the spirits of the dead (which stay about a house to protect it).

In the light of what we know about Gaiser, we can guess the significance of the snake in the story. Brack and his wife have that magic closeness to the earth and simple life and old traditions (even superstitions) which constitute strength in a time out of joint.

[17] **davon** *some of it* (almost like the Latin partitive genitive)

Schluß ermunterte er Fehleisen, von dem er durch Zufall gehört, er möchte kommen und es sich ansehen.

Fehleisen las es, und etwas an dem Brief verdroß ihn zuerst so wie der Ring ihn verdrossen hatte, als seine Mutter mit ihm ankam; erst steckte er den Brief ein und faltete ihn dann noch einmal auseinander und las ihn noch einmal: nein, sagte er sich, es war kein Gehabe darin und kein Aufschwemmen von Gefühlen, wie es oft ein Bekenntnis so unausstehlich macht.[18] Kein unmöglicher Gedanke, sagte er sich, da einmal hinzugehen. Es braucht ja nicht morgen oder übermorgen zu sein. Aber schon am Abend schrieb er eine Karte.

Von der kleinen Station aus, auf der er den Zug verließ, war es ein Weg von anderthalb Stunden. Das Häuschen war ihm beschrieben, es lag etwas seitab dem Dorf und am halben Hang, wo vormals Wein gezogen worden war, er sah die verwachsenen Stufen Schatten werfen und sah das hellrote Dach unter einem Föhrenschopf. Eine Frau erhob sich, die dort in der Tür mit einer Arbeit gesessen hatte, sie trat ein paar Schritte tiefer, blieb stehen und erwartete ihn. Der Weg war noch nicht fest, die Spuren von Bauarbeiten noch unaufgeräumt, doch gab es schon Blumen, wie sie in Bauerngärten gezogen werden: Bartnelken, Malven und Eisenhut. Jetzt am Nachmittag stand die Sonne schon schräg, und Fehleisen mußte gegen das Licht steigen. Das Licht schmerzte ihn in den Augen, wie er dort hinaufstieg, plötzlich klopfte der Schmerz ihm im ganzen Kopf. Fehleisen litt an solchen Schmerzen häufig, er hatte den Druck schon unterwegs

-5-

das Gehabe pretense, "fuss"
das Aufschwemmen overflow(ing)

seitab' off to the side of

am halben Hang half-way up the slope

der Föhrenschopf, ⸚e thatch (crown) of firs overhead

die Bartnelke, -n sweet William; **die Malve, -n** mallow; **der Eisenhut, ⸚e** monkshood

[18] **wie es oft . . .; es** recapitulates **Gehabe** and **Aufschwemmen:** *such as often make a confession* (*or avowal of affection*) *intolerable.* In English we do not use this repeated subject.

gespürt, aber ihn nicht wahrhaben wollen. Es fängt an, sagte er zu sich. Verdammtes dummes Zeug.

Sie begrüßten sich, und die junge Frau nahm ihn als einen alten Bekannten, sie führte ihn herum und hinein und zeigte ihm, wo sie lebten. Dann sagte sie: Joachim ist, wie Sie sehen, nicht im Haus. Wir wußten nämlich nicht genau, wann Sie kommen würden. So ist er zu seiner Arbeit ins nächste Dorf. Er hat da einen kleinen Auftrag.

So, einen Auftrag. Darf er jemand konterfeien?

Nein, sagte die junge Frau und lachte, obwohl es auch schon vorgekommen ist. Aber es ist ein Schwesternhaus drüben und ein kleiner Saal, in dem ihn die Oberin malen läßt. Die Oberin hat sich das ausgedacht, es wird eine Reihe von Gleichnissen aus der Schrift, lauter Lieblingsstellen von ihr, Gleichnisse von dem Verlorenen und Wiedergefundenen.

Helfen Sie mir weiter. Ich bin nicht mehr beschlagen in der Schrift.

Doch. Zum Beispiel das mit der Frau, die den Groschen verlor und ihr Licht anzündete und das Haus kehrte und suchte mit Fleiß. Und dann das mit dem Schaf und natürlich auch mit dem verlorenen Sohn.[19] Lauter Lieblingsstellen. Joachim mußte auch schon andere Lieblingsstellen malen. Ein Wirt besorgte uns Dachziegel und bekam dafür seine Gaststube ausgemalt. Auch da mußte etwas an die Wände. Wenn das Geld wieder etwas wert ist, wird es schwieriger für uns werden. Jetzt geht es uns ganz gut.

Die Frau sagte, als Fehleisen etwas ausgeruht war: Joachim dachte wir könnten nachkommen, wenn Sie

- 6 -

nicht wahr-haben wollen† not want to admit

konterfei'en do a portrait of

die (Heilige) Schrift Bible (Holy Writ)

beschlagen (*p.p.*) well versed

der Dachziegel, - roof tile

[19] All these parables may be found in Luke 15, together with the proper translations of **Groschen, mit Fleiß, verloren,** etc.

eine Probe an-stellen give it a try

das Ro'senspalier', -e rose trellis
gitterig lattice(d)

bespinnen† entwine

da sind, und ihn abholen. Der Weg ist hübsch zu gehen.

Und wir sehen uns dabei schon die Gleichnisse an.

Nein, die läßt er nicht sehen. Niemand kommt an seine Sachen, ehe sie fertig sind. Nun ja, Sie vielleicht.

Ich will keine Probe anstellen, sagte Fehleisen.

Die junge Frau hatte ein weißes Wollkleid an und trug eine Schnur von Korallen. Sie hatte eine gesunde, windbraune Haut und eine Stimme, die sich wohl anhörte.[20] Der Abend war warm; sie ließen sich Zeit und stiegen langsam zwischen den Ährenfeldern. Es war ein Samstagabend, und drüben war vor dem Schwesternhaus schon gefegt und aufgeräumt, der Bau lag feiertäglich, unversehrt mit seinen Rosenspalieren und gitterigen Jalousien; eben kam Brack heraus. Die Oberin trat mit ihm heraus auf die Schwelle und verabschiedete ihn, eine alterslose, nonnenhafte Person mit einem adligen Namen; Fehleisen mußte auch heran und sich verbeugen. Sie reichte jedem die Hand, die Dame, welche sich die Gleichnisse malen ließ, und sah jedes an, und Fehleisen blickte sie auch an und blickte an ihr vorbei mit seinen schmerzenden Augen gegen die reinliche, da und dort von Kletterrosen besponnene Wand, dachte: Wie still das ist. Still, dachte er, um böse zu machen.[21] Er dachte: Alles still, und dann Crimson Ramblers, die vielen kletternden Rosen, viel Rot, ein ganz leeres Rot, das nichts sagt und nur Schmerzen macht.—Sein Zustand hatte sich verschlimmert, und es brachte ihn auf, daß dieser Überfall sein müsse an diesem Tag, von dem er sich etwas versprochen hatte und an dem er gern gewesen wäre wie andere.

-7-

[20] **sich wohl an-hören** *be pleasant to listen to*

[21] **still . . ., um** *quiet enough to* (see footnote on **war, um . . .** above).

Denn er freute sich, daß er jetzt Brack wiedersah, je mehr etwas in ihm sich sträubte, Freude zu empfinden und wie die andern zu sein. Die Oberin hatte sie entlassen, und jetzt schüttelten sie sich noch einmal die Hände und musterten sich und gingen dann zu[22] dreien langsam dem Dorf zu und die Straße hinunter, an der erst Gehöfte locker standen, durch weitläufige Gärten getrennt, und dann die Häuser sich dichter anreihten, und sie blieben wohl einmal stehen und riefen durcheinander, wenn sie sich an etwas erinnerten, und redeten laut und leise und kamen langsam voran. Und Fehleisen, aufgekratzt von dem Gespräch, das er nicht mehr gewohnt war, rief ein wenig laut, denn er wollte etwas loben und kämpfte doch nebenher gegen seinen Störenfried: Wißt ihr, was mich am meisten freut? Daß ihr Glück habt.—

Glück—, hatte Fehleisen eben gesagt, da merkte er, daß an seiner Hand der Ring fehlte. Augenblicklich blieb er stehen und war verstummt. Zugleich hatte der Schmerz in seiner Schläfe eine solche Bösartigkeit erreicht, daß Fehleisen[23] schien, als gehöre beides zusammen, der Verlust und der Schmerz, und überbiete eines das andere in einer sinnlosen, heimtükkischen Kränkung. Ja, eine Art von Quittung schien dies auf seinen Versuch, sich zu Leuten zu halten, die Glück verdienten. Aber habe ich den Ring auch getragen? dachte er fliegend, hatte ich ihn, als ich herfuhr, am Finger? Kein Zweifel, die junge Frau bestätigte es, ihr war der Ring aufgefallen. Und der Ring war jetzt fort.

Wir müssen zurückgehen, sagte Brack.

locker *here* scattered

auf-kratzen stimulate, excite

der Störenfried, -e trouble maker (*i.e., his ailment*)

die Quittung, -en (re)payment

[22] **zu dreien** *the three of them*

[23] What case is **Fehleisen?**

Wir finden ihn, sagte die junge Frau. Er muß ja mitten auf dem Weg liegen.

Im stillen aber sagte sich jeder, daß eben dieser Umstand das Mißliche sei. Die Straße zog sich lang hin und war jetzt, am Abend vor Sonntag, von vielen Leuten begangen. Dazu gab es Fahrzeuge. Der Ring mußte schon zerwalzt sein, oder jemand hatte sich schon nach ihm gebückt. Auf die Ehrlichkeit eines Finders konnte man damals aber nicht rechnen, denn die Zeit war noch kraus, Hehlen und Beutemachen sah jeder für ein Recht an. Schlechter noch stand es draußen auf dem Grasweg zwischen den Ähren. Aber vor allem sank die Sonne soeben. In einer Viertelstunde würde nichts mehr zu unterscheiden sein.

Dennoch machten sie sich natürlich daran, ihren Weg rückwärts abzuschreiten, sie teilten sich, und eines nahm die Mitte und zwei nahmen die beiden Seiten des Wegs. Es dämmerte schnell, sie gingen einsilbig, die Augen am Boden, und die Leute vor ihren Häusern, die sie laut redend hatten kommen sehen, standen noch da und gafften sie an und starrten hinter ihnen her. [24]

Jetzt mußten sie Platz machen und zur Seite treten, denn von hinten lärmte ein Motorrad und gab Signal. Sie blieben stehen, und das Motorrad überholte. Die Straße war mitgenommen und nur notdürftig geflickt, das Fahrzeug schlingerte zwischen Löchern. Zwei Männer saßen mit krummen Rücken darauf, einer nahm die Beine herab und spreizte sie, solang es stieß auf der schlechten Stelle. Das Motorrad, sagte Fehleisen zu sich. Das bißchen Himmel, dumm [25]

- 9 -

mißlich dubious
zerwalzen roll over and crush
kraus disturbed, "out of joint"
hehlen deal in stolen goods
sich machen an set about
an-gaffen gape at
mitgenommen in bad shape (*also used for persons and things that have suffered badly in war*)
schlingern lurch
es stieß† auf they were up against *or* were running into

[24] **eines** *one of them* (like **alles** *everyone*)

[25] **Signal' geben** *blow one's horn*

26 und gelb, und der Weg voller Löcher, das gehört dazu.

27 Das fährt da herum, sagte am Zaun ein Mann, der Pfeife rauchte und den Kittel eines Waldhüters trug. Wenn das Volk herumfährt, ist der Teufel irgendwo los. Von mir aus könnten von den Gestalten da weniger unterwegs sein.

Dann grüßte er Brack und fragte: Haben Sie etwas verloren? ich sehe, Sie sind am Suchen.

Sie blieben stehen, und der Waldhüter sagte: Nein, ich habe nichts bemerkt. Einen Ring? Zu klein. So etwas findet man kaum wieder. Ich habe es einmal erlebt, auf dem Anstand; eine Jägerin verlor eine Nadel mit Steinen, und der Platz, wo sie liegen konnte, war nicht größer als eine Tischplatte. Jetzt ist es Nacht. Sie müssen morgen früh wiederkommen.

28 Er hat recht, sagte Brack, geben wir es auf. Mach dir nicht zuviel draus, Fehleisen, morgen suchen wir weiter.

29 Da nichts mehr zu tun blieb, ließen sie es bei ihrem Vorhaben. Das Gasthaus hieß „Zur Traube", und hinten im Saal, da wo Brack die Wände geschmückt hatte, fand eine Hochzeit statt. Sie saßen in der Vorderstube, und an ihnen vorbei war viel Kommen und Gehen.

Der Waldhüter hat recht, sagte die junge Frau, Suchen bringt's nicht zuwege. Aber solche Gegen-30 stände leisten sich oft ein merkwürdiges Stück. Mama hatte vor neunzehn Jahren ihren Trauring verloren. Eine Bombe riß das Haus auf bis in den Keller hinunter, und, wo meinen Sie, fand man den Ring? Nein nein,

- 10 -

der Kittel, - tunic, jacket

von mir aus as far as I'm concerned
die Gestalt, -en *colloquially* character, type

der Anstand, ⸗e *here* hunting blind

[26] **das gehört dazu** *that's all part of the picture*
[27] **das fährt da herum** *there they go, driving around*
[28] **mach dir nicht zuviel draus** *don't worry too much about it*
[29] **sie ließen es bei ihrem Vorhaben** roughly *they let i go at that*
[30] **leisten sich oft ein merkwürdiges Stück** *often a remarkable things*

der Johan'nisbeerstrauch, ⁼e currant bush

angeflogen (*p.p.*) tinged

auf Strümpfen in stocking feet

Sie raten falsch. Neunzehn Jahre war es her, und jetzt, als man Schutt räumte, hing der Ring im Vorgarten an einem Johannisbeerstrauch. Es waren schwarze Johannisbeeren, und ich aß als Kind immer so gern davon.

Eine ganz einfache Sache, sagte Fehleisen. Ich sehe, man braucht weiter nichts als schwarze Johannisbeeren.

Sie fielen in einen leichteren Ton, und Fehleisen spürte plötzlich, daß ihn sein Quälgeist entlassen hatte. Es wurde ihm freier und danach ganz leicht im Kopf, bezaubernd leicht, als sie den nächtlichen, nach Schafen, nach Staub und Korn duftenden Feldweg heimwärts gingen.

Trotzdem schlief Fehleisen unruhig und erst gegen Morgen eine Weile sehr tief. Er wachte auf, sah, daß es ein Viertel nach drei sei, erhob sich und blickte in die sprachlose grüne Landschaft hinaus. Die Sonne war noch nicht herauf, der Himmel fast weiß, von einem rosenen Kupfer angeflogen. Fehleisen spürte keinen Schlaf mehr, doch war auch das seltsame Hochgefühl des nächtlichen Heimwegs weggewischt, es war ihm zumute, als hätte er etwas Vergebliches hinter sich, und etwas Widerwärtiges stünde ihm bevor. Alles verkehrt, dachte er. Ich suche nicht weiter. Ich hätte überhaupt nicht herzukommen brauchen.[31] Ich gehöre nicht her. Was wollte ich denn eigentlich?

So kleidete er sich an, ließ einen Zettel zurück und schlich auf Strümpfen über die Schwelle. Auf den Stufen, über dem Schlangenschlupf zog er sich die Stiefel an. Der Hund sah zu, ohne Laut zu geben, und

- 11 -

[31] **brauchen,** an example of the old participial forms that look like infinitives; they appear in modals and several other verbs taking dependent infinitive without **zu**—less often with those taking **zu.**

sah ihm nach, als er rasch hangabwärts hinunterschwand.

Von Knabenzeiten her kannte Fehleisen die Gegend ziemlich gut. So wählte er einen Rennsteig, der fast schnurgerade den großen Wald durchteilte; der Weg führte den alten Namen Der Eselstritt, denn er war einst der Zuweg der Bauern zu den Öl- und Kornmühlen der reichen Ambrach gewesen. Neuerdings bildete der Forst eine Grenze zwischen den Zonen zweier Besatzungsmächte,[32] und wer in ihm nichts verloren hatte, hielt sich gerne heraus. Wer aber dort Besorgungen hatte, nahm fleißig Deckung und sicherte vor sich und hinter sich.

Fehleisen nahm keine Deckung, er stiefelte hin in seiner Unfreude und halben Reue, ging und entfernte sich eine gute Strecke,[33] erst nach einer Weile wurde er gemächlicher und blickte um sich, und der Wald fing ihm an zu gefallen. Dann lief vor ihm her auf dem feuchten Weg eine Reifenspur, sie war frisch und hatte den perlgrauen Tau von den Gräsern abgestreift. Wer ist da schon vor mir aufgestanden, dachte Fehleisen. Plötzlich, hinter einem steilen Stich, den man von unten schwer einsah, stand ein Motorrad quer im Weg. Bei dem Motorrad standen zwei Männer. Ach verdammt, dachte Fehleisen, es ist das Motorrad von gestern. Und was jetzt? Die zwei Männer hatten offenbar auf ihn gewartet und blickten ihm mit einer belästigenden Aufmerksamkeit entgegen.

Er brauchte die Umstände nicht lang zu überdenken: ein Abbiegen war so unmöglich wie ein Ausbrechen. Leute wie diese da, die in umgefärbten,

- 12 -

der Rennsteig, -e forest path

der Eselstritt *here a proper name, roughly* Donkey-track *or* Donkey-kick

Ambrach *a river*

die Reifenspur, -en tire track

der Stich, -e *here* rise, incline

[32] **Besatzungsmächte:** Along the boundaries between the zones of different occupying powers smuggling and other illicit businesses flourished, especially in the early days after the war—along with a good deal of refugee traffic in the case of Soviet Zone borders.

[33] **sich eine gute Strecke entfernen** *put a good distance behind one*

das Montur'stück, -e (army-issue) uniform

aber durchaus ansehnlichen Monturstücken steckten, die führten auch Schußwaffen, das war ihm sehr wohl bekannt. Zugleich sagte er sich auch mit einer gewissen Belustigung, daß seit gestern abend das einzige Ding, das bei ihm zu holen gewesen wäre, sich entfernt habe. Also ging er vollends heran und ließ sich anhalten. Es war deutlich, daß die zwei Freibeuter nicht seinetwegen unterwegs waren, sondern in weit ergiebigeren Händeln, von denen sie kamen oder die sie noch vor sich hatten. So verstanden sie Spaß und gebärdeten sich wie eine Obrigkeit, die zwar nichts durchgehen, aber doch mit sich reden läßt. Sie nahmen ihm etwas Geld, ließen ihm aber gönnerhaft die kleine Münze. Dann mußte er seine Finger vorstrecken, und endlich blieben nur seine Bergschuhe einer kurzen Musterung wert. Doch gab der eine Mann, der es offenbar eilig hatte, ein Zeichen der Ungeduld, worauf der erste grob wurde und Fehleisen, indem er affig eine Zigarette in die Mundspalte schob, mit einer eindeutigen Gebärde anwies, er möchte schnell und in gleicher Richtung und ohne sich umzublicken davongehen. Dem kam Fehleisen ohne einen Einwand nach. [34] [35] [36]

Der Handel hatte ihn nicht viel länger als vielleicht anderthalb Minuten aufgehalten, aber erst am Ausgang des Waldes befand Fehleisen sich so weit, daß das Spiel ihm gänzlich einleuchtete. Er mußte sogar lachen, obwohl er nüchtern und bis an die Knie herauf durchnäßt war. Schwarze Johannisbeeren, sagte er zu sich und suchte die befahrene Landstraße auf, die außerhalb des Walds Eselstritt wieder zu den Freunden zurückführte. [37]

- 13 -

[34] **Spaß verstehen** *take a joke*
[35] **Fehleisen** is accusative, object of **anwies.**
[36] **in gleicher Richtung,** i.e., from which he came

[37] **F. befand sich so weit** *F. had got far enough* (*in his thinking*). The clue to his train of thought is given in the words he says to himself.

Er kam in das Dorf, wo der Ring verloren gegangen war, und schnell durchschritt er es bis an die Stelle, an der das Motorrad sie gestern überholt hatte. Die Spur unterschied sich noch deutlich, denn es war ja erst früher Vormittag, sie schlängelte sich zwischen den Schlaglöchern und lief dann gegen eine breite, aufgeschotterte Fläche. Auch war der Waldhüter schon wieder herausgetreten und rief Fehleisen über den Zaun weg an.[38]

Ihre Freunde, sagte er, sind schon vor Ihnen dagewesen. Eine halbe Stunde vielleicht ist es her, da sind sie wieder zurück. Suchen hilft nicht viel, sage ich immer. Man kann höchstens Glück haben.

Oder man muß wissen, wo, sagte Fehleisen und ging langsamer weiter, die Augen am Boden. Dann sah er den Ring. Der Ring stak, keine zehn Schritte von da, wo sie gestern abend gestanden hatten, zwischen den bläulichen Kalksteinen. Das Motorrad hatte ihn versorgt, indem es ihn gestreift, in den Schotter gedrückt und etwas angestaubt hatte, so lag er gut versteckt und fiel nur einem auf, der erriet, wo er suchen mußte. Fehleisen brauchte sich nur zu bücken, er nahm den Ring, blies und rieb ihn und steckte ihn wieder an. Dann ging er über den Berg zurück zu den Freunden.

Sie haben den Ring, sagte die junge Frau, als er wiederkam. Wo haben Sie ihn gefunden?

Das wissen Sie doch, sagte Fehleisen. In den schwarzen Johannisbeeren.

Sie setzen sich zu ihrem Frühstück, und Fehleisen mußte alles berichten.

- 14 -

schlängeln twist
das Schlagloch, ⸚er pot-hole
auf-schottern cover with crushed rock, gravel

der Kalkstein, -e (piece of) limestone
der Schotter crushed rock

[38] **über . . . weg** here *from across*

Merkwürdig, sagte er, lauter Tatsachen. Aber richtig wahr ist es nicht.

Warum denn, sagte Brack. Es ist wahr, und deshalb stimmen sogar die Tatsachen. 39

Da spielt etwas, sagte die junge Frau, und treibt doch kein bloßes Spiel. 40

Könnt ihr mich einen Tag behalten? sagte Fehleisen. Bei euch lernt man allerhand. Ich möchte noch den Rest herausbringen. Denn wenn du nachrechnest, geht die Geschichte nicht auf. 41

auf-gehen† balance, "add up"

Warum soll sie aufgehen? sagte Brack. Wenn sie aufginge, fehlte ihr etwas. Laß den Rest ruhig stehen.

[39] That is, the inner truth is there, hence even (!) the facts agree. Inner truth and consistency is the important thing. Consistency of external fact can be deceptive.

[40] **da spielt etwas** roughly *there's some odd force at work there:* note the continuation of the word-motif of **spielen.**

[41] With **Rest** begins a final metaphor of "accounting": in the words *balance, figure, add up.* Note our similar popular metaphors like "*That doesn't add up.*"

Heinz Piontek

In 1943, at the age of 17, Heinz Piontek left the town where he was born (Kreuzburg, then on the Polish border) and entered the German army. After two years of service he found himself, in 1945, in an American prisoner-of-war camp in Bavaria. After his release, he worked in quarries, at construction jobs, as a sign-painter. For a time his only suit was a dyed army uniform (like that of the characters in Gaiser's *Fehleisen*). Yet he is aware that his is a fate shared with an entire generation. And when, in a recent self-portrait he referred to the "life-and-death enterprise" in which he had been engaged, he did not mean the external course of his life but the profession of writing itself.

Piontek takes a deeply serious view of the writer's task. In Munich, where he has lived since 1961, he begins writing at eight in the morning—prose or poetry—and characterizes his method as painstaking recall, the deep-sea diver's search for sunken memories, but also as a continuing quest for links with the present. His discipline is not merely that of long hours but also the perfectionist's endless polishing and revising. He deliberately concentrates on joining the lyric with prose fiction, a combination he finds increasingly rare among modern writers. For all of his labor Piontek's total output is relatively small: half a dozen volumes of poetry, as many radio plays, a long narrative poem for radio, a fair number of carefully crafted short stories (collections: *Vor Augen*, 1955; *Kastanien aus dem Feuer*, 1963). In the fall of 1965 he was working on the final chapter of a novel. As an editor he has done, among other things, an anthology of religious poets, and an edition and translation of John Keats. He is also an essayist and reviewer.

Piontek's work may not be notably voluminous but it has been widely recognized and honored. His poems have been extensively anthologized. The new Bantam collection *Modern European Poetry* (ed. W. Barnstone, 1966) carries a section devoted to translations of his work. In 1957 he received the "Junge Generation" literary prize, and in 1960 a fellowship to the Villa Massimo in Rome.

In a post-war literary world where even the most unorthodox and avant-garde sought the sanction of loosely organized groups, Piontek has remained, in theory and practice, independent. His closest approach to conformity was a brief period of *Naturlyrik* in directions established by Britting and Lehmann. He is also one of the most truly contemporary of authors. He writes of a world where war and reconstruction are real as *history*, but are no longer the ordering or dominant elements of reality. He is not afraid to assert his kinship with the "silent generation," free of delusions and suspicious of causes. And he does not see these characteristics as entirely negative. The basic trend of his critical and literary activity has been toward a cautious, even skeptical affirmation of life, beauty, and religious values in a context of uncertainty and mortality. It is not a sentimental or tragic pose but a posture of defense in the face of danger.

In an exceptionally perceptive essay in *Buchstab Zauberstab* (1959), he sums up the broad development of modern poetry: "a long period of crisis, starting with the Romantics, in the course of which it became increasingly clear that the answer to the crucial question 'Can poetry still provide meaningful knowledge about life?' is *no*." Content had become suspect, form was all. Although Piontek sees the difficulty and danger inherent in this sort of substantive nihilism, he does not condemn it. Individual poets, speaking in (and against) a time of scientific confidence, anticipated *our* dissolution of confidence, our anxiety in the face of meaninglessness. Piontek's individuality is apparent in his extension of the analysis to the present. He claims that most of contemporary poetry, still in the dominion of this denial of meaning, has ceased to function as a voice countering the stream of the time and is barely floating with it. The old prophecies are dulled because they have been fulfilled. A poet who uses the word "Angst" in the Age of Anxiety has ceased to speak meaningfully. The task of poetry is to provide new insight, to refuse the easy currency of accepted belief, to find "etwas Höheres, Verbindendes." For Piontek this means that modern poetry, to regain its function, must strive for the preservation of man against the disruptive forces of his civilization and his own consciousness. The components of such a new poetry are clear: simplicity (not emptiness), "das genaue Geheimnis," the assertion of truth and the defense of man, the poem as life not mask, intelligibility of form and image, respect for technique and even "rules," possibly a new classicism—in a phrase borrowed from Hofmannsthal, a "konservative Revolution."

Piontek sees the story-teller's mission as different from the poet's: not essentially a struggle against the time but a recording of it. He confirms his debt to the American short story, with its tradition and character so different from the *Novelle:* balance of elements rather than concentration on single elements, symbolization and interiorizing of life in "ordinary" not extraordinary situations, linear plot rather than *Wendepunkt*, generality of event and character, not *Sonderfall*, cessation of action rather than well-defined ending. Yet in both short story and *Novelle* Piontek sees the presence of symbolized or extended meaning. The short story, he feels, is particularly capable of manifesting the fundamentally problematic qualities of human life in the guise of everyday situations. Masters of the modern short story include, in his view: Borchert, Böll, Gaiser, Nossack, Lenz, Aichinger, and Walser. To this list his own name should be added.

Rote Pfeile

(1963)

The narrative surface of a Piontek story is typically linear and predominantly realistic. In *Rote Pfeile* much of the narrative could be considered reportorial or documentary, telling an occurrence for its own sake, and as it "happened." Indeed, certain details (the make of Lohoff's camera, for example) seem almost to have been introduced to reinforce the impression of random reality. In Piontek's narrative technique, language corresponds to "event"; both tend to be specific and matter-of-fact, that is, comprehensible in terms of ordinary experience. This combination is not inevitable: in Rilke and Kafka these two basic components of narrative are divergent. Kafka is roughly comparable to Piontek in language, but not in event; in Rilke, the event is relatively routine, the language certainly is not.

In some respects *Rote Pfeile* is a departure from Piontek's norm, witness the relatively frequent passages in which differing levels of reality are reflected in changed levels of style. Examples of such interpenetration of style and event are the workings of Lohoff's and Jens' fevered minds, revealed by the "omniscient narrator," or the association of animal imagery with outbreaks of violence. These exceptions to the mode of "ordinary reality" are perhaps a first key to other levels of Piontek's fictional world: Behind the narrative screen there lies a far less casual or variable substance.

What is narrated in this and other stories of Piontek is not undifferentiated reality but a selective representation of the human condition. As one critic says, "In subtly crystallized everyday situations, he reveals the essential nature of modern man." Such situations and the actions or interrelationships of the characters within them are paradigms, infinitely repeatable patterns of human behavior. Each one represents Piontek's "model" of some major aspect of modern life, presented largely without commentary.

In the spectrum of prose fiction running from anecdote to parable, *Rote Pfeile* approaches parable. Yet the interpretation of the parable is not dictated by Piontek, nor are the "clues" obvious. Gaiser's *Fehleisen* offers an instructive comparison. There the point is scarcely in doubt. But in *Rote Pfeile* the element of sheer narration, almost reportage, keeps the story unbiased, as it were, and conceals the point. In *Fehleisen* it is almost as if the intended message preceded the devising of the narrative frame, as in allegory. *Rote Pfeile* seems rather to present a sequence of events which somehow "happened" or might have happened, but which, among many possible and even similar sequences, seems to be of singular intensity, significance, and generality and thus commands attention and recording.

The basic elements of the story are definable, not without ambiguity or possible error, but in serviceable outline: In a physical environment of hazard and in a (metaphorical) atmosphere compounded of threat and animality, the violent disruption of a highly unstable triangle occurs, a triangle that had been maintained, under "normal" stresses, by a curious mixture of whim, irresponsibility and principle (however misguided). The traumatic change which explodes the situation is not merely the disintegration of the quiet order of physical nature but a devastating upsurge of primitive, hitherto suppressed forces of human nature.

The intensified spatial isolation of the mountain climb leaves the three characters alone with their artificial and volatile relationship, in growing awareness that it cannot last. The storm drives their nerves to the breaking point, tearing away the last covering mask of control, and exposing the elemental passions of man. The imagery at this point is dominated by animal nature, sometimes subtle, sometimes painfully obvious. The man, Lohoff, who thought he had set aside ordinary considerations of domination, rivalry, and possession—not in altruism but in "sophistication"—meets his fate in the form of complete de-humanization. He dreams of fatal struggle and in actuality kills, not simply his friend, but also whatever there was between him and the girl. It is like *hybris* and *nemesis*, but with no point of reference to any divine order. The characters, highly modern, are trapped in a world of their own making, where the only forces beyond man are the violence of an inscrutable nature and the inevitability, under crisis, of relapse into ancient passions.

ROTE PFEILE

Die Grillen. Die Grillen.

Lohoff fuhr hoch aus dem Schlaf. Er wußte nicht, daß eine Entscheidung gefallen war.[1] Er erinnerte sich nur an die Sonne, die über seinen Himmel gekreuzt war wie ein riesenhaftes Positionslicht, aus – an, aus – an. Jetzt hörte er die Grillen auf den Bergwiesen, und die Dämmerung zuckte von den Stromschlägen ihres Gesanges. Ihm war, als müßte er sich auf die Fensterscheiben stürzen, alles Glas in seinem Zimmer mit Fäusten einschlagen. Rote Pfeile schwärmten an seinen Augen vorbei.

Da fiel ihm die gestrige Verabredung ein, die sie alle nicht ganz ernst gemeint hatten. Er konnte es nicht mehr verstehen, wieso sie am Abend so lahm und schüchtern gewesen waren. Er stand sofort auf und lief hinüber ins Bad. Ungeduldig zog er die Klinge über seine Stoppeln, fuhr mit dem Kopf ins Wasser. Die Grillen draußen schrien stürmisch in den Morgen und rissen seine Überlegungen mit. Er dachte an viele Dinge zugleich.

Als Lohoff wieder auf den Gang hinaustrat, war er in einem Leinenanzug, in groben Schuhen. Er klopfte nebenan, und da sich nichts rührte, ging er

- 1 -

das Positions'licht, -er navigation light, beacon

der Stromschlag, ⸚e pulsation

[1] **eine Entscheidung fällt** *a decision is made*

weiter zur übernächsten Tür und schlug mit der Faust dagegen. Eine schlaftrunkene Stimme meldete sich. Lohoff erinnerte an die Abmachung, aber die Stimme schickte ihn zum Teufel.

[2] „Ach was! Wird ein fabelhafter Tag, kann ich euch sagen."

Drinnen wurde geflüstert.

Unten in der Küche traf er die Wirtin noch im Unterrock an, mit hängenden Haaren, dickem rosenrotem Gesicht. Sie machte eine beschwörende Geste, und er sah erst wieder hin, als sie den Kragen des Morgenrocks unterm Kinn zusammenzog, wie wenn sie Halsschmerzen hätte.

„Können wir in einer halben Stunde frühstücken?"

Die Wirtin blinzelte. Dann warf sie einen Klumpen Butter ins Feuerloch,[3] schimpfte auf Iris und Kathi und versuchte ihn auszufragen. Aber Lohoff machte diesmal den Mund kaum auf, nickte nur und ging langsam rückwärts zur Tür.

Oben kam Rudja hoch und lässig auf ihn zu, in etwas sehr Dünnem. Es war noch ziemlich dunkel auf dem Korridor, und erst als sie dicht vor ihm stand, konnte er erkennen, daß sie einverstanden war. Sie schlang die Arme um ihn, und er zitterte unter ihrer Wärme.

[4] „Ich habe ihn hochgeboxt", sagte sie. „Natürlich machen wir mit." Er umarmte sie, sein Glück war ein wilder Kummer. Dann hörten sie Schritte, Rudja löste sich von ihm und fing an von Jens zu sprechen. „Ein sagenhaftes Faultier", sagte sie.

sagenhaft fabulous

- 2 -

[2] **ach was** *don't be silly; come off it*
[3] **das Feuerloch** is the round hole in the top of an old-fashioned stove, into which a pan fits.
[4] **ich habe ihn hochgeboxt** *I slapped him around until he woke up; I shook him awake*

Jens kam aus der Tür.

„Vergeßt nicht, was Warmes mitzunehmen", meinte Lohoff.

Jens sagte kein Wort und ging in das auf der anderen Seite gelegene Badezimmer.

„Ich beeil mich", sagte Rudja, und es funkelte unter ihren Wimpern.

die Wimper, -n eyelash

Mit seinen Kameras behangen, verließ Lohoff die Pension. Er ging hinter das Haus, wo die Gäste ihre Wagen abgestellt hatten, schloß den seinen auf, ein langgestrecktes Kabriolett, bog in die Straße ein und stoppte vor dem Tor. Für ihn war die Sonne noch nicht aufgegangen, aber drüben, jenseits des Tales, fingen schon die Zinnen der Wand Feuer, und scharfe enthüllende Schatten legten ihre Formationen frei.

enthüllen reveal

Beim Frühstück redete nur Rudja. Lohoff aß fast nichts, aber der Student Jens schlang mürrisch seine ganze Portion hinunter, auch noch alles, was Lohoff übrigließ, und trank vier Tassen Kaffee dazu. Jens war fünfundzwanzig, etwas älter als Rudja. Er hatte eine Figur wie ein Stierkämpfer. Sein Haar war kurz und hell und sah wie eine Steppe aus über dem verbrannten Gesicht. Die pummelige Wirtstochter bediente sie. Es war Iris, und ihre romaneverschlingende Mutter war stolz auf den Namen. [5]

Als Jens sich eine Zigarette anzündete, meinte Lohoff, daß man auch im Auto rauchen könnte, und stand auf.

Mit Rudja in der Mitte gingen sie vors Haus. Rudja hatte einen prachtvollen Gang. Sie lachte, es klang wie ein Gurren. In der Haustür lehnend, ver-

gurren coo (of doves)

- 3 -

[5] **Iris** comes from the Greek word for rainbow: *goddess of the rainbow;* **roma'neverschlingend: der Roman',** **-e** *novel* + **verschlingen** *devour*

folgten Iris und Kathi die Abfahrt, stießen sich kichernd an und winkten faul hinterher.

6 Es ging durch lange Schatten in die Tiefe. Der Mais abgeblüht, das Heu geschnitten, Herbstzeitlosen überall. Unten in der Stadt ließ Lohoff volltanken und schob das Verdeck zurück: ein kühler süßer Geruch in den Gassen, wo die Jalousien hochrasselten und die Schwalben über alte frischgeweißte Fassaden zickzackten. Die Burg hatte einen nassen Helm und verschattete Augen wie ein übernächtigter Posten.

„Wunderbar, so früh am Morgen", sagte Rudja und dehnte sich auf dem Sitz.

Jens rauchte.

„Wie weit ist es noch?" fragte sie.

„Fünfzehn Kilometer bis zur Klamm", sagte Lohoff.

Als sie aus der Stadt heraus waren, schien die Sonne in den Wagen, und der Wind riß an Rudjas Haar. Lohoff fuhr gut, noch wenig Verkehr auf den Chausseen, sie bogen ab von der spiegelglatten Hauptstraße und kamen auf immer schlechtere Fahrbahnen, die allmählich anstiegen, und dann schraubte sich ihr Weg durch den Wald hoch mit Rinnen und Schlaglöchern.

Auf einem Holzplatz stiegen sie aus. Der Photograph reichte ihnen ihre Sachen aus dem Wagen, und 7 er wählte von seinen Kameras nur die Leica mit dem Summaron dreikommafünf aus.

„Es gibt zwei Möglichkeiten", sagte er. „Einen fast dreistündigen Wanderweg zur Hütte oder neunzig

- 4 -

abgeblüht past, gone by
die Herbstzeitlose, -n meadow-saffron

die Schwalbe, -n swallow

übernächtigt bleary(-eyed)
der Posten, - sentinel, guard

die Klamm, -en ravine, gully

schrauben twist

[6] **es ging** "impersonal construction": *their way lead*

[7] **die Leica** *make of camera,* **mit dem Summaron 3,5** *with the 3.5f lens*

der Scheißkrieg (vulgar) lousy war

Minuten durch die Klamm. Die Klamm ist verboten, also ganz das richtige für euch."

„Wieso?" fragte Rudja.

„Während des Krieges konnte man sich nicht um die Stege kümmern. Sie sollen zum Teil vermorscht sein."

„Scheißkrieg", sagte Jens.

„Erst das untere Drittel ist wieder begehbar, wie ich mir sagen ließ."[8]

Jens scharrte[9] mit den Füßen. Nicht mehr feierlich, was der alles weiß![10]

Rudja sagte: „Können ja umkehren, wenn es nicht zu schaffen ist."

Sie kamen an eine Tafel, die zur Klamm einwies, und darauf stand alles zu lesen, was sie eben von Lohoff gehört hatten. Plötzlich stiegen die Felsen senkrecht hoch, die Luft wurde feucht und kalt. Jens übernahm die Spitze. Er lief leichtfüßig und war lange vor ihnen an der ersten Brücke, die über eine Staumauer hinwegführte. Das Wasser hier wie aus einem Block,[11] sie konnten die Kiesel am Grunde zählen. Später verloren sie Jens aus den Augen. Das Geröll in der Tiefe war schneeweiß gewaschen, die kleinen Brücken schwangen unter ihnen, sie mußten sie einzeln passieren. An den Fällen dröhnte das Wasser.

Jens stand hinter einem Stein und sah sie herankommen. Zuerst die schwarze Rudja in ihrem roten Pullover und den schmalen Hosen, einen Campingsack über der Schulter. Sie balancierte mit den Armen. Es war, als folge Lohoff einem Magneten. Er stampfte, und immer wieder glitten seine scharfen Augen über

- 5 -

[8] **wie ich mir sagen ließ** *so I'm told, they tell me*
[9] **scharren** *scrape one's feet* (in audiences a sign of disapproval)
[10] **nicht mehr feierlich, was der alles weiß** approximately: *beats all, what he knows*
[11] **wie aus einem Block** *like a solid* (*transparent*) *mass*

[12] sie hin. Jens wartete. Du stampfst ganz schön für dein Alter! Bilde dir bloß nicht ein, daß Rudja verrückt nach dir ist. Don't call it love. Dann sprang er aus seiner Deckung, und Rudja schrie spitz wie ein Vogel.

Nach einer halben Stunde kamen sie an einen Übergang, dessen Mittelstück weggebrochen war. Sie entschlossen sich, den Bach zu durchwaten. Als sie in das eisige Wasser stiegen, meinten sie, in Feuer zu treten. Es ging ihnen nur bis zu den Knien, doch es riß sie fast um. Sie hielten sich an den Händen fest, torkelten über die seifenglatten Kieselsteine. Der Bach toste zwischen riesigen Blöcken durch, und der Wasserstaub durchnäßte sie.

Die nächsten zwei Übergänge waren tadellos, dann wurde es schlechter, und dann war's fast bequem für sie. Sie schwitzten in der kalten Luft, ihre Sohlen brannten, sie sahen zu den Felswänden auf und schrien durch den Donner des Wassers. Mit einemmal standen sie mitten im Licht. So weit sie sehen konnten, lauter Grashänge und Grillen [13] im Gras und darüber die lautlosen Klippen. Vor der Hütte bewegten sich schwarze Punkte.

Die Hütte war ein großer Holzbau auf einem Steinsockel. Tische und Bänke waren draußen in die Erde gerammt. Ein fetter Italiener und eine fette Italienerin saßen ganz allein unter dem ganz blauen Himmel, er in Hemdsärmeln, mit einem halben Pfund Käse in der Hand, sie geschwätzig, harte Eier schälend. Lohoff fiel ein Photo von Cartier-Bresson [14] ein, eine

- 6 -

durchwa'ten wade across

torkeln stagger, stumble
seifenglatt smooth and slippery as soap
tosen roar, rush

der Steinsockel, - rock foundation

[12] Note the occurrence of what seems to be direct address, without quotation marks. What could this represent? Compare also, above, **"Nicht mehr feierlich . . ."**

[13] Note the reappearance of the **Grillen.** Watch fo further instances and try to explain the motif.

[14] **Cartier-Bresson** a famous modern photographer, on of whose studies shows just such a scene on the Seine

Idylle mit dicken Anglern und Weibern ohne Blusen am Seineufer.

Sie setzten sich schnaufend in den leichten Wind, und heraus kam ein Kalb von einem Schäferhund und dann ein Mann wie ein Steinblock. Sie wollten Milch von ihm. Er ging wieder weg, der Hund schnüffelte. Die drei Zinnbecher, die der Wirt anbrachte, waren so kalt, daß ihnen die Finger weh taten. Er ließ sich bei ihnen nieder, souverän, unverrückbar. Seine Jacke und seine Strümpfe waren aus Schafwolle. Er warf einen prüfenden Blick auf Rudja, und sie holte tief Luft. Dann fing er mit Lohoff ein Gespräch an.

15 16

unverrück'bar imperturbable

„Die Wand? No, kein Kunststück. Aber eine schöne Aussicht." Wie hypnotisiert blickten sie alle drei auf einmal zum Bundkofel hin, der sich wie ein gelbes Sägeblatt in das Blau hineinfraß. „Ihr dürft bloß die Markierung nicht verlieren, die allerdings schlecht ist."

17

Der Photograph sah jetzt auf die Hand des Wirts, die eine wüste Narbe trug.

„Der lebt nicht mehr, der mir das Messer in die Hand getrieben hat", sagte der Wirt gleichmütig. „Übrigens nicht der einzige Kratzer. In der Schulter ein Splitter, sechs Monate Lazarett, und ein Bajonettstich unter der Brust. Sie haben im Krieg wahrscheinlich auch Ihr Fett wegbekommen", sagte er zu Lohoff.

18

Jens stand einfach auf.

„Der Hund ist scharf", sagte der Wirt. „Geben Sie Obacht."

scharf *here* vicious

Aber Jens ging schnurgerade auf den Schäferhund zu und schlug ihm gegen die Rippen. Der Hund

- 7 -

[15] **ein Kalb von einem Schäferhund** *a sheep-dog the size of a calf*
[16] **sie holte tief Luft** *she drew a deep breath*
[17] **der Bundkofel** is the name of a fictitious mountain.
[18] **sein Fett wegbekommen** *have a rough time of it; get kicked around*

knurrte, und plötzlich bellte er leicht auf, es klang wie ein Jauchzen. Jens rannte hinaus auf die Weide, der Riesenköter hinter ihm her, ein schwarzes Geschoß, und er sprang an ihm hoch, begeistert verspielt.

„Einmal bin ich mit einem Kahn im Eismeer abgesoffen", erzählte der Wirt, „ausgerechnet im November. Zwei Stunden sind wir gegen den Sturm geschwommen, die Kumpels weg, einer nach dem andern, aber ich immer unter den Wellen durch, ganz methodisch, immer mit dem Kopf durch die Wand. Und nachher im gefrorenen Zeug acht Stunden übers Eis."

Dann wollte er wissen, wo der Herr zu Hause sei. Lohoff sagte es.

„Da bin ich einmal durchgefahren, da haben wir gemeutert, wohl, wohl, zwei Jahre nicht im Urlaub und nun für irgendwelche Kümmeltürken wieder die Kastanien aus dem Feuer, no, da haben wir einfach losgeballert, als das Zugpersonal nicht Richtung Heimat fahren wollte. Famoser Haufen, zwei Divisionen, siebzigtausend Mann. Gerade die Hälfte noch am Leben."

Als Lohoff gezahlt hatte, stand der Wirt auf, drehte ihnen grußlos den Rücken, als ob sie längst nicht mehr da wären, pfiff nach dem Hund und ging an den Italienern vorbei, die verstummten, ins Haus zurück.

Lachend kam ihnen Jens entgegen.

„Der verdammte Bramarbas", sagte er. „Habt ihr endlich genug in eurer mistigen Vergangenheit gewühlt?"

- 8 -

der Riesenköter, - giant hound
verspielt absorbed in the game

ab-saufen† **(ist)** fall in the drink
ausgerechnet of all times

der Kumpel, -s buddy, pal

der Kümmeltürke, -n, -n bum, good-for-nothing

los-ballern cut loose

famos' (*colloq.*) great, first-rate

der Bramarbas, -se braggart, boaster
mistig murky, mucky
wühlen rummage around, wallow

„Er ist grandios", sagte Rudja.

Und Lohoff, mitten aus einem Gedanken heraus: „Man kann auch anders leben." 19

So setzten sie sich in Marsch auf die Wand. Der Pfad schlängelte sich über die Matten, zuerst noch ein Kühweg, doch Vieh sahen sie nirgends, nur die wunderschönen sanften Glocken waren zu hören. Der Boden war naß von Rinnsalen, hundert Quellen mußte es hier geben, und auch diesmal wußte Lohoff wieder alles und unterhielt sie mit der besonderen geologischen Beschaffenheit des Geländes und erzählte was von einem hochberühmten Kraut, das hier und sonst bloß noch im Himalaya gedieh. Sie zogen ihn beide auf, und auch er lachte nun, und einträchtig stiegen sie weiter.

das Hima'laya H. Mountains
gedeihen† thrive

Ein Knarren war in der Luft. Sie blickten auf. Nicht weit von ihnen, von einem Waldhang herunter, führten zwischen Masten dicke Seile bergab, und ein schwerer Stamm tauchte mitten im Blau auf und glitt an zwei Seilrollen in die Tiefe.

das Seil, -e rope
die Seilrolle, -n rope pulley

„Wäre schön, so eine Abfahrt", sagte der Student. 20

Sie wandten sich um und sahen unter sich die Hütte liegen und in ihrer Nähe die beiden Zollhäuser auf der Paßhöhe. Die Sonne schien warm herab, aber der Wind nahm zu, und so machte ihnen die Wärme nichts aus. Seltsam fremd kamen drei Pferde aus einer Mulde hoch. 21 Ihre Schweife schlugen in den Wind, ihre Felle blitzten. Ohne Furcht grasten und wanderten sie, zu unglaublichen Zielen unterwegs.

der Schweif, -e tail
das Fell, -e hide, coat

- 9 -

[19] **man kann auch anders leben** *there are other ways to live*, i.e. other than ours, other than the civilized way or the way of the cities.

[20] In view of what happens later, these words are profoundly ironic.

[21] Animals and animal images become increasingly frequent in the story. Watch them as bearers of metaphorical meaning.

„Was kriege ich, wenn ich durchhalte?“ fragte Rudja.

„Hör dir das an!“ sagte Jens. „Dabei ist sie in Form wie ’ne Gemse.“

Rudja schürzte die Lippen. „Wirst du wenigstens ein paar Bilder fürs Familienalbum von uns machen, Robby, oben auf dem Gipfel?“

„Die heilige Rudja selbdritt“, sagte Jens.[22]

„Ich hab dich satt, mein Kleinod“, sagte Rudja.

Lohoff amüsierte sich.

„Ich hab euch beide satt.“ Rudjas Kopf war klein unter der schwarzen Krone, ein Schlangenkopf. „Am liebsten möchte ich umdrehen“, sagte sie und reckte die Arme in die Richtung, in der die Hütte lag.

Jens pfiff durch die Zähne. „Da bin ich, Herr Wirt!“[23]

„Der träumt jetzt von zwei Divisionen“, sagte Lohoff.

Rudja mußte lachen und zertrat eine Grille, ohne es zu merken. Sehr dünn war das Gezirp geworden. Bald versank es ganz unter ihnen. Dafür begannen die Steine zu reden. Noch war die Markierung gut: rote Pfeile, alle wie gegen den Gipfel geschossen und nun verstreut im Gras, auf Felstrümmern und Bukkeln.

Nur ein Geröllfeld trennte sie noch von den Zinnen. Es lag im Windschatten, und mit einem Schlag fing die Luft an zu brennen, und die Pfeile zitterten vor ihren Augen. Immer wieder sahen sie hoch auf die Masse von gelb und weiß blendendem Fels. „Ihr seid ja verrückt!“ sagte Rudja.

- 10 -

die Gemse, -n chamois, mountain goat
schürzen purse

das Gezirp chirp, singing

der Buckel, - hummock

mit einem Schlag at one stroke, all at once

[22] **selbdritt′** *with two companions;* **selb-** plus ordinal numeral indicating that the person referred to makes the n-th of the group. The whole is a parody of the titles of religious paintings, etc.

[23] Whose words are these?

im Stich lassen† let . . . down
lotrecht vertical
hoch-wuchten thrust mightily upward
flimmern glitter, glimmer

die Platte, -n ledge
der Steingrieß coarse gravel
geriffelt fluted
die Halde, -n rock pile
zerscherben fragment, pulverize
der Kalk *here* limestone
das Band, ⸚er striation

heikel difficult, ticklish

Auch Jens war beeindruckt, und sogar Lohoff schien sich seiner Sache nicht mehr ganz sicher zu sein.

„Wir halten uns eben an den Weg."

Und Rudja: „Schöner Weg!"

Doch die Pfeile ließen sie nicht im Stich. Hinter den ersten Zacken, die lotrecht hochwuchteten, führte der Trampelpfad weiter, mitten hinein in den Stein. Es flimmerte, rauschte hohl, ein anderes Element. Jetzt ging Lohoff voran, und der Hirsch Jens, schon etwas lahm, machte den Schluß. Über Platten stiegen sie, schweren Schotter, über Steingrieß, dann wieder geriffelter Fels, Rinnen, Halden mit zerscherbtem Kalk, der Berg zeigte seine Schädelseiten, Adern und Bänder glommen, die Türme drehten sich um sie, die Himmelsrichtungen verschwammen. [24]

Rudja hielt sich gut, auch dann, als sie hinter dem Joch über einen Steig mußten, bei dem es rechts und links in die Tiefe ging. Wenn es heikel wurde, packte Lohoff sie an den Händen, zog sie nach. Die Sonne prallte auf den Stein und schlug ein in die Körper und in die Pulverkammern der Körper. Sie fieberten vor Anstrengung. Lohoff suchte mit den Augen die roten Pfeile im Geröll, aber seine Hände griffen immer wieder genau in die Luft, um Rudja zu sich heranzuziehen. Wie einer, der an Starkstrom hängt, dachte er, häng ich an dir. Nie werde ich loskommen! Der Schweiß rann ihm übers Gesicht, seine Füße wurden bleiern, klumpige Hufe, das Blut rauschte durch die Bahnen mit einem hohen Ton.

„Du rennst dahin, als hättest du eins vor den Kopf [25]

- 11 -

[24] **Schädelseiten** (pl.) literally *sides of the skull;* the bare heights of the mountain are likened to a human head, with its veins and bands (= muscle ridges).

[25] **eins vor den Kopf bekommen** *get one in the face, be hit in the face*

bekommen", meuterte Jens hinter ihm. „Mann, wir sind längst nicht mehr auf dem Weg!"

Rudja fuhr auf. „Warum hast nicht du geführt!?"

„Ich jedenfalls gehe zurück. Am Kar habt ihr nämlich die Abzweigung verpaßt. Ihr seht überall rot, wie?"

„Wir gehen in dieser Richtung weiter", sagte Lohoff.

„Und du, Rudja?" fragte Jens kalt.

26 „Was heißt hier Rudja? Du *willst* wohl nicht hören, daß ich bei Robby bleibe!"

„Laß sie in Ruhe", sagte Lohoff scharf.

Rudja sah Jens in die Augen. „Los, komm."

Aber Jens stieg den Hang hinunter, Steine kollerten ihm nach. Gleich sah er winzig aus in der Öde, und er

27 verging wie ein dunkler Tropfen auf dem glühenden Stein. Minuten später kamen sie durch ein richtiges Tor im Fels, an dem der Photograph die rote Markierung wieder entdeckte, er holte Atem, um nach Jens zu rufen, aber da verschloß ihm eine verschwitzte Hand den Mund.

Auf dem Gipfel wallte der Wind heran. Rudja riß die Arme hoch und schrie hingerissen in die kühle blaue endlose Weite hinein. Lohoff hatte sein Zeug abgeworfen, auch er badete in der Kühle. Dann suchten sie Schutz vor der heimtückischen Strahlung, aber kein Fetzen Schatten hier oben, und dann preßte Lohoff das Mädchen wieder an seine Brust, und Rudja machte sich los, glitt zu Boden und zog die Knie an und legte die Stirn auf die Knie.

- 12 -

das Kar, -e glacial hollow

die Abzweigung, -en turn-off, fork in path

kollern roll, tumble

heran'-wallen come over in waves

der Fetzen, - shred

[26] **was heißt hier Rudja?** *who are you calling Rudja? what do you mean Rudja?*

[27] Try analyzing the remarkable simile and relating it to other elements of the story.

Eine halbe Stunde später wuchs Jens' Gesicht über der Felsbarriere hoch. Finster wie ein Wolf kam er an, warf sich neben dem Paar nieder und setzte gierig seine Zigarette in Brand. Schatten lagen wie Gruben unter seinen Augen. Rudja und der Photograph kauten ihren Proviant, Jens jedoch nahm keinen Bissen zu sich, gar nichts, aber er trank ihnen in einem Zug den Tee weg, von dem sie ihm etwas angeboten hatten. Und Lohoff, der aus purem Hochmut auf keiner ihrer Fahrten jemals ein paar Bilder von ihnen geschossen hatte, erhob sich schlapp und visierte sie mit der Kamera an: Rudja ohne Schuhe, jammernd und lachend über ihre geschundenen Füße, und den rauchenden Jens. Dann versuchten alle drei zu schlafen, mit gegen die Sonne verhüllten Häuptern, Lohoff neben dem Studenten und Rudja neben Lohoff auf dem Plateau.

Aber Jens schlief nicht. Er lag auf der Seite, sein Blick bohrte sich in den Stein neben seiner Wange, und er haßte Rudja dafür, daß sie nicht bei ihm lag. Doch der Haß war nicht stark genug, seine Gedanken an ihre Augen und an die Kraft und den vollkommenen Bau ihrer Glieder auszulöschen, und er dachte mit einer wütenden Sehnsucht an sie. Über den Bergen schoß ein Wölkchen bleigrau herauf. Kalte Böen fauchten durch das Licht.

Beim ersten Donnerschlag fuhren alle drei hoch.

Wie eine Sturmflut jagte das Gewitter heran, von Westen und Norden gleichzeitig. Hals über Kopf brachen sie auf. Sobald sie nicht auf jeden Tritt achten mußten, spähten sie nach dem Himmel. Ungeheuer

- 13 -

der Proviant' provisions

schlapp limp, lazy
an-visie'ren sight, aim (a camera) at
schinden† tear, skin

die Bö, -en gust of wind
fauchen swish, hiss

Hals über Kopf head over heels, headlong

schnell riß es die Regenfronten hoch. Schon sausten die ersten grauen Fahnen über die Sonne. Im flackernden Licht konnten sie die Schroffen und Senken kaum wiedererkennen. Der Photograph wollte sie zu einem langsameren Tempo überreden, damit sie nicht fehlgingen, doch sollten sie sich hier oben überrollen lassen vom Gewitter? Sie stolperten weiter, bis sie mit einemmal in ein heiseres Schreien gehüllt waren und nichts mehr sehen konnten und sich ans Gestein klammerten. Ein riesiger Schwarm von Dohlen rauschte weg. Sie lachten hohl über ihren Schrecken, während der Wind sich gegen sie warf, und dann kamen die Wolken im Tiefflug, zerfetzten die Sicht, und sie konnten sich nur noch bis zu einer Stelle vortasten, wo der Fels ein wenig überhing, und sich niederhocken und warten.

der Schroffen, - towering cliff
die Senke, -n crevasse

die Dohle, -n jackdaw, crow

Lohoff sagte laut in das Heulen und Brodeln hinein, daß er schon einmal bei Gewitter im Berg gewesen sei.

brodeln rumble; boil

„Weißt du vielleicht auch, daß es meine letzte Tour mit dir ist?“ fragte der Student höhnisch.

„Du hast uns was eingebrockt!“[28] sagte Rudja zu Lohoff, ohne ihn anzublicken.

In diesem Augenblick stürzte der Regen herunter wie ein Dach. Der Gebirgsstock dröhnte, als ob er mit Hämmern zermalmt werden sollte. Die Steine kamen ins Rollen. Im Dunkel hing ein brandiger Geruch. Einzelne Blitze fuhren so dicht herab, daß Lohoff sie nicht mehr als Strahl zu erkennen vermochte: flammende Scheiben, Fächer und Mauern, gewaltige Baumkronen aus Feuer prasselten zu Tal. Ein trok-

der Gebirgsstock mountain mass

die Scheibe, -n disc, sheet
der Fächer, - fan
prasseln crackle, crash

- 14 -

[28] **einem etwas einbrocken** *play a mean trick on someone*

kener, unvorstellbarer Knall zerriß ihr Gehör, und gleichzeitig wankten sie von einer schwindlig machenden Glut. Ihre Zähne knirschten, jeder Knochen erschüttert bis ins Mark – und dann, nach nicht zu zählender Zeit, in der die Stille wie ein Getöse war, [29] suchten die Männer mit ihren tauben Händen nach Rudja und fanden einen von Schluchzen gestoßenen Körper.

Als es Lohoff einfiel, auf die Uhr zu schauen, war es gegen drei Uhr. Durch den wie gehetzt abziehenden [30] Spuk schlug das Blau durch, schon lagen die Felsen wieder in der Sonne, goldfarben und noch leicht dampfend von Nässe. Auf unsicheren Beinen krochen die drei aus ihrer Nische, sich wie Hunde schüttelnd. Sie schlurften den Pfad hinunter, und erst allmählich wurden sie wieder lockerer in den Gelenken, aber auf ihren Gesichtern war die Finsternis zurückgeblieben, die nicht wich.

Noch ehe sie das Kar erreichten, war ihr Weg zu Ende. Mit aufgerissenen Augen starrten sie auf den Hügel von Brocken, der während des Wetters aus der Wand heruntergehagelt war und den schmalen Durchgang, das Tor im Fels, verschüttet hatte.

„Aber das gibt's doch nicht!" schrie Jens, zitternd [31] vor Wut.

Rudjas Augen funkelten Lohoff an. Sie war ganz grau im Gesicht.

„Ihr seid ja übergeschnappt! Als ob ich etwas dafür könnte!"

„Ich möchte dir den dicken Hals umdrehen!" Jens hob die Fäuste.

- 15 -

knirschen grate, grind

taub *here* numb

von Schluchzen gestoßen racked by sobs

dampfend steaming, steamy

schlurfen shuffle, drag

Kar *see above*

über-schnappen crack up, lose one's mind

etwas dafür können† be able to help it

[29] **nach nicht zu zählender Zeit** *after a period of time that was beyond counting*

[30] **der wie gehetzt abziehende Spuk** *the tumultuous storm which fled across the sky in wild haste (as if pursued by some force).*

[31] **aber das gibt's doch nicht** *things like that just don't (can't) happen;* an expression of incredulity

„Komm her! Komm doch her!"

Wie auf ein unhörbares Kommando hin wurden sie still und drehten einander den Rücken zu, die Hände in den Taschen. Lohoff starrte in die Schlucht, hundert Meter hinunter. Auf der Gegenseite standen die Zacken des Kofels wie Palisaden. Schweigend ging er ein Stück zurück, bis er einen Platz fand, von dem er sich an einigen guten Griffen in die Schlucht hinunterlassen konnte. Er hangelte,[32] stieß sich ab und sprang, er wich geschickt einem Absturz aus, und oben am Rand Jens und Rudja, die seine gewagte Tour beobachteten und seine wild auf und ab gehende Brust schnaufen hörten. Jens zog an seiner feuchten Zigarette. Als Lohoff unten nicht mehr weiter konnte und komisch mit den Beinen strampelte, lachte er los. Rudja fiel ein, doch mitten in ihrem Gelächter warf sie einen zornigen Blick auf Jens, und ihr Mund verzerrte sich.

„Saukerl!"

Jens zuckte zusammen.

„Er setzt alles aufs Spiel, damit wir hier herauskommen, und du stehst da und paffst!"

Und Jens unsicher: „Du bist gut."

Der Grund der Schlucht war nicht zu erreichen. Lohoff gab sich nach dreißig Metern geschlagen,[33] arbeitete sich wieder nach oben. Auf einmal ließ Rudja den Studenten stehen. Allein humpelte sie zum Gipfel hoch, und auf dem Plateau streifte sie den roten Pullover ab, packte ihn bei den Ärmeln und schwenkte die rote Flagge im Kreis. Sie schrie dazu, schrie und heulte um Hilfe, bis ihr die Stimme versagte. Ihr

der Kofel, -s dome

der Absturz, ⸚e sudden drop-off

strampeln kick

der Saukerl, -e beast, rotter

aufs Spiel setzen risk

paffen puff away, smoke

humpeln hobble

[32] **hangeln** a mountain-climbing term: *climb (let oneself down) hand over hand*

[33] **gab sich geschlagen** *admitted defeat*

Körper warf schon einen langen Schatten. Die Sicht war unvergleichlich schön.

pala'vern hold a conference, huddle

Als sie wieder beisammen waren, palaverten sie lange über alle Rettungsmöglichkeiten, die ihnen einfielen. Was blieb ihnen weiter übrig, als auf Hilfe aus dem Tal zu warten? Der Wirt würde sich ihrer erinnern und Alarm schlagen bei der Bergwacht. Sie liefen hin und her zwischen den Felsen, suchten die Ferne ab, schlugen die Arme umeinander wie Fuhrleute.

Alarm' schlagen† sound the alarm
ab-suchen search, scan
der Fuhrmann, -leute drayman, wagon driver

Etwas oberhalb der Nische, wohin sie vor dem Gewitter geflohen waren, entdeckten sie einen bequemeren Winkel. Dort konnten sie sich zur Not ausstrecken. Und nachdem es zu dämmern begonnen hatte, kauerten sie sich eng nebeneinander auf den kalten Stein. Unruhig und groß leuchteten ihre Augen aus den erschöpften Gesichtern – Augen von Eulen in der Nacht.

Nach einer Weile fing Jens im Finstern an zu kauen. Erst jetzt kam den beiden anderen zu Bewußtsein, wie hungrig sie waren. Sie hatten keine Krume mehr übrig, und ihre Zungen lagen rauh und schwer vor Durst in den Schlünden.

der Schlund, ⸗e throat

„Möchtest du was, Rudja?"

„Hör zu", sagte Lohoff ruhig, „du hast heute einen sehr schlechten Tag, Jens. Es hat dich zuviel aufgeregt. Aber das hast du wohl gemerkt, daß wir Schluß machen müssen, ein für allemal Schluß, wenn wir hier herauskommen. Ich werde Rudja heiraten, und du wirst sie nicht wiedersehen."

ein für allemal *once and for all*

„Das würde dir passen", sagte Jens aus dem

- 17 -

Dunkel, und seine Stimme zitterte. „Frag einmal Rudja, was sie darüber denkt."

„So geht es nicht länger", sagte Rudja.

„Du hast uns ruiniert", sagte Jens zum Photographen, „du und kein anderer!" Er konnte sich nicht mehr beherrschen. „Eine Nutte hast du aus ihr gemacht!"

„Bitte, hör auf! Bitte!"

Was weißt du schon, du ahnungsloser Engel! dachte Lohoff.

„Du wirst es büßen", sagte Jens und drehte sich weg und schwieg.

Die Nacht mit übermäßig scharfen Sternen. Alle großen Bilder drehten sich um den Felsen, die Milchstraße führte von einem Ende der Welt zum anderen, und die unter die Sterne versetzten Tiere berührten sich nicht, und zwischen ihnen war nichts als schwarze Klarheit.

Der Student auf dem Stein spürte, wie es ihn schüttelte, heiße und eisige Schauer, er wälzte sich, er zündete mit bebenden Fingern seine letzte Zigarette an, es ging wirr zu in seinem Schädel, und der Berg lag ihm auf der Brust. Er träumte, Felsen, Felsen, die ihn umringten, die alle ausschauten wie der Wirt von der Hütte, sie rückten gegen ihn an, er rannte vor und fiel, nichts zu machen, er fiel. I've lost my battle.

Lohoff lag noch wach. Auch hinter seiner Stirn rauschten die Bilder. Riccardo Moncalvo[34], seine Hohlwege im Nebel, die Schafherden, die durchzogen, und

die Nutte, -n *tart, bad woman*

das Bild, -er *here* constellation

sich wälzen toss and turn

der Schädel, - skull, brain

der Hohlweg, -e defile, narrow pass

[34] **Riccar'do Moncal'vo** is a well-known photographer, and the photographic subject alluded to is an actual one.

schleifen drag
das Euter, - udder

außer Kraft setzen cancel

bis aufs Blut to the quick

das Mark marrow, core

die Weiche, -n groin

die Pranke, -n paw

mächtige Böcke dazwischen, die ihr Gehörn schleuderten und ihr Gemächte schleiften wie Euter. Ab und zu vermochte er zu denken und dachte, daß er gescheitert war. Er hatte von sich geglaubt, ohne Vorurteile zu sein: ein Mann, der nicht darauf bestehen wollte, daß sich ihm der Mensch unterwarf, den er liebte. Ich war entschlossen, es außer Kraft zu setzen, das alte Gesetz, das uns degradiert. Immer wieder wollte ich Rudja neu überwältigen, um ihr die Freiheit zu schenken. [35]

Aber auch er hatte den Bann von Bock und Hahn nicht abschütteln können, Jens reizte ihn bis aufs Blut, unmöglich, ihn noch länger neben Rudja zu dulden! Schwarz wurde es ihm vor Augen, und da er zu sich kam, hielt der Junge das Mädchen in seinen Armen, die Sterne standen still, Fäuste von Sternen, und jetzt war er bereit, es endlich zu tun, steinern zu sein wie der Stein, in dem sie nisteten, endlich den Auftrag auszuführen, den aus dem Schlaf, ohne eine einzige Frage und glühend bis ins Mark vom alten todbringenden Gesetz. Er riß Jens hoch, er, der Bock des Berges auf eisernen Hufen, riesig aufgerichtet sein alter göttlicher Schatten, er umarmte den Jungen, drängte ihn Schritt für Schritt gegen den Rand der Schlucht, ihre Lungen pfiffen, ihre Muskeln wie Vipern, und er stieß zu, stieß dem anderen mit aller Macht das Knie in die Weiche. Lautlos löste sich Jens, griff in die Luft und verschwand. Rudja klatschte und klatschte in die Hände. [36]

Ein Geräusch drang an Lohoffs Ohr. Er öffnete die Augen. Über ihm stand der Große Bär und hob die Pranken, die blitzten.

- 19 -

[35] **das Gemächte** *male parts:* Lohoff's hallucinatory vision is dominated by the sexuality which demands possession and male rivalry—feelings he has unsuccessfully tried to negate in his relationship with Rudja and the unstable triangle with Rudja and Jens.

[36] Note that another source of metaphor is introduced: inorganic nature.

Gegen vier Uhr früh wurde es so kalt, daß sie sich alle drei erhoben und sich warmstampften auf dem Fels. Unendlich langsam wurde es Morgen. Sie sahen übel aus, ihre Stimmen tierisch heiser, Tau war in der Luft, der Himmel fing an zu glühen: eine Messerwunde. Aber dann bekamen sie Mut und beschlossen, daß sie es nun zu dritt versuchen wollten, durch die Schlucht zu entkommen.

Sie fanden einen günstigeren Abstieg als Lohoff am Vortag, und sehr vorsichtig kletterten sie an dem zerklüfteten Hang in die Tiefe.

zerklüftet fissured

Jens war still, von einer ruhigen Stärke, die sie verwunderte. Sie prüften jeden Felstritt, sprangen sich gegenseitig bei, immer aber stand Jens an den gefährlichsten Punkten und hielt ihnen die Hände hin.

Auf einem Geröllband mußten die Männer verschnaufen, die Hälfte geschafft, und ihre Herzen schlugen aufgeregt unter den Kitteln. Rudja kam heruntergeglitten, sie konnten sie noch nicht erreichen, als es jäh zu brummen anfing und zu poltern, dann sahen sie, wie sich Rudja gellend zur Seite warf, und Jens konnte über den Felsvorsprung nicht hinwegschauen, aber Lohoff sah ihn, den Steinrutsch, wie eine Keule, in Staub gehüllt, genau über seinem Platz.

verschnaufen stop for breath

brummen rumble

gellen scream

die Keule, -n club

Auch er schrie und sprang. Es gab nur eine Stelle, auf die er sich retten konnte. Dort stand Jens. Und er prallte wuchtig gegen Jens, der wild in die Luft griff und verschwand. Dann rasselten die Steine, der einmal ins Rollen gekommene Berg, nicht aufzuhalten, dann [37]

wuchtig with great force, violently

- 20 -

[37] **der einmal ins Rollen gekommene Berg** *the mountain, once it had started rolling*

gab es einen dumpfen Aufschlag in der Schlucht, und dann donnerten die Brocken auf.

Als Rudjas Gesicht über ihm hing, begann Lohoff langsam zu begreifen, was geschehen war. Ein Splitter hatte sie verwundet, in Fäden lief das Blut über ihre totenfahle Haut, ihre Augen glotzten und der Mund wie eingerissen ins Gesicht.[38]

„Geh. Geh. Geh. Geh weg."

Lohoff brachte keinen Ton heraus. Er wollte nicht gehen, denn er sah, daß sie nicht mehr weiter konnte. Er streckte wieder die Hände nach ihr aus, doch Rudja hob einen Stein auf. Da floh er abwärts, abwärts – und die Felsen standen ihm bei wie Komplizen.

Im Gras schrien die Grillen. In der Hüttentür lehnte der Wirt. Er machte keinen Schritt auf Lohoff zu, bloß der große Hund fuhr auf, aber er kuschte sofort wieder und hechelte mit rosiger Zunge. Unter dem tief verächtlichen Blick des Wirts tat Lohoff die letzten Schritte. Es schien, als wisse er alles.

„Ja, den Toten werden wir wohl abseilen müssen", sagte er, als der Photograph mit seinen Worten am Ende war.

„Durch die Luft?" fragte Lohoff.

Und dann mußte er wieder an Rudja denken, so aussichtslos es auch war – bis er drüben gegen den leichten blauen Himmel die Pferde sah.

„Die drei Pferde", sagte er, und der Mund blieb ihm offen.

Der Wirt schaute Lohoff ins Gesicht. „Wieso drei?

- 21 -

glotzen stare

kuschen lie down

hecheln pant

ab-seilen let down by rope

[38] **wie eingerissen ins Gesicht** *like an opening torn into her face*

Ich habe doch zwei von ihnen einspannen lassen und den Sohn in die Stadt geschickt."

ein-spannen hitch up

Lohoff fiel auf die nächste Bank, während der Wirt hineinging, um zu telephonieren. Dort saß er lange, die Sonne brannte auf seinen kalten dumpfen Kopf nieder. Er merkte es nicht. Er merkte nur, daß der Apparat noch vor seiner Brust baumelte. Ein kindisches Lachen trat auf sein Gesicht. Er dachte an den eingespannten Film.

baumeln dangle

ein-spannen load (film in a camera)

Ein paar Bilder in einer dunklen Kammer.

Fragen

(The questions employ words listed in the vocabulary or closely related to them. Any others are translated in parentheses.)

Keller, Seite 5 bis 20

1. Welche Eigenschaften Bertrades ließen so viele Edelleute auf ihre Hand hoffen? 2. Warum interessierte sich der Kaiser auch für den Fall? 3. Welches sind die Charakterzüge Zendelwalds, die Keller zuerst in Erscheinung treten läßt? 4. Wie kann man auch aus Zendelwalds Kampfweise ersehen, daß er eher träumerisch als praktisch ist? 5. Was für einen Eindruck bekommen wir von Zendelwalds gesamtem (*entire*) Besitz? 6. Inwiefern stellt Zendelwalds Mutter die Kehrseite (*reverse*) seines Charakters dar? 7. Geben Sie einige Beispiele für die Tätigkeit seiner Mutter! 8. Aus welcher Ursache (*cause*) wird seine Mutter erst recht zornig über Zendelwald? 9. Welche Nachricht bringt der fremde Ritter? 10. Die Vermutungen der Mutter über Bertrade bringen Zendelwald zum Lachen. Aus welchen Gründen eigentlich? Wie nimmt sie es aber auf? 11. Wodurch wird auch auf seiner Reise klar, daß Zendelwald ein echter Träumer ist? 12. Wie wird ihm zumute, als er tatsächlich Bertrades Burg erblickt? 13. Warum geht er wohl in die kleine Kirche? 14. Wie kommt die Jungfrau Maria in die Geschichte? 15. Erzählen Sie, wie die Jungfrau den Teufel besiegt! 16. Beschreiben Sie mit eigenen Worten die zwei starken Ritter! 17. In welcher Hinsicht behandelt die Jungfrau die beiden besiegten Ritter auf ähnliche (*similar*) Weise? 18. Die Jungfrau gesellt sich an Zendelwalds Stelle zur schönen Bertrade. Ist sie dabei in allem das Gegenteil (*opposite*) von Zendelwald? 19. Wie wissen wir, daß Bertrade Gefallen an „Zendelwald" gefunden hat? 20. Warum ist Zendelwald zugleich glücklich und unglücklich darüber, daß er das Fest versäumt hat? 21. Erzählen Sie, wie es dazu kommt, daß Zendelwald selber an Bertrades Seite sitzt! 22. Warum hat er keine großen Schwierigkeiten, das passende Wort zu finden? 23. Wie kommt der richtige Sachverhalt endlich ans Licht? 24. Man hätte erwarten können, daß Bertrade sich ärgern würde, denn eigentlich liegt ein Betrug vor. Warum ist das nicht der Fall? 25. In welcher Hinsicht wird der Charakter Zendelwalds plötzlich anders? 26. Warum kehren Zendelwald und Bertrade im Vorbeigehen ein jedes Mal in das Kirchlein ein?

Ebner-Eschenbach, Seite 23 bis 39

1. Beschreiben Sie das Äußere des Mannes, dem Hopp den Hund abkauft! 2. Wie ist der Kerl in die Lage (*situation*) gekommen, den Hund verkaufen zu wollen? Wodurch wissen wir das? 3. Hat der Forstgehilfe ohne Gefühl den Hund ausgeliefert? 4. Was ist an dem Hund so besonders schön? 5. Bringt Hopp den Hund ohne Schwierigkeit nach Hause? 6. Warum wird Hopps Frau so eifersüchtig auf den Krambambuli? 7. In welcher Hinsicht sehen Hopp und seine Frau die Dinge verschieden an? 8. Der zweite Handel um den Hund mißlingt. Wie? 9. Wie wird es auch im Wirtshaus klar, welch ein tiefes Verständnis zwischen dem Hund und seinem Herrn besteht? 10. Welche Beziehung zum Anführer der Bande haben die verschiedenen Leute, die ihn als „den Gelben" kennen? 11. Welche Folgen hat für die weniger Schuldigen das Treiben der wirklichen Verbrecher? 12. Einen wie tiefen Eindruck auf den Oberförster macht der Eid, den die Verbrecher geschworen haben sollen? 13. Beschreiben Sie den Zwischenfall (*episode*) im Lindenrondell! 14. Unter welchen Umständen wird die Leiche des Oberförsters gefunden? 15. Warum will Krambambuli das Gewehr apportieren? 16. Warum nimmt Hopp in der Nacht noch seinen Hund vor? 17. Wo kommt Hopp zuerst auf die Spur des Verbrechers, und wie weiß er eigentlich, wen er vor sich hat? 18. Warum schreit Hopp „den Gelben" an? 19. Wie ist es gekommen, daß Hopp ihn nicht getroffen hat? 20. Beschreiben Sie den Konflikt, in den der arme Hund gerät und die „Lösung", die er gefunden hat! 21. Wodurch spielt der Hund eine bestimmende Rolle im Schicksal seines ehemaligen Herrn? 22. Was hätte Hopp mit seinem Hunde getan, wenn der Krambambuli ihn nicht angesehen hätte? 23. Wie weiß man, daß der Hund bei seinem „Entschluß" fest geblieben ist? 24. Wäre es nach Ihrem Ermessen (*judgment*) besser gewesen, wenn Hopp den Hund gefunden und heimgeholt hätte?

Mann, Seite 43 bis 56

1. Warum werden am Anfang der Geschichte das Gebäude, in dem Tobias Mindernickel seine Wohnung hat, sowie dessen Bewohner so genau beschrieben? 2. In welcher Hinsicht ist Tobias altmodisch gekleidet? 3. Was können wir aus seiner Kleidung und seinem Aussehen schließen? 4. Wie benimmt sich Tobias den Kindern und seinen Nachbarn gegenüber? 5. Die Unterlegenheit und Haltlosigkeit Mindernickels, sagt der Autor, könne entweder in . . . oder in . . . seinen Ursprung haben. 6. Was tut Tobias, nachdem er aus dem Wohnzimmer in sein Schlafzimmer getreten ist? 7. Durch wessen Schuld ist eigentlich der Junge gestrauchelt? 8. Wie ändert sich Tobias' Haltung, nachdem er dem Kinde behilflich sein konnte? 9. Welche Änderung in dem Benehmen der Nachbarn verursachte der Vorfall mit dem Kind, und wie lange dauerte sie? 10. Wie können wir auch aus der kleinen Szene auf dem Lerchenberg ersehen, daß Tobias immer furchtsam und unentschlossen handelt? 11. Wie bringt Tobias den jungen Hund nach Hause? 12. Wie wird er dann im Grauen Wege empfangen? 13. Wie fängt Tobias an, den Hund zu trainieren? 14. Unter welchen Umständen schlägt das scheinbar so gute Verhältnis zwischen Herrn und Hund plötzlich so erschreckend um? 15. Wie findet dann die Annäherung wieder statt? 16. Welche Stimmung herrscht jetzt in dem verstörten Gehirn Mindernickels? 17. Warum kommt es dazu, daß Tobias nur ganz selten das Haus verläßt? 18. Wann ist Tobias eigentlich mit dem Betragen des Hundes ganz zufrieden? 19. Warum wird der arme Hund eines Tages grausam bestraft? 20. Geben Sie sehr genau den Vorfall mit dem großen Messer wieder! 21. Wie behandelt Tobias den Hund, als dieser verwundet da liegt? 22. Was ist das Sonderbare und Erschreckende an diesem Vorfall? 23. Wie ändert sich die Pflege je nach dem Grade der Gesundung? 24. Wie ist Tobias' Gesicht, während er dem freudigen Treiben Esaus zusieht? 25. Warum will jetzt Tobias den Hund so traurig und mitleidig anreden und in den Armen halten? 26. Erzählen Sie das wieder, was Mann „ausführlich zu erzählen sich weigert"!

Rilke, Seite 59 bis 71

1. Wie betont Rilke die Eintönigkeit dieser Landschaft? 2. Wie sind die Reiter gekleidet? 3. Wieso verstehen diejenigen, die kein Deutsch können, was der Deutsche spricht? 4. Warum sind diese aus so vielen Ländern hergerittenen Männer plötzlich einander so nah? 5. Was für eine Bedeutung hat wohl die Rose für den Franzosen? 6. Warum ist es so bezeichnend (*indicative*), daß der von Langenau ein Herbst- und Erntelied singt? 7. Was gibt der Franzose dem Deutschen beim Abschiednehmen, und was soll das bedeuten? 8. Wie spiegelt die Sprache die ganze Aufregung der kleinen Szene „ein Tag durch den Troß" wider? 9. Welcher neue Ton kommt dann wiederum in die Sprache, wo Spork auftritt? 10. Welchen Aspekt des Krieges soll die erschütternde Szene beim Baum darstellen? 11. Der Cornet steckt den Brief zu dem Rosenblatt und denkt „Vielleicht findet ihn einmal Einer". Woran denkt er wohl? 12. An welche andere Figur in der Schilderung der Kriegszeiten erinnert der erschlagene Bauer? 13. Wie beschreibt Rilke das Gefühl des endlich Rastenkönnens? 14. Geben Sie einige Beispiele seiner Wort- und Satzmusik, die den Anfang des Tanzes beschreibt! 15. Wie drückt Rilke die Schönheit der Frauen aus? 16. Warum möchte der Cornet wohl weit fort und in Waffen sein? 17. Was haben die „Trümmer der Zeit" mit der Liebesaffäre zu tun? 18. In welcher Hinsicht ist die ganze Atmosphäre des Schlosses in dieser Nacht sehr unheildrohend? 19. Rilke läßt uns nicht direkt gewahren, daß das Schloß brennt und der Feind so nah ist, sondern . . . 20. Sollen wir annehmen, daß der Cornet in vollem Bewußtsein aus dem Schlosse stürzt und in den Feind? Was spricht dagegen? 21. Daß die Fahne am Ende langsam verlodert, ist ohne Zweifel symbolisch. Wie? 22. Wie können die Säbel wie eine Wasserkunst aussehen, und warum wählt Rilke gerade dieses Bild?

Kafka, Seite 77 bis 93

1. Was wissen wir am Anfang von Georgs Freund? 2. Wie denkt sich Georg offenbar des Freundes Zukunft? 3. Was würde dem Freunde bevorstehen, wenn Georg ihn bewegen könnte, nach Hause zurückzukehren? 4. Sollen wir uns vielleicht vorstellen, daß hinter diesen Argumenten etwas ganz anderes steckt? 5. Welche Gründe gibt der Freund für seine lange Abwesenheit an, und was hält Georg davon? 6. Wie ist es mit Georgs Geschäft gegangen? Warum? 7. Wozu hatte der Freund früher Georg überreden wollen? 8. Wie reden Georg und Frieda über die Möglichkeit eines Besuchs von seiten des Freundes? 9. Mit welchen Worten berichtet Georg seine Verlobung? 10. Warum soll der Freund die erfolgte Verlobung begrüßen? 11. Wie versucht Kafka (oder Georg) glaublich (*credible*) zu machen, daß der Sohn seit Monaten nicht in des Vaters Zimmer war? 12. Welche Winke (*hints*) haben wir, daß Georg ganz dem Einfluß des Vaters unterliegt (*is subject to*)? 13. In der langen Rede des Vaters sehen wir, wie er nach und nach (*gradually*) seine mißtrauischen Vermutungen ans Licht bringt. Erklären Sie dies! 14. Womit erreichen diese Vermutungen ihren Höhepunkt? 15. Was versucht Georg nach dieser erstaunlichen Anklage des Vaters zu tun? 16. Welche Tatsachen führt Georg an (*cite*), um die Existenz seines Freundes zu beweisen? 17. Welche religiösen Anspielungen (*allusions*) kommen hier vor? 18. Welche Schuldgefühle zeigt Georg zuerst? 19. Wie nimmt er sich vor, die begangenen „Fehler" auszugleichen? 20. Was wirft der Vater Georg in seiner langen Rede (wo er die Bettdecke zurückwirft) vor? 21. In welchen Bildern werden jetzt Georgs Schuldgefühle dem Freunde gegenüber ausgedrückt? 22. Der Vater macht drei Anklagen nacheinander gegen seinen Sohn, und zwar welche? 23. Wie werden Georgs Unterlegenheit und seine Furcht ersichtlich? 24. Welche letzte schreckliche Hoffnung hat Georg? 25. Aus welchen drei Quellen (*sources*) hat der Vater die Kraft geschöpft, den Sohn zu vernichten? 26. Des Vaters Zorn ist offenbar sehr gegen die Verlobung des Sohnes gerichtet. Warum ist das? 27. Wie vollzieht der Sohn des Vaters Urteil?

Ernst, Seite 97 bis 101

1. Was für eine Stellung hat jetzt Manfred, und worauf hofft er? 2. Was ist der Inhalt (*content*) des Briefes? 3. Was könnte Marie bewegt haben, den Brief in das Kästchen zu legen und die Gesellschaft zu meiden? 4. Wie stellt sich Manfred Gott und das Schicksal vor? 5. Was hat Melanies Vater gegen Manfred? 6. Marie verteidigt Manfred sehr lebhaft. Was sollen wir daraus entnehmen? 7. Wozu hat Marie den Vater überredet? 8. Erzählen Sie den Vorfall am Briefkasten! 9. Worin sieht Manfred den Mangel seines ersten Briefes? 10. Warum wird Marie bei der Ankunft rot und verlegen? 11. Und warum sieht Melanie so bleich aus? 12. Welche neue Nachricht hat Manfred erhalten? 13. Ist der Ausgang auch für Marie erfreulich oder nicht? 14. Versuchen Sie, die am Ende der Einführung zum „geraubten Brief" erwähnte Frage auf deutsch zu beantworten!

Wiechert, Seite 105 bis 113

1. Beschreiben Sie nach Lage und Aussehen die Ehrentafel! 2. Wie unterscheidet sich der Namenszug des gefallenen Lehrers von den anderen? 3. Was für ein System der Erkundung haben die Tertianer gegen einen neuen Lehrer? 4. Erklären Sie die verschiedenen Imperativformen („Setzt euch!" usw.)! 5. In welchem Sinne weiß auch der Kandidat, daß „der Würfel fällt"? 6. Was ist der gewöhnliche Ausgang dieser Probe? 7. Erzählen Sie, wie einmal das System der Schüler fehlschlug (*failed*)! 8. Wie aber ging es mit Georgesohn? 9. Welchen Einfluß haben die plötzlichen Zornausbrüche Georgesohns auf die Schüler? 10. Wie macht Jonas auch dem ein Ende? 11. Welcher Unfall bereitet dem

Kandidaten die letzte und tiefste Niederlage? 12. Was hören die Schüler von dem verschwundenen Kandidaten? 13. Was bringt die alten Schüler wieder zusammen? 14. Inwiefern ist jetzt Jonas anders (in mehr als einer Hinsicht)? 15. Was meint Jonas, wenn er sagt, dreißig hätten es „wieder gutgemacht"? 16. Wie hat sich auch der Kandidat in der Zwischenzeit geändert? 17. Unter welchen Umständen erscheint wieder das Motiv des Gebets? 18. Welcher Widerstreit entsteht über den vergoldeten Namen und zu welcher Entscheidung kommt man?

Borchert, Seite 119 bis 147

1. Aus den Traumbildern Fischers gestalten sich die eigentlichen Kriegsereignisse, die der Geschichte zugrundeliegen (*serve as basis for*). Erzählen Sie, was „wirklich" passierte! 2. Welche Geräusche spielen in Fischers Gedanken eine Rolle? Warum sind sie wohl so wichtig? 3. Kann man aus den ersten zwei oder drei Seiten genau sagen, was Fischer in Wirklichkeit tut, während er diese Visionen aus der Vergangenheit sieht? 4. Warum ist die Episode mit dem kleinen Mädchen so rührend? 5. Was steckt hinter Fischers Erinnerungen an die Lokomotive? 6. Zu welchem Zweck betont Borchert die eingeschobene Episode mit Timm und dem Russen? 7. Wieso kann Borchert die lautmalenden Wörter „pink, pank" in diesen verschiedenen Zusammenhängen (*connections*) gebrauchen? 8. Die Struktur der Stelle, wo die Zahl 57 immer wieder vorkommt, erinnert an den Stil des Märchens. Inwiefern? 9. Welchen Eindruck sollen die Schilder (*signs*) an der Straße auf Fischer (und auf den Leser) machen? 10. Die Skatspieler haben scheinbar nicht so viel mit der Geschichte zu tun wie andere Gestalten. Wozu sind sie wohl da? 11. Welchem Zweck dient die Erwähnung des *ersten* Weltkrieges (1917 auf dem Brief)? 12. Was meint Borchert, wenn er sagt, das Geschäft gehe für den Mann in der dunklen Ecke gut? 13. Welche Rolle soll der „Dichter" spielen? 14. Warum ist die Gestalt des Obergefreiten so tief ironisch? 15. In dem darauffolgenden Absatz (*paragraph*) sammeln sich fast alle bisherigen Motive, und der Ausdruck „das ist gut" kommt wiederholt vor. Erklären Sie weshalb! 16. Das mit der Urania-Lebensversicherung ist tief ironisch. Wieso? 17. Wie wird Evelyn geschildert, und inwiefern ist das Bild von ihr etwas ganz Neues in der Geschichte? 18. Wann weiß man eigentlich erst, was das Mädchen neben den Schienen will? 19. Fußballspiel und Matthäus-Passion stehen ganz eng beieinander. Was haben sie gemeinsam? 20. Hier sammeln sich die verschiedenen Motive wieder. Wie kann man also die Struktur der ganzen Geschichte beschreiben? 21. Die Hampelmänner sind offenbar symbolisch. Wieso? 22. Was hat Borchert über Wissenschaft und Forschung zu sagen? 23. Endlich hört hier Fischer auf, einfach passiv zu sein. Was versucht er zu tun? Was soll es wohl heißen, daß es ihm nicht gelingt? 24. Wieder einmal gruppieren sich alle Motive und Gestalten der Geschichte, und zwar in der Szene auf der Straßenbahn. Warum läßt Borchert die Geschichte auf diese Weise schließen?

Gaiser, Seite 151 bis 165

1. Welche besondere Schwierigkeit hat die Nachkriegszeit für Fehleisen? 2. Wie weit reicht die Erbitterung, die Fehleisen fühlt? 3. Woher hat seine Mutter das Gold für den Ring? 4. Welche besondere Anweisung hat die Mutter für die Goldschmiedin? 5. Was sagt Fehleisen zu dem Geschenk? 6. Was für ein Mann ist Brack gewesen? 7. Wo ist Brack jetzt wohnhaft (wohnhaft sein *be settled, reside*), und wie ist er dahin gekommen? 8. Warum gibt Fehleisen der Bitte Bracks schließlich nach? 9. Was hat Fehleisen offenbar vom Kriege als Erbe mitgebracht? 10. Es ist wichtig, daß das, was Brack malt, aus der Bibel kommt. Auch daß es gewisse Gleichnisse sind. Erklären Sie! 11. Wie lassen die

Schmerzen, die Fehleisen leidet, ihn die Rosen am Schwesternhause sehen? 12. Bei welchem Wort bemerkt Fehleisen zuerst den Verlust des Ringes? 13. Weil der Schmerz zur gleichen Zeit so schrecklich wird, glaubt Fehleisen, daß die beiden irgendwie zusammengehören. Wie mag das sein? 14. Offenbar muß Fehleisen den Ring wiederfinden. Was hat dies mit dem symbolischen Wert des Rings zu tun? 15. Wie kommt das Motorrad in die Geschichte? 16. Welchen Trost hat Bracks Frau Fehleisen zu bringen? 17. Welche zwei Bedeutungen dürften die Worte Fehleisens haben: „Ich suche nicht weiter"? 18. Warum ist der Wald so gefährlich? 19. Erzählen Sie den Vorfall mit den zwei Motorradfahrern! 20. Warum sagt Fehleisen plötzlich zu sich: „Schwarze Johannisbeeren"? Was ist ihm jetzt klar? 21. Was haben Fehleisen und der Waldhüter einander zu sagen? 22. Warum ist es so, daß Fehleisen genau weiß, wo er zu suchen hat? 23. Fehleisen möchte noch einen Tag bei Bracks bleiben. Was ist damit gewonnen? 24. Können Sie auf deutsch sagen, was der Ring für eine symbolische Bedeutung hat?

Piontek, Seite 171 bis 192

1. In dem ersten langen Absatz kommen schon einige Motive vor, die für den weiteren Verlauf der Geschichte wichtig sind. Sie sind daran zu erkennen, daß sie hier ein bißchen unerwartet oder ungewöhnlich sind. Welche wären es wohl? 2. Was scheint am Anfang das Verhältnis von Lohoff, Rudja und Jens zu sein? 3. Warum stoßen sich Iris und Kathi kichernd an? 4. Wie ändert sich die Landschaft, indem sie höher steigen? 5. Was sind in der ganzen Episode an der Berghütte die wesentlichsten Punkte, d.h. für den Gang der Handlung (besonders was den Charakter des Wirts angeht)? 6. Wenn man weiß, daß das Heruntergleiten des schweren Stammes (an den dicken Seilen) und die Worte Jens' darüber eine ironische Vorwegnahme (*anticipation*) sind—was könnte das bedeuten? 7. Wie werden die Spannungen (*tensions*) zwischen den Personen der Geschichte deutlich? 8. Wie wird die wachsende Gefahr des Aufstiegs in der Erzählung wiedergespiegelt? 9. Welche tiefere Bedeutung hat die Tatsache, daß Jens jetzt zurückgeht? 10. Das Herannahen des Gewitters bedeutet sowohl innerlich wie auch äußerlich eine Steigerung (*increase, intensification*) der Spannungen. Wieso? 11. Wie wird der furchtbare Schicksalsschlag des Bergrutsches (*landslide*) eingeleitet und geschildert? 12. Wie reagieren (*react*) die drei auf die neue Lage der Dinge? 13. Welchen Eindruck macht unter diesen Umständen die Erklärung Lohoffs gegenüber Jens? 14. Jetzt fangen die beiden Männer an, wirre Traumbilder zu erleben. Was ist der wesentliche Inhalt dieser Visionen? 15. Wie wird in der Vision Lohoffs das Ende der Erzählung vorweggenommen? 16. Erzählen Sie, wie Jens stirbt! 17. Welche Rolle spielen hier nach Ihrem Ermessen Absicht und Zufall? 18. Am Schluß kommen wieder diese Motive vor: die Grillen, der Wirt, das Abseilen, die Pferde, die Kamera. Sofern möglich, erklären Sie die Bedeutung eines jeden Motivs!

Vocabulary

For all nouns, the plural is indicated, and for masculines the genitive singular if it is not **-(e)s.**

Separable verb prefixes are followed by hyphens.

The accent mark shows stress on the preceding syllable, but stress is indicated only if it is not on the first syllable (or on the syllable after an inseparable prefix—on whatever part of speech).

Every effort has been made to provide a complete and accurate vocabulary. The assistance of the computer made the editor's task vastly easier, the results much more reliable. Except for numbers and exact or nearly exact cognates (see separate list p. xxxv), no words have been omitted. (See also the note under **un-,** and footnote 4 to Borchert's story.) For some common words, like the prepositions, it is impossible to cover all meanings. Otherwise the student will find a full range of translations, adequate for an understanding of any passage in these stories.

For economy of presentation—without sacrifice of completeness:

(1) Lexical items given in marginal notes are not repeated in the vocabulary.

These are all words or usages of low frequency, occurring only in the given passage. Not all nonce words, however, are given marginal glosses. When a word of relatively high frequency happens, by accident, not to occur more than once in the ten stories (e.g. **ähnlich**) or when the student might reasonably be expected to infer its meaning (e.g. **Abstieg** *descent*), the word appears only in the vocabulary.

(Words incorporated in the footnotes are, with a few obvious exceptions, repeated in the vocabulary, at least in their basic meaning.)

(2) Verb prefixes (separable only) are noted as such and listed independently, with their basic meanings. No entry is provided for a compound verb consisting of one of these prefixes, in a listed meaning, and a simple verb which also appears separately. For example, **herein** *in* and **kommen** *come* are both given, **hereinkommen** *come in* is not. If any special meaning is involved, either in prefix or verb, the compound is included in its alphabetical position.

(3) Negatives of listed adjectives are not specially noted, nor are infinitives and past participles (of listed verbs) used as nouns and adjectives, respectively.

(4) Principal parts of strong and irregular verbs, in their uncompounded forms, are given in a single section at the end.

This avoids the ambiguity likely to result from abbreviating principal parts.

There is no unnecessary repetition of forms. The dagger after an infinitive refers the student to this list.

ab (*as verb prefix and adverb*) off, away, down; **ab und zu** now and then
sich **ab-arbeiten** work oneself to death
ab-biegen† (ist) turn aside, turn off
der **Abend, -e** evening; **das Abendbrot** supper; **abends** in the evening
das **Abenteuer, -** adventure
aber but; however
abermals again
die **Abfahrt, -en** descent
ab-geben† give, transfer
abgemagert emaciated
abgeneigt averse
ab-halten† hold
ab-hängen† depend
ab-holen (come and) get, pick up
ab-lassen† desist
der **Ablauf** (downward) course
ab-machen settle; **die Abmachung, -en** agreement
die **Abneigung** dislike, aversion
die **Abreise** departure; **ab-reisen** (ist) depart, leave
der **Abschied, -e** departure, leave
ab-schließen† conclude
die **Absicht, -en** intent(ion), plan
ab-stellen park, leave (a car)
der **Abstieg, -e** descent, way down
die **Abteilung, -en** department, division, compartment
ab-tragen† carry off; demolish
ab-tun† get rid of, finish off
abwärts downward
ab-wehren ward off
abwesend absentminded; **die Abwesenheit** absence
das **Abzeichen, -** mark
ab-ziehen† retreat; **der Abzug, ⸚e** retreat
ach oh
achten regard, respect, pay attention; **achtlos** heedless
der **Acker, ⸚** field
die **Ader, -n** vein
adlig noble
affig apish, vulgar
ähnlich similar, like
die **Ahnung, -en** notion, idea; **ahnungslos** unsuspecting
die **Ähre, -n** ear of corn; **das Ährenfeld, -er** field of corn
die **Albernheit** silliness
all all, every; **alles** everything, all, everybody
allein' alone; yet, but
allerdings to be sure, it is true
allerhand all sorts of things
allerhöchst- greatest possible
allerlei all kinds of
allgemein general
alljähr'lich every year
allmäh'lich gradual
als when, as; as if; than; but
alsbald' immediately, straightway
alsdann' then
also therefore, so; (well) then
alt old; **altbekannt** old familiar; **der Alte, -n, -n** old man; **die Alte, -n, -n** old woman; **älter** older, rather old, elderly; **das Alter** age; old age; **altersblank** shiny with age; **alterslos** ageless; **altmodisch** old-fashioned
das **Amt, ⸚er** office, job; **die Amtspflicht, -en** official duty
sich **amüsie'ren** have a good time, make fun, be amused
an to, at, by, *etc.;* on; (*also verb prefix*)
an-befehlen† enjoin
an-bellen bark at
an-bieten† offer
der **Anblick, -e** sight; **an-blicken** look at
an-bringen† bring (out)
das **Andenken, -** souvenir; memory
ander- other, else, different; next; **ändern** change; **anders** else, other; different(ly), otherwise; **anderthalb** one and a half
an-deuten indicate
an-fallen† attack; assail; fall upon
an-fangen† start, begin; **anfangs** in the beginning
sich **an-freunden** become friends
der **Anführer, -** ringleader
an-geben† indicate
an-gehen† (ist) approach; entreat; concern
die **Angelegenheit, -en** matter, affair
angenehm pleasant
das **Angesicht, -er** face, countenance
der **Angriff, -e** attack
die **Angst, ⸚e** fear, anxiety; **Angst haben**† be afraid; **sich ängstigen** be afraid; **ängstlich** anxious
an-halten† check, stop (in one's course); last, persist
an-heben† be lifted up; begin (to speak)
die **Anhöhe, -n** hill
an-hören listen to; sound (as if, like)
die **Anklage, -n** accusation
(sich) **an-kleiden** dress
an-kommen† (ist) come, arrive
an-legen aim
anmutig charming
die **Annäherung, -en** approach, advance
die **Annahme, -n** assumption; **an-nehmen**† assume; accept

an-packen attack, take hold of
sich **an-reihen** follow in line
an-rücken (ist) advance
an-rufen† call to; challenge
an-schauen look at
die **Anschrift, -en** address
an-sehen† look at, take a look at, regard; (*with dat.*) tell by looking at; **ansehnlich** respectable, good-looking; **die Ansicht, -en** view, opinion
an-siedeln settle
an-springen† (ist) jump up on
anstatt′ instead (of)
an-stauben cover with dust, get dusty
an-staunen gape at
an-steigen† rise, climb
die **Anstellung, -en** position, job
an-stimmen strike up
sich **an-stoßen**† nudge one another
die **Anstrengung, -en** exertion
der **Anteil, -e** portion
das **Antlitz, -e** countenance
an-treffen† come upon
an-treten† enter upon
der **Antrieb, -e** spur, incentive
an-tun† do to, subject to
die **Antwort, -en** answer; **antworten** answer
an-weisen† instruct, indicate
das **Anzeichen, -** indication, sign
an-zeigen report, announce
an-ziehen† attract; put on; draw up
an-zünden light
der **Apparat′, -e** camera
die **Arbeit, -en** work, piece of work; **arbeiten** work; **der Arbeiter, -** worker; **die Arbeiterhand, ⸚e** working-man's hand
arg bad, severe; **der Ärger** annoyance, vexation; **ärgerlich** annoyed; **ärgervoll** annoyed, spiteful
arm poor
der **Arm, -e** arm; **der Ärmel, -** sleeve
ärmlich poor, wretched, in poverty; **die Armut** poverty
die **Art, -en** kind, type, manner, way, sort, fashion
der **Arzt, ⸚e** doctor
der **Ast, ⸚e** branch
der **Atem** breath; **der Atemzug, ⸚e** breath; **atmen** breathe
auch too, also; . . . ever; even
auf on, *etc.;* **aufs reinlichste,** *etc.* in the neatest fashion, most neatly, *etc.;* **auf und ab** up and down; **auf . . . zu** up to . . .
auf (*as verb prefix and adverb*) up; open
auf-bellen let out a bark
auf-blühen (ist) bloom, open like a flower
auf-brechen† (ist) set out
auf-bringen† bring up; irritate
auf-dämmern dawn
der **Aufenthalt** stay; stopping place, abode
auf-fahren† (ist) start up, wake up with a start; strike out angrily
auf-fallen† (ist) strike, be striking, attract attention
auf-fordern summon; challenge; invite, ask
auf-gehen† (ist) rise
aufgerissen wide open
auf-halten† hold up, stop
sich **auf-häufen** pile up, accumulate
sich **auf-heben**† rise up; contrast
auf-hören cease, stop
auf-lesen† gather up
auf-lösen resolve, dissolve, break up; solve
auf-machen open
aufmerksam attentive, watchful; **die Aufmerksamkeit** attention
auf-muntern encourage
auf-nehmen† take up, take in (hand), adopt
auf-passen (auf) watch for; be intent upon
sich **auf-raffen** pull oneself together, collect oneself
auf-räumen clean up, clear away
aufrecht erect, upright; **aufrecht-erhalten**† maintain
auf-regen excite; **die Aufregung, -en** excitement
auf-richten erect; set up; **sich auf-richten** rise up; **aufrichtig** sincere
der **Aufruf, -e** summons, call; **auf-rufen**† call, summon, order up
auf-rühren stir up; revive
der **Aufschlag, ⸚e** impact, crash
auf-schlagen† open; raise
auf-schließen† unlock, open
auf-schreien† cry out
auf-sparen save
auf-spüren track down
auf-stehen† (ist) stand up, rise, get up
auf-suchen seek out, look for
auf-tauchen (ist) show up, appear
der **Auftrag, ⸚e** mission, assignment, commission
auf-treiben† find, get hold of
auf-wachen (ist) wake up
auf-ziehen† bring up, raise; tease, make fun of
der **Augapfel, ⸚** eyeball; **das Auge, -n** eye; **der Augenblick, -e** moment; **augenblicklich** momentarily, instantly; **die Augenbraue, -n** eyebrow; **der Augenring, -e** circle (spot) around the eye; **augenscheinlich** obviously, apparently; **die Augenschwäche, -n** weakness of vision
aus out of, from, *etc.;* over; out; off
aus (*as verb prefix and adverb*) out
aus-bessern repair
aus-bilden develop
sich **aus-bitten**† beg
aus-brechen† break out, break away

aus-breiten extend, outspread, spread out
der **Ausbruch, ⸚e** outbreak, outburst
aus-denken† conceive, think up
der **Ausdruck, ⸚e** expression; **aus-drücken** express; **ausdrücklich** explicit
auseinan'der-falten unfold
aus-fragen question, interrogate
aus-führen carry out; **ausführlich** in detail; **die Ausführung, -en** execution; explanation
der **Ausgang, ⸚e** exit, end
ausgetreten worn down (by being walked on)
ausgezeichnet excellent
aus-gleichen† compensate for
aus-halten† stand, be able to stand
das **Ausland** foreign land(s), foreign parts; **Auslands-** (*compounding form*) foreign . . .
aus-liefern hand (turn) over, surrender
aus-löschen† (be) extinguish(ed)
aus-machen settle; matter, make a difference
aus-malen portray, depict; paint
aus-rauben plunder
aus-ruhen rest
aus-sagen declare; express fully; report
aus-schauen look
aus-schmücken adorn, decorate
aus-sehen† look
außer except, outside of, besides, *etc.;* **außer sich** beside oneself; **außerdem** besides; **das Äußere** external appearance; **außerhalb** outside of
die **Aussicht, -en** view; prospect(s), outlook, chance; **aussichtslos** hopeless
aus-spreizen spread (out)
aus-stoßen† utter, emit
die **Ausübung** practice, exercise
die **Auswanderung, -en** emigration
der **Ausweg, -e** opening, way out (of difficulty)
aus-weichen† (ist) avoid, shun, elude
aus-ziehen† undress, take off
der **Autoomnibus, -se** bus; **der Autoschlosser, -** mechanic

der **Bach, ⸚e** brook
backen† bake
das **Bad, ⸚er** bath(room); **baden** bathe; swim; **das Badezimmer, -** bathroom
die **Bahn, -en** way; course; alley; **der Bahnsteig, -e** platform
der **Bajonett'stich, -e** bayonet cut
bald soon; **bald . . . bald** . . . now . . . now . . .
der **Balken, -** beam
das **Bandelier', -e** shoulder-belt, bandolier
bändigen subdue, tame
bang(e) anxious, worried
die **Bank, ⸚e** bench
der **Bann** (magic) spell; **bannen** hold fast (by magic spell)
die **Barmher'zigkeit** mercy
der **Bart, ⸚e** beard
der **Bau, -ten** building; **die Bauarbeit, -en** construction work
der **Bauch, ⸚e** belly, stomach
bauen build
der **Bauer, -s (-n), -n** peasant, farmer; **der Bauerngarten, ⸚** farmer's garden
der **Baum, ⸚e** tree; **die Baumkrone, -n** treetop; **der Baumzweig, -e** branch of a tree
der **Beamte, -n, -n** official, government employee
bebändert beribboned
beben tremble, quake
der **Becher, -** cup
bedächtig discreet, cautious
bedauern feel sorry for
bedecken cover
das **Bedenken, -** misgiving
bedeuten mean, signify; **bedeutend** significant, considerable; **die Bedeutung, -en** meaning; **bedeutungslos** meaningless
bedienen serve; **sich bedienen** use; **die Bedienerin, -nen** maid
bedrohen threaten
bedruckt printed, with print
bedürfen† need
sich **beeilen** hurry
beeindrucken impress
beenden finish, end
befahren (*participle*) well-travelled
der **Befehl, -e** order; **befehlen†** order, command
befestigen affix, fasten
befinden† find; **sich befinden†** be located, be, find oneself; **befindlich** located, residing
die **Beförderung, -en** promotion
befragen ask
sich **begeben†** go, make one's way; happen; **die Begebenheit, -en** incident, happening
begegnen (ist) meet
begehbar passable; **begehen†** travel
begeistert enthusiastic; **die Begeisterung** enthusiasm
der **Beginn** beginning; **beginnen†** begin
begleiten accompany
beglückt blest, fortunate
begraben† bury
begreifen† comprehend; **begreiflich** understandable; **begreiflicherweise** understandably; **der Begriff, -e** concept, idea; **im Begriffe sein†** be about to, be in the process of
begründen establish, found
begrüßen greet, acclaim
behalten† keep, retain; put up; remember

behandeln treat; **die Behandlung, -en** treatment
behängen† cover, hang, drape
sich **beherrschen** control oneself; **die Beherrschung** self-control
behutsam careful
bei with, at, near, *etc.;* at the house of; while, as one . . .
beide both, two; **die Beiden, die beiden** the two (of them)
der **Beifall** applause; approval; **beifällig** approving
bei-geben† assign, attach
bei-kommen† (ist) catch up with
das **Beileid** condolence; **der Beileidsbrief, -e** letter of condolence
das **Bein, -e** leg; **auf den Beinen** on the prowl, in action
beina'he almost
das **Beinkleid, -er** (*pl.*) trousers
beisam'men together
beisei'te (*as verb prefix*) aside
das **Beispiel, -e** example; **beispielsweise** for example
bei-springen† (ist) lend a hand
beißen† bite
bei-stehen† stand by, assist
bei-wohnen attend
bekannt familiar, well-known; **der Bekannte, -n, -n** acquaintance
das **Bekenntnis, -se** confession, protestation
bekommen† get
bekräftigen affirm, emphasize
sich **bekümmern** be concerned
belästigen annoy
beleidigen offend
bellen bark, howl
die **Belustigung, -en** amusement
sich **bemächtigen** master
bemerken notice; **bemerkenswert** worthy of note; **bemerklich** noticeable; **die Bemerkung, -en** observation; remark
bemitleiden sympathize with
sich **benehmen**† act, behave; **das Benehmen** behavior, attitude
beneiden envy
der **Benzin'fleck, -e** gasoline spot
beobachten observe, watch; **die Beobachtung, -en** observation
bequem comfortable, easy
sich **beraten**† take counsel, consult
bereit ready; **bereiten** prepare; make available; **bereits** already
der **Berg, -e** mountain, hill; **bergab'** downhill; **bergauf'** uphill; **der Bergschuh, -e** mountain boot; **die Bergwacht, -en** mountain rescue party; **der Bergwald, ⸚er** mountain forest; **die Bergwiese, -n** mountain meadow
der **Beruf, -e** profession, vocation
berühmt famous
berühren touch
die **Besatzungsmacht, ⸚e** occupation, (occupying) power
die **Beschaffenheit** nature, quality
sich **beschäftigen** occupy oneself, busy oneself; **die Beschäftigung, -en** occupation
die **Beschämung** embarrassment, shame
beschatten shade
bescheiden modest; **die Bescheidenheit** modesty
beschließen† decide
beschnüffeln sniff (over)
beschränken restrict
beschreiben† describe
die **Beschützerin, -nen** protectress, patroness
besehen† inspect, look over
beseitigen put aside, eliminate
besiegen conquer; **der Besieger, -** conqueror
sich **besinnen**† recall, recollect; reflect
der **Besitz** possession; **besitzen**† possess, own, have; **die Besitzergreifung** seizure, appropriation, confiscation; **die Besitzerin, -nen** owner; **die Besitzung, -en** possession
besonder- special, particular; **besonders** especially
besorgen arrange, take care of, get; **die Besorgung, -en** thing to do, errand
besser better; **best-** best
beständig constant, continual
der **Bestandteil, -e** component (part)
bestätigen confirm
bestatten bury
bestehen† consist; undergo; exist; insist
besteigen† mount
bestellen order; till, cultivate
die **Bestie, -n** beast
bestimmen destine, intend, assign; **bestimmt** definite, certain, destined; **die Bestimmtheit** definiteness
bestrafen punish
bestürmen besiege
bestürzt startled, dismayed
der **Besuch, -e** visit; **besuchen** visit; attend
betäuben stun, stupefy; **die Betäubung** bewilderment, insensibility, stupefaction
sich **beteiligen** participate
beten pray
beteuern assert, affirm
die **Betonung, -en** emphasis
betrachten look at, contemplate, regard
sich **betragen**† behave; **das Betragen** behavior
betreffen† concern

betreiben† run, manage
betreten† enter
betrügen† betray, deceive; **der Betrüger, -** deceiver
das **Bett, -en** bed; **die Bettdecke, -n** blanket; **betten** bed down
beugen bend; **sich beugen** bend (down)
die **Beute** booty; **das Beutemachen** looting, appropriating things
die **Bevölkerungsklasse, -n** class of the population
bevor'-stehen† be in the offing (to be expected)
bewegen move, make . . . move; **sich bewegen** move; **die Bewegung, -en** motion, stir
bewirten entertain; minister to
der **Bewohner, -** inhabitant, occupant
bewundern admire
bewußtlos unconscious; **das Bewußtsein** consciousness, awareness
bezahlen pay
bezaubernd enchanting
bezeichnen designate, indicate, mark
die **Beziehung, -en** relation(ship)
biegen† bend, turn
die **Bierflasche, -n** beer bottle; **bierflaschengrün** beer bottle green
bieten† offer
das **Bild, -er** picture, image
bilden constitute, form
das **Billett', -e** ticket
billig inexpensive; fair; **billigen** approve
binden† bind, tie
bis (up) to, until, as far as; until, till; **bisher'** before (*adv.*); **bishe'rig** previous
bißchen (little) bit
der **Bissen, -** bite
die **Bitte, -n** request; **bitte** please; **bitten**† ask, beg
blank shining, shiny
blasen† blow
blaß pale
das **Blatt, ⸚er** leaf, petal, page, sheet
blau blue; **bläulich** bluish
bleiben† (ist) remain, stay; be left
bleich pale
bleiern leaden, like lead; **bleigrau** lead-gray
der **Bleistift, -e** pencil
blenden dazzle, be dazzled
der **Blick, -e** glance, look; eye, vision; **blicken** look, glance
blindlings blindly
blinzeln wink
der **Blitz, -e** lightning (flash); **blitzen** flash, shine
der **Block, ⸚e** block; boulder
blöde dull, witless, dull-witted; **die Blödigkeit** timidity
bloß bare; mere, simple, just
blühen bloom, be in blossom
die **Blume, -n** flower; **blumenblau** flower-blue; **der Blumentopf, ⸚e** flowerpot
die **Bluse, -n** blouse
das **Blut** blood; **bluten** bleed; **der Blutdurst** bloodthirstiness; **blutdurstig** bloodthirsty
die **Blüte, -n** bloom
blutig bloody; **blutigrot** bloody-red; **das Blutkreuz, -e** bloody cross; **blutrot** blood-red; **blutrünstig** bloody
der **Bock, ⸚e** ram, he-goat
der **Boden, ⸚** ground, soil; floor
böhmisch Bohemian
die **Bösartigkeit** (degree of) malice, maliciousness; **böse** angry; wicked, evil, bad; **der Böse, -n, -n** the Evil One, the devil
der **Bote, -n, -n** messenger; **die Botschaft, -en** mission; message; embassy
der **Brand, ⸚e** fire; **in Brand setzen** light; **brandig** burnt
der **Branntwein, -e** brandy; **das Branntweingläschen, -** little brandy glass
der **Bratkartof'felgeruch'** smell of roast potatoes
brauchen use, need; take
braun brown; **das Braun** brown
brausen roar, thunder
die **Braut, ⸚e** fiancée; bride; **die Brautzeit, -en** engagement
brechen† break
breit broad, wide
brennen† burn
das **Brett, -er** board
der **Brief, -e** letter; **das Briefchen, -** little letter; **der Briefkasten, -** mailbox; **brieflich** in letters, epistolary
die **Brille, -n** glasses
bringen† bring, take; **es zu . . . bringen** manage (to)
der **Brocken, -** piece of rock, broken rock
der **Brokat', -e** brocade
das **Brot, -e** bread; loaf; **der Brotherr, -n, -en** employer
die **Brücke, -n** bridge
der **Bruder, ⸚** brother
brüllen roar, thunder
der **Brunnen, -** spring, well
brüsk brusque
die **Brust, ⸚e** chest, breast
der **Bub(e), -(e)n, -(e)n** boy, lad
der **Buchstabe, -n, -n** letter
bücken bend over
bunt of many colors, gaily-colored
die **Burg, -en** castle; fortress
der **Bürger, -** citizen, burgher; **bürgerlich** middle class; civilian

das **Büro′, -s** office
der **Bursch, -en, -en** fellow, lad
bürsten brush
büßen pay for

die **Chaussee′, -n** highway
der **Chef, -s** boss
der **Chor, ⸗e** choir
christlich Christian
die **Chronik, -en** chronicle
der **Cornet′, -s (-e)** cornet, standard bearer

da there; here; then; since, as; when; **da und dort** here and there
da (*as verb prefix*) there
da(r)- (*with preposition*) there- . . . . , . . . it, that; *with following infinitive or* **daß**, "*anticipatory*" *and not translated*
dabei′ with that, *etc.;* at the same time, in so doing; there; yet
das **Dach, ⸗er** roof
dafür′ for it, *etc.;* in compensation for that, in exchange; but then
daheim′ at home
daher′ from there, this way; therefore
dahin′-rennen† run along
damals then, at that time
die **Dame, -n** lady
damit′ with it, *etc.;* so that
dämmern get dark; **dämmernd** twilight, darkening; **die Dämmerung** twilight; dawn
dankbar grateful; **die Dankbarkeit** gratitude; **danken** thank; **das Dankgebet, -e** prayer of thanks
dann then; **dann und wann** now and then
dannen thence; **von dannen** away
dar-stellen depict, represent, act the part of
darum′ around it, *etc.;* therefore
da-sein† be there, be here; **das Dasein** existence, life
daß that, so that
die **Dauer** duration; **dauern** last
der **Daumen, -** thumb
davon′ (*as verb prefix*) away
davon′-streben try to get away, press ahead
dazu′ for that, *etc.;* in addition, along with . . . , beside(s)
dazwi′schen between them, among them, *etc.;* in between, in among; between times
die **Decke, -n** ceiling; blanket, cover; **der Deckel, -** cover, lid; **die Deckung** cover, hiding spot; **das Deckzeug** covers
sich **dehnen** extend, spread
dem′nach according to this
demütig humble, meek
denken† think, imagine
denn for; anyway, then; than
dennoch nevertheless, still
der, die, das the; he, *etc.;* that (one); who, which, that
derje′nige that one, the one
dersel′be the same; it, *etc.*
deshalb therefore, for that reason
desto the more, so much the . . .
deutlich distinct, clear
deutsch German; **das Deutschland** Germany
dicht close, thick
der **Dichter, -** poet, writer
dick thick, fat
das **Dickicht, -e** thicket, thick woods
der **Dieb, -e** thief
der **Diener, -** servant; **der Dienst, -e** service, duty
dieser this (one); the latter; he, *etc.*
diesmal this time
das **Ding, -e** thing
doch yet, nevertheless, however, still, though, but; surely, after all
der **Donner** thunder; **donnern** thunder; **der Donnerschlag, ⸗e** thunderclap
der **Doppelgänger, -** double
das **Dorf, ⸗er** village
dort there; **dorthin′** there, over there; **dortig** local, there
dran = **daran**
der **Drang** urge, drive, impulse; **(sich) drängen** press, push
drauf = **darauf; draus** = **daraus**
draußen outside
(sich) **drehen** turn, twist
drein = **darein** into it; along; **hinter . . . drein** along behind
drin = **darin**
dringen† press, penetrate, force one's way; urge; **dringlich** pressing, urgent
drinnen inside
dritt third; **zu dritt** all three; **das Drittel, -** third
drohen threaten, menace; **die Drohung** menace
dröhnen boom, roar, rumble; shake
drüben over there
drüber = **darüber**
der **Druck, ⸗e** pressure; **drücken** press, squeeze, push
du you
ducken duck, bend down
duften be fragrant, smell (sweet)
dulden tolerate
dumm stupid, dumb; **die Dummheit, -en** stupidity
dumpf dull
dumpfig musty, dank
dunkel dark; **dunkelgrün** dark green

dünn thin
durch through, by, *etc.;* (*as verb prefix*) through
durchaus' at all; quite; absolutely
der **Durchblick, -e** view through
durchdrin'gen† penetrate
durcheinan'der in confusion; all at the same time
der **Durchgang, ⸚e** passage
durch-gehen† (ist) go through, get by
durch-halten† hold out, see it through
durchhau'en† cut through
durchja'gen go through in a hurry
durchlö'chern perforate
durch-machen go through
durchnä' ßen wet through
durchschau'en see through
sich **durch-schlagen†** make one's way, get by
durchschrei'ten† walk through
durch-streichen† cross out
durchtei'len cut in two, divide evenly
dürfen† be allowed, may, can, *etc.*
der **Durst** thirst
das **Dutzend, -e** dozen

eben precisely, exactly, just (now); **das Ebenbild, -er** image, likeness; **die Ebene, -n** plain; **ebenfalls** likewise; **ebenso** just as; **ebensolch-** identical, similar
echt real, genuine
die **Ecke, -n** corner
edel noble; **der Edelmann, Edelleute** noble; **der Edelstein, -e** jewel
ehe before; **ehemalig** former; **eher** rather
die **Ehre, -n** honor, credit; **ehren** honor, do honor; **das Ehrenmal, -e** memorial; **der Ehrenmann, ⸚er** man of honor, gentleman; **die Ehrentafel, -n** commemorative (memorial) tablet; **ehrlich** honorable; **die Ehrlichkeit** honesty
das **Ei, -er** egg
die **Eiche, -n** oak; **eichen** oaken
der **Eid, -e** oath
die **Eifersucht** jealousy; **eifersüchtig** jealous
eifrig eager, zealous
eigen own, proper, particular; **eigenhändig** with one's own hands; **die Eigenschaft, -en** characteristic, attribute, aspect of character; **eigensinnig** self-willed, stubborn; **eigentlich** actual(ly), real(ly), anyway; **die Eigentümlichkeit, -en** peculiarity
die **Eile** haste; **eilen** (ist) hurry; **eilends** hastily; **eilig** hasty, hurried; **eilig haben** be in a hurry
ein one; a(n)
ein (*as verb prefix*) in
(-) einan'der (. . .) one another, each other
sich **ein-bilden** imagine; **die Einbildung, -en** fancy, imagining; imagination
der **Einblick, -e** look, insight
eindeutig unambiguous
eindringlich urgent, forcible
der **Eindruck, ⸚e** impression
einemmal: mit einemmal suddenly
einerlei one and the same, immaterial; **einfach** simple
ein-fallen† (ist) sink, fall in; join in; occur to
ein-fangen† catch, trap
sich **ein-finden†** make one's appearance, show up
der **Einfluß, ⸚e** influence
ein-führen introduce
ein-graben† engrave
ein-händigen hand over
ein-hauen† light into, strike (out) at
einheimisch native, local, indigenous
einige some, a few, several; **einigemal** a few times
ein-kaufen buy
die **Einkehr** stop(ping in); **ein-kehren** (ist) stop
die **Einladung, -en** invitation
ein-legen earn
ein-leuchten be clear, make sense
einmal once; just; occasionally; **auf einmal** all of a sudden; **nicht einmal** not even; **noch einmal** once more, again
ein-nehmen† take, have
ein paar a few
ein-rennen† (ist) run at
ein-richten arrange; **sich einrichten** set oneself up; establish oneself; adapt
eins one
einsam lonely
ein-schenken pour, serve
ein-schlafen† (ist) fall asleep
ein-schlagen† break in; beat in; set off on
ein-sehen† see
einsilbig monosyllabic, saying little
ein-spinnen† spin round, entangle
einst once
ein-stecken put (stick) in, put in pocket
ein-stellen turn off, stop
ein-stürzen (ist) collapse, be demolished
ein-tauschen get in exchange, trade
die **Eintrittskarte, -n** ticket
einverstanden in agreement
der **Einwand, ⸚e** objection
ein-weihen initiate; **die Einweihung, -en** dedication
ein-weisen† show the way, point
ein-werfen† mail (letter)
ein-wickeln wrap up
einzeln single, individual; **der Einzelne, -n, -n** individual; **das Einzelwesen, -** individual being
ein-ziehen† (ist) move in
einzig single, only, sole

das **Eisen** iron; **die Eisenbahn, -en** railroad (car); **eisern** iron
eisig icy; **das Eismeer** polar sea; **der Eisschrank, ⸚e** ice-box
eitel vain
elend wretched, miserable
der **Ellbogen, -** elbow
die **Eltern** (*pl.*) parents
der **Empfang, ⸚e** reception, receipt; **empfangen†** receive
empfehlen† recommend, commend, introduce; **die Empfehlung, -en** recommendation
empfinden† feel
empor′ (*as verb prefix*) up
sich **empö′ren** rebel
das **Ende, -n** end; **endgültig** definitive, permanent, definite; **endlich** finally; **endlos** endless
eng tight, narrow, confined
der **Engel, -** angel
entdecken discover
entfalten unfold
sich **entfernen** get away, withdraw, be removed; **entfernt** remote; die **Entfernung, -en** distance; removal
entfliehen† (ist) flee
entfremden alienate
entge′gen toward, in the direction of
entge′gen (*as verb prefix*) toward, to (meet)
das **Entge′genkommen** reception, response
entgehen† (ist) escape
sich **enthalten†** refrain
entheben† relieve of responsibility
entkommen† escape
entlang′ along
entlassen† release, discharge, dismiss, let go; **die Entlassung, -en** release
entleeren empty
entnehmen† take out
entreißen† tear from, snatch away
entrichten pay
entrüsten incense, enrage
entscheiden† decide; **die Entscheidung, -en** decision; **entschieden** definite, distinct
sich **entschließen†** decide; **entschlossen** decisive, decided; **die Entschlossenheit** decisiveness; **der Entschluß, ⸚e** decision
entschuldigen excuse
das **Entsetzen** terror, horror; **entsetzlich** terrible; **entsetzt** horrified
entspringen† (ist) arise, originate
entstehen† (ist) arise
entstellen distort, disfigure
(sich) **entwickeln** develop
sich **entwinden†** struggle out of
entwischen (ist) escape
sich **entziehen†** evade, refuse
entzünden inflame
er he; it
das **Erbarmen** pity
erbauen build; edify; **erbaulich** edifying
das **Erbe** inheritance
erbeben tremble, vibrate
erben inherit
die **Erbitterung** bitter spitefulness, anger; embitterment
erblicken catch sight of, see
erbrechen† break in
die **Erde, -n** earth, world; soil, ground; **das Erdgeschoß, -e** ground floor; **erdig** earthy
das **Ereignis, -se** occurrence
erfahren† discover, find out, learn; experience; **die Erfahrung, -en** experience; **der Erfahrungskreis, -e** range of experience
erfinden† invent; **der Erfinder, -** inventor; **erfinderisch** inventive; **die Erfindung, -en** invention, fancy
der **Erfolg, -e** success
erfolgen (ist) take place
erfolgreich successful
erfreuen delight, please; **erfreulich** gratifying, delightfully pleasant
erfüllen fill; fulfill
das **Ergebnis, -se** result
ergehen† (ist) happen
ergiebig profitable
erglänzen gleam
erglühen glow
ergrauen (ist) turn grey
ergreifen† seize, lay hold on
erhaben sublime, noble
erhalten† receive, get, obtain, acquire; keep, maintain, support, sustain
erheben† lift, raise; **sich erheben** rise, be lifted, get up; **(über)** transcend, exceed
erheitern amuse, cheer
erhöhen raise
sich **erholen** recover
erinnern remind (of); **sich erinnern** remember; **die Erinnerung, -en** memory
erkennen† recognize, tell
erklären explain; declare; **die Erklärung, -en** explanation; declaration
erkunden reconnoiter; **sich erkundigen** inquire
erlauben allow; **die Erlaubnis** permission
erleben experience, have the experience; live to see, survive
erlegen kill, shoot
die **Erleichterung** relief
erleiden† suffer
erlernen learn

erlösen rescue, release
ermessen† measure
ermorden murder
ermüden exhaust, tire
ermuntern encourage
ernst serious
die **Ernte, -n** harvest
erraten† guess, surmise correctly
erregen arouse, excite
erreichen reach, attain
erringen† gain, win
erröten blush
das **Ersatz'bataillon', -s** reserve (replacement) battalion
erscheinen† (ist) appear; **die Erscheinung, -en** phenomenon; appearance
erschießen† shoot (and kill)
erschlagen† slay, kill
erschöpfen exhaust
erschrecken frighten; **erschrecken**† take fright, be frightened, be alarmed; **das Erschrecken** terror; **erschreckend** frightening
erschüttern shake; shock
ersehen† see, perceive
ersetzen replace
ersichtlich obvious
erspähen catch sight of
ersparen spare, save
erst first, *etc.;* only, not until
erstarren fix, freeze in fear
das **Erstaunen** astonishment; **erstaunt** astonished
erstens first (of all)
ersterben† (ist) die, fade
ersticken choke, suffocate; muffle
ertappen catch
erteilen give, impart
ertragen† endure, bear
ertrinken† (ist) drown
erwachen (ist) awake
erwählen choose; select
erwähnen mention
sich **erwärmen** get warmed up (enthusiastic)
erwarten expect, wait for; **die Erwartung, -en** expectation
erwecken wake(n)
sich **erwehren** resist, help, avoid
erwerben† acquire, gain
erwidern reply, answer
erwischen catch
erwürgen choke
erzählen tell (a story), narrate, talk
es it; he, she
essen† eat; **das Essen, -** meal, dinner
etwa about, perhaps, say; **etwaig** possible, eventual
etwas something, somewhat, a little; some
die **Eule, -n** owl
die **Ewigkeit, -en** eternity
die **Existenz', -en** being, existence, living

fabelhaft great, fabulous
der **Faden, ⸚** thread, string
fahl sallow, sickly
die **Fahne, -n** standard, flag; streamer
die **Fahrbahn, -en** roadway; **fahren**† (ist) ride, drive, go, come, travel; **die Fahrt, -en** trip, journey; **das Fahrzeug, -e** vehicle
der **Fall, ⸚e** case; fall
die **Falle, -n** trap
fallen† (ist) fall; die (in battle)
fällen pass (sentence)
falsch wrong, false
die **Falte, -n** fold, wrinkle; **falten** fold
fangen† catch, capture
die **Farbe, -n** color; **die Färbung** color(ation)
fassen take (lay) hold of, seize, hold, reach; apprehend, comprehend; contain; **sich fassen** control oneself, take hold of oneself
fast almost
faul lazy; **das Faultier** lazybones
die **Faust, ⸚e** fist
die **Feder, -n** feather
fegen sweep
fehlen lack, miss, be lacking, be missing, not have; be wrong; **der Fehler, -** mistake; **fehl-gehen**† go wrong, lose one's way
die Feier, -n ceremony; **feiern** celebrate; **feiertäglich** festive
fein refined, fine, elegant, excellent
der **Feind, -e** enemy; **feindlich** hostile; **feindselig** hostile
feingebaut finely formed
das **Feld, -er** field; **die Feldnacht, ⸚e** night in the field; **der Feldweg, -e** path through the field
der **Fels, -en, -en** (rock) cliff; **die Felsbarrie're, -n** rock barrier; **der Felstritt, -e** step in the rock; **die Felstrümmer** (*pl.*) fragments of rock; **der Felsvorsprung, ⸚e** projecting rock; **die Felswand, ⸚e** rock wall, rock face
das **Fenster, -** window; **der Fensterbord, -e** window sill; **das Fensterkreuz, -e** cross-bars of a casement window, casement; **die Fensterscheibe, -n** window pane
die **Ferien** (*pl.*) vacation; **das Ferienhäuschen, -** vacation cottage
fern far, remote, distant; **die Ferne, -n** distance, distant parts; **in der Ferne** far away
fertig finished, through, ready
fest (*as verb prefix*) fast

das **Fest, -e** festival, feast, fête, banquet, celebration
fest solid, firm, fast, fixed; **die Festigkeit** firmness
der **Festzug, ⸚e** festive procession
fett fat
feucht damp
das **Feuer, -** fire, firing
fiebern be feverish
die **Figur′, -en** figure, build
finden† find; **der Finder, -** finder
der **Finger, -** finger; **das Fingerbein, -e** leg thin as a finger; **die Fingerspitze, -n** finger tip
finster dark, somber; **die Finsternis** darkness
die **Fläche, -n** surface
flackern flicker
die **Flagge, -n** flag
die **Flamme, -n** flame; **flammen** flame
die **Flasche, -n** bottle
flattern flutter
der **Fleck, -e** spot
flehen implore, plead
das **Fleisch** meat
der **Fleiß** diligence; **fleißig** industrious; carefully, well
flicken patch, repair
fliegen† (ist) fly; **fliegend** momentary, fleeting
fliehen† (ist) flee
die **Flinte, -n** gun
der **Fluch, ⸚e** curse; **fluchen** curse
flüchten (ist) flee; **der Fluchtversuch, -e** attempt at escape
der **Flug, ⸚e** flight; **der Flügel, -** wing
der **Flur, -e** entryway, hall
der **Fluß, ⸚e** river
flüstern whisper
fluten flood, flow
die **Folge, -n** consequence, result; **folgen** (ist) follow
fördern advance, further, bring ahead
die **Form, -en** form, shape; **formen** (take) shape; **die Förmlichkeit, -en** formality
forschen investigate, inquire, do research
der **Forst, -e** or **⸚e** forest; **der Förster, -** forester; **das Forst′personal′, -e** forest personnel
fort (*as verb prefix*) away; on
fort away, gone, on
fort-fahren† (ist) continue
das **Fortkommen** advancement, progress
der **Fortschritt, -e** progress
fort-setzen continue
fortwährend continually
die **Frage, -n** question; **fragen** ask, question
(das) **Frankreich** France; **der Franzo′se, -n, -n** Frenchman
die **Frau, -en** woman, lady, wife; **das Frauenauge, -n** woman's eye; **frauenhaft** feminine, like a woman; **das Frauenherz, -ens, -en** woman's heart; **das Fräulein, -** young lady, Miss
frech fresh, impudent
frei free, vacant; **der Freibeuter, -** freebooter, brigand; **die Freiheit, -en** freedom; **der Freiherr, -n, -en** baron; **frei-legen** lay bare; **freilich** truly, to be sure; **der Freiwillige, -n, -n** volunteer
fremd strange, foreign; **fremdartig** foreign-looking, strange; **die Fremde** foreign land(s); **der Fremde, -n, -n** stranger
fressen† eat; **sich fressen**† eat one's way
die **Freude, -n** joy, pleasure; **der Freudenschrei, -e** cry of joy; **der Freudentag, -e** happy day; **die Freudenträne, -n** tear of joy; **freudig** joyful; **freudlos** joyless; **freuen** please; **sich freuen** be happy
der **Freund, -e** friend; **die Freundin, -nen** (girl) friend; **freundlich** friendly; **die Freundlichkeit** friendliness; **die Freundschaft, -en** friendship; **freundschaftlich** friendly, intimate
der **Friede, -ns, -n** peace
frieren† freeze, be cold
frisch fresh; **frischgeweißt** freshly whitewashed
der **Friseur′, -e** barber; **die Frisur′, -en** hair-do
froh happy, glad; **fröhlich** happy
fromm pious; honest; excellent, good, kindly
die **Frucht, ⸚e** fruit
früh early; **früher** earlier, former, sooner, before, before that; **das Frühjahr, -e** spring; **das Frühlingswetter** spring weather; **das Frühstück, -e** breakfast; **frühstücken** have breakfast; **das Frühstücksgeschirr, -e** breakfast things (or dishes); **der Frühstückstisch, -e** breakfast table; **frühzeitig** early, premature
der **Fuchs, ⸚e** fox
fühlen feel
führen lead, conduct, take, carry, direct
füllen fill
der **Fund, -e** find, discovery
funkeln sparkle, flash
für for, *etc.*
die **Furche, -n** furrow, line, crease
die **Furcht** fear; **furchtbar** fearful, awful; **fürchten** fear; **fürchterlich** frightful; **furchtlos** fearless; **furchtsam** timid
der **Fürst, -en, -en** prince
der **Fuß, ⸚e** foot; (der) **Fußball** soccer; **der Fußballplatz, ⸚e** soccer field; **der Fußboden, ⸚** floor; **das Fußende, -n** foot; **der Fußgänger, -** pedestrian; **die Fußspitze, -n** tip of one's toe; **der Fußsteig, -e** footpath; **der Fußtritt, -e** kick
das **Futter** feed; **füttern** feed
der **Gang, ⸚e** walk, trip; hall, corridor; way of walking

ganz whole, entire, complete; quite, very; **gänzlich** entire
gar very, quite; (*before negative*) . . . at all; **gar zu gerne** all too gladly
der **Garten, ¨** garden; **der Gärtner, -** gardener
der **Gasarm, -e** bracket of a gas light
die **Gasse, -n** street
der **Gast, ¨e** guest; **das Gasthaus, ¨er** inn; **die Gaststube, -n** main room, public room (of an inn)
die **Gebärde, -n** gesture; bearing; **sich gebärden** act, behave, carry on
das **Gebäude, -** building
das **Gebein, -e** bones
geben† give; **es gibt,** *etc.* there is, there are, *etc.*
das **Gebet, -e** prayer
gebieten† command; rule
der **Gebrauch** use
(sich) **gebühren** be fitting, be proper for, be the proper one for
der **Geburtstag, -e** birthday
das **Gedächtnis, -se** memory; **ins Gedächtnis rufen†** remind of
der **Gedanke, -ns, -n** thought, idea; **die Gedankenarbeit** mental activity; **gedankenlos** thoughtless, without thinking
gedenken† remember; mention
das **Gedicht, -e** poem
geduldig patient
geeignet suited, qualified
gefährlich dangerous
gefallen† please; like
das **Geflügel** birds
das **Gefühl, -e** feeling(s), emotion
gegen against, toward, *etc.;* about
die **Gegend, -en** region
der **Gegenruf, -e** answer; **der Gegensatz, ¨e** contrast; **die Gegenseite, -n** opposite side; **gegenseitig** mutual
der **Gegenstand, ¨e** object
gegenü'ber opposite, across from (*also verb prefix*); in relation to; **das Gegenü'ber** person across the table, vis-à-vis
die **Gegenwart** presence; present
der **Gegner, -** opponent
geheimnisvoll mysterious
gehen† (ist) go; walk; work
das **Geheul** howl(ing)
das **Gehirn, -e** brain
das **Gehöft, -e** farm
das **Gehör** hearing
gehorchen obey
gehören belong
das **Gehörn** horns
der **Geist, -er** spirit, mind, intellect; **der Geistliche, -n, -n** clergyman
das **Gelächter** laughter
das **Gelände** terrain, area
das **Geländer, -** parapet, balustrade, railing
gelangen (ist) get; arrive
gelb yellow
das **Geld, -er** money
gelegen situated
die **Gelegenheit, -en** opportunity
gelehrt learned; **der Gelehrte, -n, -n** scholar
geleiten accompany
das **Gelenk, -e** joint
die **Geliebte, -n, -n** beloved, sweetheart
gelingen† (ist) succeed
gelten† be worth; be a matter (or question) of, be (well) thought of, be accepted, pass for
gemächlich comfortable
der **Gemahl, -e** husband; **die Gemahlin, -nen** wife
die **Gemeinde, -n** community, congregation; **gemeinsam** (in) common
genau exact, right
genesen† (ist) recover
genug enough; **genügen** suffice, be enough
gerade just (then), precisely; straight, direct; **geradezu'** positively, absolutely
geraten† (ist) fall, get (into a state of . . .)
das **Geräusch, -e** sound, noise
das **Gerede** idle talk
gereichen redound to, contribute to, conduce to
das **Gericht, -e** court; **gerichtlich** court
gering slight, insignificant; **geringschätzig** disdainful
gern(e) gladly, like to . . . ; **gern haben†** like
das **Geröll(e)** rubble; boulders; **das Geröllband, ¨er** pebble-covered strip; **das Geröllfeld, -er** field strewn with boulders
der **Geruch, ¨e** smell
das **Gerücht, -e** rumor
das **Gesamtwerk** complete works
der **Gesang, ¨e** song
das **Geschäft, -e** business; store; business deal; **geschäftlich** business; **der Geschäftsmann, Geschäftsleute** business man; **die Geschäftsreise, -n** business trip; **der Geschäftszweig, -e** branch (of business)
geschehen† (ist) happen
das **Geschenk, -e** gift
die **Geschichte, -n** story; affair; history
geschickt clever, skillful
das **Geschlecht, -er** race, generation
das **Geschöpf, -e** creature
das **Geschoß, ¨e** shot, bullet
das **Geschrei** shouting

geschwätzig garrulous
geschwind quick, fast, swift
der **Geselle, -n, -n** fellow; **die Gesellschaft, -en** company; party; society; **gesellschaftlich** social
das **Gesetz, -e** law
das **Gesicht, -er** face
gespannt tense, taut
das **Gespräch, -e** conversation
die **Gestalt, -en** figure, form, shape, stature; **sich gestalten** take form
die **Geste, -n** gesture
gestehen† confess
das **Gestein** rock
gestern, das Gestern yesterday; **gestrig** yesterday's
gesund healthy, well, sound; **gesunden** (ist) recover; **die Gesundheit** health
das **Getöse** roaring
das **Getränk, -e** drink
gewachsen (*participle*) equal to, "up to"
gewagt daring
gewahren perceive
die **Gewalt, -en** force; **gewaltig** mighty, powerful; **gewaltsam** violent, forcible, fierce
das **Gewehr, -e** gun
gewinnen† win
gewiß certain, sure; **gewißlich** surely
das **Gewitter, -** storm
sich **gewöhnen (an)** get used to; **gewöhnlich** usual, ordinary; **gewohnt** used to
gewunden curving
das **Gezweig** branches
gezwungen constrained, forced
gierig greedy, rapacious
giftig poisonous, venomous
der **Glanz** luster, splendor, light, radiance; **glänzen** gleam, shine
das **Glas, ⸚er** glass; **glasig** glassy
glatt smooth, slick
der **Glaube, -ns, -n** belief, faith; **glauben** believe, think
gleich (*prep.*) like; (*adv.*) immediately, right away, *etc.;* (*adj.*) equal, same; **gleichen**† resemble; **das Gleichgewicht** equilibrium; **gleichgültig** indifferent, inconsequential; **gleichmütig** calm; **das Gleichnis, -se** parable; **gleichsam** so to speak, as it were; **gleichwohl** nonetheless; **gleichzeitig** simultaneous, at the same time
gleiten† (ist) glide, slide
das **Glied, -er** limb
glimmen† glow
die **Glocke, -n** bell; **das Glöckchen, -** little bell
das **Glück** happiness, luck, good fortune; **Glück haben** be lucky, be happy; **glücken** succeed; **glücklich** happy, fortunate, lucky, safe; **glücklicherweise** fortunately; **glückselig** happy, blissful
glühen glow; burn; **die Glut, -en** heat, glow
gnädig gracious
goldfarben golden; **die Goldschmiedin, -nen** (woman) goldsmith, jewelry maker
gönnerhaft magnanimous
gotisch Gothic
der **Gott, ⸚er** god, God; **gotteslästerlich** blasphemous; **göttlich** divine
das **Grab, ⸚er** grave
der **Grad, -e** degree, extent
der **Graf, -en, -en** count; **die Gräfin, -nen** countess; **gräflich** count's
grämlich morose, gloomy
grandios' great, tremendous
grasen graze; **der Grashang, ⸚e** grassy slope; **graskalt** grassy cool; **der Grasweg, -e** grassy path
gräßlich horrible, terrible, dreadful
grau grey; **gräulich** greyish
grausam cruel
greifen† reach, grab, seize
die **Grenze, -n** boundary, bound, limit; **grenzen** border
der **Griff, -e** grasp; hand-hold
die **Grille, -n** cricket
grimm(ig) fierce, bitter
grinsen grin
grob coarse, brusque, rude
der **Groschen, -** "farthing"; (*Bible:*) piece of silver, silver coin
groß large, great, big; tall; **die Großmutter, ⸚** grandmother
die **Grube, -n** cave, hole, pit
grummeln rumble, grumble
grün green
der **Grund, ⸚e** ground; bottom; soil; reason, cause; **das Grundstück, -e** piece of property; **die Grundlage, -n** foundation
die **Gruppe, -n** group
grüßen greet; **grußlos** without a word (of greeting)
günstig favorable
gut good, well, nice; **gutgemeint** well meant; **gutheißen**† approve; **gut-machen** make amends, make up for
der **Güterwagen, -** freight car

das **Haar, -e** hair
haben† have
hageln hail
hager gaunt
der **Hahn, ⸚e** cock, rooster

halb half; **halbgeschlossen** half-closed; **die Hälfte, -n** half
der **Hals, ⸚e** neck, throat; **Halsschmerzen** (*pl.*) sore throat
halten† hold; stick; stay, stop; keep; consider; **sich halten†** keep; attach oneself; hold up; **haltlos** unsteady, irresolute; **die Haltung** bearing, manner, attitude, posture
der **Handel, ⸚** deal, transaction, business; **handeln** act; bargain
handhaben execute, manage; **die Handhabung** administration; execution
die **Handlung, -en** action
der **Hang, ⸚e** slope; cliff; **hangabwärts** down the slope
hängen† hang, be attached
harren wait (for), await
hart hard, harsh, severe; hardboiled
der **Hase, -n, -n** rabbit, hare
der **Haß** hatred; **hassen** hate; **häßlich** ugly
die **Hast** haste; **hastig** rapid, hasty
hauchen breathe
hauen† chop
der **Haufen, -** heap, pile; mob; troop; group; **häufig** frequent
das **Haupt, ⸚er** head; **der Hauptmann, Hauptleute** captain; **die Hauptstadt, ⸚e** capital, big city; **die Hauptstraße, -n** highway
das **Haus, ⸚er** house; **das Häuschen, -** little house, cottage; **der Haushalt** household, housekeeping; **der Häusler, -** cottager, settler; **die Haustür, -en** house door, front door
die **Haut, ⸚e** skin; **die Hautfarbe, -n** complexion
heben† lift, raise
das **Heer, -e** army
heftig violent
heil whole, unhurt; **das Heil** welfare, good, salvation; **heilen** heal, cure
heilig holy; (*with name*) Saint . . . ; **der Heilige, -n, -n** saint
die **Heilung** healing, recovery
heim (*as verb prefix*) home
das **Heim, -e** home, dwelling; **die Heimat** home (-land); **das Heimatschlößchen, -** little home castle, own little castle; **die Heimatstadt, ⸚e** home town
heimlich secret
heimtückisch treacherous
heimwärts homeward; **der Heimweg, -e** way (walk) home; **Heimweh haben†** be homesick
die **Heirat, -en** marriage; **heiraten** marry
heiser hoarse
heiß hot, warm, ardent, fiery
heißen† be called, be named; command; mean; be said
heiter cheerful, happy
der **Heizer, -** stoker, fireman
der **Held, -en, -en** hero; **die Heldengedenkfeier, -n** memorial service for war heroes
helfen† help; **der Helfer, -** helper, assistant
hell bright, piercing; **hellgrün** bright green; **hellrot** bright red
der **Helm, -e** helm(et); **helmlos** helmetless; **die Helmzierde, -n** helmet decoration
das **Hemd, -en** shirt; **der Hemdsärmel, -** shirtsleeve
der **Henker, -** executioner, hangman
her ago; here; *often untranslated*
her (*as verb prefix*) here, up
herab′ down(ward)
herab′ (*as verb prefix*) down
herab′lassend condescending
heran′ (*as verb prefix*) up, near, close
sich **heran′-machen** accost, make advances to
herauf′ (*as verb prefix and adverb*) up
heraus′ (*as verb prefix and adverb*) out
heraus′-bringen† bring (or take) out; work out, figure out; bring forth
herbei′ (*as verb prefix*) up, near
herbei′-führen bring about
der **Herbst, -e** autumn; **der Herbsttag, -e** autumn day
herein′ (*as verb prefix*) in
her-geben† give out, hand over
her-laufen† (ist) **hinter** run after
sich **her-machen über** fall upon
der **Herr, -n, -en** gentleman, man, lord, Lord, master, Mr.; **die Herrenfrau, -en** noble lady; **herrenlos** without a master; **der Herrgott** Lord God, the Almighty; **herrisch** imperious
herrlich splendid, glorious; **die Herrlichkeit, -en** splendor
herrschen prevail
herü′ber (*as verb prefix*) over, across
herum′ (*as verb prefix and adverb*) around
herun′ter (*as verb prefix and adverb*) down
herun′ter-kommen† (ist) decline, become run down
hervor′ (*as verb prefix*) out, forth
hervor′-sehen† protrude
hervor′-stehen† protrude
das **Herz, -ens, -en** heart; **herzklopfend** palpitating; **herzlich** hearty, sincere
herzu′ (*as verb prefix*) up
das **Heu** hay
heulen howl; whimper
heute today; **heute abend** this evening; **heute nacht** tonight; **heutig** of today
die **Hexe, -n** witch; **der Hexenmeister, -** sorcerer
hie = **hier** here

hierauf′ hereupon
hierbei′ in this case, in doing this
hierher′ (*as verb prefix and adverb*) here, to this place
hierin′nen inside here
die **Hilfe** help; **hilflos** helpless
der **Himmel, -** heaven, sky; **die Himmelsgabe, -n** gift of Heaven; **die Himmelsrichtungen** (*pl.*) north, south, east, and west; **himmlisch** heavenly
hin (over) there; *often untranslated;* **hin und her** back and forth; **hin und wieder** now and again
hin (*as verb prefix*) up, up to, out to, to, there, along, over
hinab′ (*as verb prefix and adverb*) down
hinauf′ (*as verb prefix and adverb*) up
hinaus′ (*as verb prefix and adverb*) out
sich **hinaus′-werfen**† unfurl
das **Hindernis, -se** obstacle
hin-deuten hint at, point to
hindurch′ through(out)
hindurch′ (*as verb prefix*) through
hinein′ (*as verb prefix*) in; **in . . . hinein′** into
hinein′-bringen† bring in, involve
hinein′-fügen insert
hinein′-ragen tower, rise
die **Hingebung** devotion
hin-gehen† (ist) pass, be spent
sich **hin-halten**† hold itself out
hin-jagen (ist) drive, rush
hinlänglich sufficient
sich **hin-legen** lie down
hin-nehmen† take
hin-reichen reach
hin-reißen† draw (or attract) powerfully, carry away
hin-schreiben† write down
sich **hin-setzen** sit down, take one's seat
hin-stiefeln march along
hin-stürzen (ist) fall over (or down)
hinten behind, (at the) back; **hinter** behind, beyond, *etc.;* **hinter . . . her** after; **hinteran′** along behind; **der Hintere, -n, -n** posterior, rear end; **der Hinterfuß, ⸗e** hind foot; **der Hinterhalt** ambush; **hinterher′** (*as verb prefix and adverb*) behind, along behind; after(ward); **der Hinterhuf, -e** rear hoof; **der Hinterlader, -** breechloader
hinterlas′sen† leave (behind), bequeath
das **Hinterzimmer, -** back room
hinü′ber (*as verb prefix*) over
hinun′ter (*as verb prefix and adverb*) down
hinweg′ (*as verb prefix*) off; away
hin-ziehen† attract; **sich hin-ziehen**† extend
hinzu′-fügen add
das **Hirn, -e** brain
der **Hirsch, -e** stag, deer

hoch high, tall; advanced
hoch (*as verb prefix*) up, up high; **hochberühmt** very famous; **hoch-fahren**† (ist) start; wake up suddenly; **das Hochgefühl, -e** exhilaration; **hochgelegen** (situated) high up; **der Hochmut** haughtiness; **hochragend** towering, high; **die Hochschule, -n** university, institute; **hochschwingen**† swing high in the air
höchstens at most, at best
hoch-wachsen† (ist) show up, rise up
die **Hochzeit, -en** wedding
hocken squat
der **Hof, ⸗e** yard, court, farm
hoffen hope; **die Hoffnung, -en** hope; **hoffnungslos** hopeless; **hoffnungsvoll** hopeful
die **Höflichkeit** courtesy; **der Hofraum, ⸗e** yard
die **Höhe, -n** height(s); **in der Höhe** above, up high
hohl hollow; **die Höhle, -n** cave, cavern; socket
der **Hohn** mockery, derision; **höhnen** mock, make fun of; **höhnisch** mocking, scornful; **das Hohngeheul** howl (roar) of scorn
hold sweet, lovely, gracious
holen get, fetch, take, bring, draw
die **Hölle, -n** hell
das **Holz, ⸗er** wood; **der Holzbau, -ten** wood structure; **der Holzknecht, -e** woodsman, lumberjack; **der Holzpfeiler, -** wooden pillar; **der Holzplatz, ⸗e** timber clearing; **der Holzschläger, -** woodcutter; **die Holztreppe, -n** wooden stair
horchen listen
hören hear, listen; **das Hörensagen** hearsay
der **Hornruf, -e** bugle call
die **Hose, -n** trousers, pants
hübsch pretty, handsome
der **Huf, -e** hoof; **der Hufschlag, ⸗e** hoofbeat
die **Hüfte, -n** hip
der **Hügel, -** hill
hüllen envelop
der **Hund, -e** dog, hound; **das Hündchen, -** little dog; **das Hundegebell** barking of dogs; **der Hundetraum, ⸗e** dog's dream
Hunger haben† be hungry; **hungrig** hungry
hupen honk
der **Hut, ⸗e** hat
der **Hüter, -** guardian
die **Hütte, -n** hut; shack; **die Hüttentür, -en** hut door

ich I
ihr you
ihrerseits for her part
immer always, ever; **immer besser,** *etc.* better and better, *etc.;* **immerfort** continually; **immerhin′**

in any event; **immer noch** still; **immerwährend** perpetual; **immerzu′** continually, all the time
imstan′de sein† (ist) be capable of
in in, at, *etc.*
indem′ as, while; by . . . -ing
indes′ while
indes′sen while; meanwhile
infam′ unspeakable, infamous
das **Innere** interior, inside(s), inner being; **innerlich** inwardly; **innig** deep, inward, fervent
insofern′ in so far, to the extent . . .
inwendig inward
inzwi′schen meanwhile
irdisch earthly
irgend any; **irgendein, irgendwelch-** some, any; **irgendwie** somehow; **irgendwo** somewhere (or other)
sich **irren** make a mistake, be mistaken; **irrsinnig** insane
der **Italie′ner, -**; **die Italie′nerin, -nen** Italian; **italie′nisch** Italian

ja yes; indeed, after all, *etc.*
die **Jacke, -n** coat, jacket
die **Jagdgeschichte, -n** hunting story; **der Jagdhund, -e** hunting dog; **die Jagdtasche, -n** game bag; **jagen** hunt, chase; drive, rush, dash; **der Jäger, -** hunter; **das Jägerhaus, ⸚er** (ranger's) lodge; **die Jägerin, -nen** huntress, woman hunter; **der Jägerrock, ⸚e** hunter's coat; **der Jägersmann, ⸚er** huntsman
jäh sudden
das **Jahr, -e** year; **das Jahrhun′dert, -e** century; **das Jahrzehnt′, -e** decade
die **Jalousie′, -n** ($j = \check{z}$) jalousie (window), louvered window blind
jammern wail
jauchzen rejoice
jawohl′ yes indeed
je ever; each; **je . . . je . . .** the . . . the . . . ; **je nachdem′** according as, according to how
jedenfalls in any case; **jeder** every, each; **jedermann** everyone, anybody, *etc.*; **jederzeit** at all times; **jedesmal** every time
jedoch′ however
jemals ever; **jemand** someone, anyone, *etc.*
jener that (one); the former; he; **jenseits** beyond, across
jetzt now
das **Joch, -e** yoke; ridge
die **Johan′nisbeere, -n** currant; **der Johan′nisbeerstrauch, ⸚er** currant bush
der **Jubel** rejoicing, jubilation
die **Jugend** youth; **der Jugendfreund, -e** childhood friend; **das Jugendjahr, -e** year of youth; **jung** young; **der Junge, -n, -n(s)** boy; **die Jungfrau, -en** maid(en); Virgin (Mary); **jungfräulich** maidenly
der **Junimorgen, -** June morning
just just (then)

das **Kabriolett′, -e** convertible
der **Kahn, ⸚e** boat
der **Kaiser, -** emperor
kalt cold
die **Kammer, -n** room
der **Kampf, ⸚e** battle, fight, struggle; **kämpfen** fight, dispute; **die Kampfhandlungen** (*pl.*) hostilities; **die Kampfweise, -n** manner of fighting
die **Kano′ne, -n** cannon, gun
kaputt′ machen break, ruin
kärglich scanty
die **Karte, -n** card
die **Kartof′fel, -n** potato
der **Käse** cheese
die **Kasta′nie, -n** chestnut
der **Kasten, - (⸚)** box; **das Kästchen, -** (jewel) box
die **Katze, -n** cat
kauen chew, munch
sich **kauern** cower together, huddle together
der **Kauf, ⸚e** purchase; **kaufen** buy; **der Kaufmann, Kaufleute** merchant
kaum scarcely, hardly, barely
die **Kehle, -n** throat
kehren (ist) turn, return
kehren sweep
kein no, not a; **keiner** none; **keineswegs** by no means, not at all
der **Keller, -** cellar
kennen† know, be familiar with; **kennen-lernen** get acquainted with, learn (or come) to know
der **Kerl, -e** fellow
die **Kette, -n** chain
keuchen pant, puff, gasp
kichern giggle, chuckle
der **Kiesel, -** ; **das Kieselstein, -e** pebble
das **Kind, -er** child; **das Kinderjahr, -e** childhood year; **das Kinderlied, -er** children's song; **der Kindertag, -e** childhood day; **die Kindesbeine** (*pl.*) childhood; **kindisch** childish; **kindlich** childlike; **das Kindsein** being a child
das **Kinn, -e** chin
das **Kirchlein, -** little church; **kirchlich** churchly, religious
der **Kittel, -** tunic, jacket, lab coat
die **Klage, -n** complaint, lament; **der Klagelaut, -e** mournful sound; **klagen** mourn; complain, lament; **kläglich** wretched
sich **klammern** cling fast

der **Klang, ¨e** sound
klar clear; **die Klarheit** clearness, clarity
die **Klasse, -n** class; grade
klatschen clap
das **Klavier′, -e** piano; **der Klavier′unterricht** piano lessons
das **Kleid, -er** dress, clothes, garment; **kleiden** dress; **die Kleidung** clothing, dress
klein small, *etc.;* **die Kleinigkeit, -en** trifle, trivial matter
das **Kleinod, -e (-ien)** treasure, jewel, gem
klettern climb, clamber; **die Kletterrose, -n** climbing rose
die **Klinge, -n** blade
die **Klingel, -n** bell; **klingeln** ring
klingen† sound
die **Klippe, -n** cliff
klirren clatter, jangle
klopfen clap, pat; beat; knock
klug intelligent, smart
der **Klumpen, -** lump; **klumpig** club-like, leaden
der **Knabe, -n, -n** boy, lad; **die Knabenzeit, -en** boyhood days
knacken crack
der **Knall, -e (¨e)** clap, detonation; **knallen** go off, fire, explode; shoot
knarren creak, crackle
das **Knie, -e** *or* **Kni′e** knee; **knie(e)n** kneel
der **Knochen, -** bone; **der Knochengriff, -e** bone handle
der **Knopf, ¨e** button
knurren growl
kochen cook
komisch funny
kommandie′ren order, command; **das Komman′-do, -s** order
kommen† (ist) come; go, get
die **Kommo′de, -n** chest of drawers
der **Kompli′ze, -n, -n** accomplice
der **König, -e** king; **die Königin, -nen** queen; **königlich** kingly, regal
können† be able, *etc.*
der **Kopf, ¨e** head; **das Kopfkissen, -** pillow; **die Kopfschmerzen** (*pl.*) headache
der **Korb, ¨e** basket; refusal, turn-down
das **Korn, ¨er** grain
der **Körper, -** body
das **Korrespondenz′verhältnis, -se** epistolary (or correspondence) relationship
kosten cost
die **Kraft, ¨e** power, strength, vigor; **kräftig** strong, vigorous
der **Kragen, -** collar
krank sick; **kränken** hurt, annoy, offend; **die Krankheit, -en** disease; **die Kränkung** hurting
der **Kranz, ¨e** wreath, chain of flowers
kratzen scratch, make a scratching or scraping sound; **kratzend** scratchy, harsh; **der Kratzer, -** scratch
das **Kraut, ¨er** herb
der **Kreis, -e** circle
das **Kreuz, -e** cross; club (in cards); **kreuzen** cross
kriechen† (ist) crawl, creep
der **Krieg, -e** war
kriegen get, catch
die **Kriegsfahrt, -en** expedition; **die Kriegsjahre** (*pl.*) war years
die **Krone, -n** crown
die **Krücke, -n** crutch
die **Krume, -n** crumb
krumm bent
die **Küche, -n** kitchen
kucken (= gucken) look
die **Kugel, -n** bullet
die **Kuh, ¨e** cow; **der Kuhgeruch, ¨e** cow smell; **der Kühweg, -e** cow path
kühl cool; **die Kühle** coolness
kühn bold
der **Kummer** grief, pain; **kümmern** bother, concern; care
kund-tun† display, reveal; **kund werden**† be made known
künftig future
die **Kunst, ¨e** art; skill; **der Künstler, -** artist; **künstlich** artful, skillful; **das Kunststück, -e** (great) trick
das **Kupfer** copper
das **Kurio′sum, -a** curious thing
kurz short, brief; in short
der **Kuß, ¨e** kiss; **küssen** kiss

lächeln smile; **lachen** laugh; **lächerlich** ridiculous
der **Laden, -** store, shop
laden load
das **Lager, -** bed
lahm lame; **lähmen** paralyze, cripple
die **Lampe, -n** lamp; **das Lämpchen, -** little lamp
der **Landarzt, ¨e** country doctor; **die Landschaft, -en** landscape, part of the country; **der Landsmann, Landsleute** compatriot, countryman; **die Landstraße, -n** highway
lang long; tall; along, the length of . . . (= **entlang); lange** long, (for) a long time; **langgestreckt** long, elongated, extended; **längs** along
langsam slow; **die Langsamkeit** slowness, deliberateness
längst long ago, long since
die **Lanze, -n** lance
der **Lärm** racket, noise; **lärmen** come up noisily, roar

lassen† let, leave, allow, cause, have, make; stop; **läßt sich,** *etc.*, can be, is to be
lässig lazy, indolent, relaxed
der **Lastwagen, -** truck
die **Later′ne, -n** lantern, street light
das **Laub** foliage
lauern lie in wait; **lauernd** watchful, alert
der **Lauf, ⸚e** course; barrel; run(ning); **laufen**† (ist) run, walk
lauschen listen
laut (a)loud; **der Laut, -e** sound; **lautlos** without a sound, soundless
lauter nothing but; all (this); **läutern** refine, purge
das **Lazarett′, -e** (military) hospital
leben live; **das Leben, -** life; **leben′dig** living, alive; **die Lebensversicherung** life insurance; **die Lebensweise, -n** way of life; **die Lebhaftigkeit** vigor, animation; **leblos** lifeless; **die Lebzeit, -en** lifetime
lecken lick
der **Ledersack, ⸚e** leather bag
lediglich solely, entirely
leer empty; **leeren** empty
legen lay, put, place; **sich legen** lie down
der **Lehm** clay; mud
lehnen lean
lehren teach; **der Lehrer, -** teacher, instructor
der **Leib, -er** body
die **Leiche, -n** corpse
leicht easy, light, slight; **leichtfüßig** light-footed; **leichtgebaut** lightly (or flimsily) built; **leichthin′** casually; **die Leichtigkeit** ease
das **Leid** hurt, harm; sorrow; **leiden**† suffer, be passive; permit, stand (for), bear; **die Leidenschaft, -en** passion; **leider** unfortunately; **leid sein**†, **leid tun**† be sorry (for)
der **Leierkasten, -** hurdy-gurdy; **der Leierkastenmann, ⸚er** organ-grinder
leihen† lend
die **Leine, -n** leash
der **Leinenanzug, ⸚e** linen suit
leise gentle, soft, quiet
leisten accomplish, do; afford; **die Leistung, -en** accomplishment
leiten lead, guide
lenken direct, guide
lernen learn
lesen† read; gather; lecture
letzt- last; **zum letztenmal** for the last time; **letzter-** latter
leuchten gleam, flash, glow, shine
die **Leute** (*pl.*) people
licht bright; **das Licht, -er** light; **lichtblau** pale blue; **lichtgelb** pale yellow
das **Lid, -er** eyelid
lieb dear, beloved, charming, good; **lieben** love, like; **mein Lieber** my dear fellow; **lieber** preferably, rather; **lieber haben**† prefer; **liebevoll** loving, affectionate; **lieb haben**† love; **der Liebhaber, -** lover; gallant; **die Liebkosung, -en** caress, endearment, blandishment, affection; **die Lieblingsstelle, -n** favorite passage; **Liebste** darling; **am liebsten** like most of all to . . .
das **Lied, -er** song; **das Liedchen, -** little song, tune
liegen† lie, lie down, be down, be hospitalized
die **Linde, -n** linden; **die Lindenblüte, -n** linden blossoms; **der Lindengarten, ⸚** garden of linden trees
lindern allay, soothe
die **Linie, -n** line
link left; **die Linke, -n** left hand; **links** (to the) left
die **List, -en** stratagem, ruse
das **Lob** praise; **loben** praise
das **Loch, ⸚er** hole
die **Locke, -n** lock, hair
locken lure, entice
locker loose
der **Löffel, -** spoon; **das Löffelchen, -** small spoon(ful)
lohnen reward, repay
los loose; wrong; let's go
los-drücken fire, squeeze the trigger
lösen loosen, detach, break free
los-kommen† get away, get out alive; **los-lachen** burst out laughing; **sich los-machen** free oneself; **los-schreien**† burst out screaming; **los-stürzen** (ist) rush at, fall upon; **los-werden**† get rid of
der **Löwe, -n, -n** lion
die **Luft, ⸚e** air; breeze; breath
lügen† lie
der **Lump, -en, -en** scoundrel, rascal
die **Lust, ⸚e** pleasure; desire; **Lust haben**† want
lyrisch lyrical

machen make; do; go; **sich machen an** set about
die **Macht, ⸚e** power, force, might; **mächtig** mighty, powerful
das **Mädchen, -** girl; **Mädchen-** (*compounding form*) young girl's . . .
der **Magen, -** stomach
mager thin, gaunt
das **Mahl, -e** meal
mahnend admonishing, reminding
der **Mais** corn
makellos flawless
das **Mal, -e** *or* **⸚er** time; mark, monument; **-mal** . . . time(s)
mal = einmal
malen paint, draw; trace; **der Maler, -** painter

man one
manch many a, (*pl.*) some; **manchmal** sometimes, occasionally
der **Mangel, ⁼** want, lack
die **Manipulation′, -en** operation, manipulation
der **Mann, ⁼er** man; husband; **die Männerhand, ⁼e** man's hand(writing); **das Männlein, -** little man
der **Mantel, ⁼** coat, cloak, cape; **die Mantelfalte, -n** folds of a cloak *or* coat
das **Märchen, -** (fairy)tale
die **Mark, -** mark (coin, ca. 25 cents)
die **Markie′rung, -en** sign, marker(s)
marsch! march!; **sich in Marsch setzen** set out, march off; **marschie′ren** march
das **Maschi′nengewehr, -e** machine gun
das **Maß, -e** measure; **maßlos** unbounded
die **Masse, -n** mass; **das Massengrab, ⁼er** mass grave
der **Mast, -e** mast, pylon, pole
matt pale, dull
die **Matte, -n** meadow
die **Mauer, -n** wall
das **Maul, ⁼er** mouth
die **Maus, ⁼e** mouse
mehr more
mehrere several
der **Meilenstein, -e** milestone
meinen think, say, mean
meist most(ly); **am meisten** most; **meistens** mostly
meisterlich masterful
melden report, announce
die **Menge, -n** crowd, multitude, quantity
der **Mensch, -en, -en** man, human being, person; **das Menschengedränge, -** throng of people; **die Menschenwürde** human dignity; **menschlich** human
merken notice; **merkwürdig** remarkable; **die Merkwürdigkeit, -en** remarkable fact
die **Messe, -n** mass
das **Messer, -** knife; **die Messerwunde, -n** knife wound
der **Metall′griff, -e** metal handle
die **Meuterei′** mutiny; **meutern** mutiny
die **Miene, -n** expression; **das Mienenspiel** expression
die **Milch** milk; **das Milchgeschäft, -e** milk store, dairy; **die Milchstraße** Milky Way
mild(e) gentle; **die Milde** gentleness
minder less; **mindest-** least
mischen mix
mißgünstig envious
mißlin′gen† (ist) fail, be unsuccessful
mit with; along; *etc.*
mit (*as verb prefix and adverb*) along
mitleidig sympathetic
mit-reißen† sweep along
das **Mittagessen, -** lunch
die **Mitte, -n** middle, center
mit-teilen communicate, tell, explain; **die Mitteilung, -en** communication
das **Mittelstück, -e** middle part
mitten (in the) mid(dle); **mitten d(a)rin′** in the midst of them; **mittendurch′-brechen†** break in two; **mitten hinein′** into their midst; **mitten in** in the middle (midst) of
mittler- middle (part of)
mögen† like, may, should like, should, *etc.*
möglich possible; **die Möglichkeit, -en** possibility; **möglichst** as . . . as possible
der **Monat, -e** month
der **Mond, -e** moon; **mondblaß** pale as moonlight; **der Mondschein** moonlight
der **Mörder, -** murderer
morgen tomorrow; **das Morgen** tomorrow
der **Morgen, -** morning; **das Morgengrauen** light of morning; **der Morgenregen, -** morning rain; **der Morgenrock, ⁼e** housecoat; **morgens** in the morning; **die Morgensonne** morning sun
das **Motorrad, ⁼er** motorcycle
müd(e) tired
mühsam with difficulty, wearily; **mühselig** wearisome
die **Mulde, -n** hollow
der **Mund, -e** & **⁼er** mouth; **die Mundspalte, -n** opening (or corner) of the mouth; **der Mundwinkel, -** corner of the mouth
das **Munitions′schleppen** ammunition carrying
munter joyous, cheerful, gay; **die Munterkeit** good spirits
die **Münze, -n** coin, "change"
murmeln mutter, murmur
mürrisch gloomy, sullen
der **Musiker, -** musician
der (die) **Muskel, -n** muscle; **muskulös′** muscular, sinewy
müssen† have to, must, *etc.*
mustern inspect, look over; **die Musterung** inspection
der **Mut** courage, spirit
die **Mutter, ⁼** mother; **das Mutterauge, -n** mother's eye; **das Mütterchen, -** little (or dear) mother; **mütterlich** maternal, mother's
na (ja) well
nach to, toward; after; according to, *etc.*
nach (*as verb prefix*) after
der **Nachbar, -s (-n), -n; die Nachbarin, -nen** neighbor; **das Nachbarhaus, ⁼er** neighboring house
nachdem′ after

nach-denken† reflect, think, meditate; **nachdenklich** thoughtful, pensive
nach-geben† give in
der **Nachhang** afterthought
nachher′ afterward
nach-kommen† (ist) follow along, obey
nach-lassen† leave (behind); diminish, slip; **nachlässig** negligent, careless
der **Nachmittag, -e** afternoon; **die Nachmittagsstunde, -n** afternoon hour
nach-rechnen figure back
nach-schauen look to see
nach-sehen† look after, watch as one disappears
nächst next, nearest; **nächstens** soon
die **Nacht, ⸚e** night; **nächtens** at night; **das Nachtlager, -** lodging (bed, camp) for the night; **nächtlich** nocturnal, (at) night; **nachts** at night
nachträglich as an afterthought, in retrospect
der **Nacken, -** (back of the) neck
nackt naked
die **Nadel, -n** needle; pin; **das Nadelöhr, -e** eye of a needle
der **Nagel, ⸚** nail
nagen gnaw
nah(e) near, close; **die Nähe** vicinity, proximity; **nahen** (ist) approach, near
nähen sew
näher nearer, closer; better; **Näheres** details, more; **sich nähern** approach
die **Nahrung** nourishment, food
der **Name** (*or* **Namen), -ns, -n** name; **namens** by name of; **der Namensvetter, -** namesake; **der Namenszug, ⸚e** inscribed name, signature
nämlich you see, because; same, very
die **Narbe, -n** scar
die **Nase, -n** nose; **das Nasloch, ⸚er** nostril
naß wet, moist; **die Nässe** wetness, humidity
die **Natur′, -en** nature; constitution; **natür′lich** natural(ly); **die Natur′lyrik** nature poetry
ne = eine
der **Nebel, -** fog
neben beside, next to, near; along with, *etc.;* **nebenan′** alongside, next door; **nebenbei′** incidentally; **nebendran′** alongside; **nebenher′** at the same time, besides
necken tease; **neckisch** teasing
nehmen† take
der **Neid** envy; **neidisch** envious
(sich) **neigen** incline; bow, bend down; **die Neigung, -en** inclination; devotion, kind disposition
nein no
nennen† name, call
neu new, recent; **aufs neue, von neuem** anew; **neuerdings** recently; **neugeboren** newborn, newly born; **neugierig** curious; **die Neuigkeit, -en** news
nicht not; **nun einmal nicht** certainly not; **nicht mehr** no longer; **nichts** nothing; **der Nichtsnutz, -e** good-for-nothing
nicken nod
nie never
nieder low, down; inferior
nieder (*as verb prefix*) down
nieder-brechen† crash down
nieder-brennen† burn down; shoot down
nieder-drücken weigh down, depress
die **Niederlage, -n** defeat; **die Niederlande** (*pl.*) Netherlands, Low Countries
nieder-lassen† let down; sit down
nieder-schlagen† prostrate, depress
niederträchtig base, low; **niedrig** low
niemals never; **niemand** no one, nobody
nimmermehr never
nirgends nowhere
die **Nische, -n** niche, hollow spot
nisten nestle, take refuge
no = na well
noch still, yet, even, in addition, *etc.;* **noch einmal** (once) again; **noch etwas** something else; **noch immer** still; **nochmal** again
nonnenhaft nun-like
der **Nord(en)** north
die **Not, ⸚e** distress; emergency; need, urgency; **zur Not** if need be; **notdürftig** scanty, poor; **nötig** necessary; **nötigen** compel; **die Nötigung** necessity; **notwendig** necessary
nüchtern sober; empty; matter-of-fact, prosaic
die **Null, -en** zero
nun now; well; **nunmehr** now, henceforth, from this time on
nur only, just, *etc.;* **nur noch** only; from now on
nützen be of use; **nutzlos** useless

ob whether, if, to see if, I wonder if; **als ob** as if
Obacht geben† watch out, be careful
oben up, upstairs, above; **bis oben** all the way up; **wieder nach oben** back up; **obendrein′** on top of that, besides; **der Oberförster, -** Chief Forester; **der Obergefreite, -n, -n** corporal; **oberhalb** above; **die Oberin, -nen** head deaconess; **der Oberleutnant, -s** first lieutenant
obgleich′ although
die **Obrigkeit, -en** authorities, government agency
obwohl′ although
die **Öde** wasteland, emptiness
oder or
offen open; **offenbar** obvious; **die Öffentlichkeit** public; **öffnen** open
oft; öfters often

der **Oheim, -e** uncle
ohne without; **ohnehin′** anyway, in any case
das **Ohr, -en** ear; **der Ohrring, -e** earring
die **Öl- und Kornmühle, -n** oil and grain mill
das **Opfer, -** victim
der **Optiker, -** optician
ordentlich downright; properly, really
ordnen arrange, fix; **die Ordnung, -en** order
die **Orgel, -n** organ
der **Ort, ⸚er** & **-e** place, spot; **die Ortschaft, -en** locality
der **Ost(en)** east; **östlich** eastern

das **Paar, -e** pair; couple; **ein paar** a couple, a few; **ein paarmal** a few times
packen seize
das **Papier′, -e** paper
die **Partei′, -en** party; part
passen suit, fit (in); pass
die **Paßhöhe, -n** (height of the) pass
passie′ren pass, cross
die **Patro′ne, -n** cartridge
die **Patro′nin, -nen** patroness
die **Pause, -n** pause; (school) recess
die **Pein** pain, torture; **peinigen** torment; **peinvoll** painful
die **Pension′, -en** pension, boarding house, inn
perlgrau pearl-gray
das **Personal′, -e** personnel, staff
der **Perso′nenwagen, -** (railroad) coach
der **Pfad, -e** path
der **Pfarrer, -** pastor
die **Pfeife, -n** pipe
pfeifen† whistle
der **Pfeil, -e** arrow
das **Pferd, -e** horse
das **Pflaster, -** pavement; **pflastern** plaster; **der Pflasterstein, -e** paving stone
die **Pflege** care; **pflegen**(†) be accustomed to; tend, take care of; devote oneself to; carry on
die **Pflicht, -en** duty, obligation
pflügen plow
der **Pfosten, -** (door) post
die **Pfote, -n** paw
das **Pfund, -e** pound
phantasie′ren daydream
der **Photograph′, -en, -en** photographer
die **Plage, -n** trouble, bother
das **Plakat′, -e** placard, poster
der **Platz, ⸚e** place; seat; **Platz machen** get out of (make) way
plaudern chat, talk
plötzlich sudden
plündern plunder, loot
pochen knock, beat, throb
poltern beat, rumble
die **Pose, -n** stance, attitude
der **Postbote, -n, -n** mailman, postman
die **Pracht** splendor; **prächtig, prachtvoll** splendid
prallen beat, bounce, crash
der **Preis, -e** prize; price
der **Priester, -** priest
das **Privat′zimmer, -** private room
die **Probe, -n** test; **proben** test, try; **probie′ren** try, test
die **Professur′, -en** professorship
der **Prozeß′, -e** trial
prüfen test; **prüfend** searching
prügeln beat
das **Pulver, -** powder; **die Pulverkammer, -n** powder room; **der Pulvermann, ⸚er** powder man; **die Pulvermine, -n** (land) mine
der **Punkt, -e** point; **pünktlich** punctual
pur pure, sheer

die **Qual, -en** torment; **der Quälgeist, -er** tormenting (evil) spirit, demon
die **Quelle, -n** spring
quer diagonally, crosswise

die **Rache** revenge
das **Rad, ⸚er** wheel
ragen tower; extend
der **Rand, ⸚er** edge, brim, rim
rasch quick, swift
rascheln rustle
rasen rage; **rasend** furious, mad, raging
rasie′ren shave
rasseln rattle, clatter
die **Rast** rest
der **Rat** advice; consultation; counselor, *etc.*; **raten**† advise, consult; guess; **ratlos** perplexed
rätselhaft puzzling
der **Raub** booty; **rauben** steal; **der Räuber, -** robber; **der Raubschütze, -n, -n** (game) poacher
rauchen smoke
rauh rough, coarse, raw
der **Raum, ⸚e** room, space; **räumen** clear, clear away
raus = heraus
der **Rausch** intoxication, stupor
rauschen rush, rustle
rechnen calculate, count, figure
recht real, right; very; **das Recht, -e** right; **der Rechte, -n, -n** right man; **die Rechte** right hand; **rechter Hand** on the right; **rechtfertigen** justify, vindicate; **recht haben**† be right; **rechts** to the right

recken stretch
die **Rede, -n** speech, talk, conversation; **reden** speak, talk
der **Regen, -** rain; **die Regenfront, -en** rain front
regie'ren rule
reglos; regungslos motionless
reiben† rub
reich rich
das **Reich, -e** kingdom, empire, realm
reichen pass; reach, extend; suffice, be enough
der **Reichtum, ⁼er** wealth
reif ripe, mature
die **Reihe, -n** row, series
rein clean, pure, neat; **reinlich** neat
die **Reise, -n** trip, journey; **reisen** (ist) travel; **der Reisetag, -e** day of travel(ing)
reißen† tear, pull, jerk
reiten† ride; **der Reiter, -** rider, horseman; **die Reiterei', -en** cavalry; cavalcade; **der Reitersmann, -leute** horseman
reizen irritate, provoke
reizend charming
rennen† (ist) run
der **Rest, -e** rest, remnant, remains, balance
retten rescue, save; **die Rettung** rescue, salvation; **die Rettungsmöglichkeit, -en** possibility of rescue
die **Reue** regret
richten direct, point, send; judge, execute; **der Richter, -** judge
richtig correct, right; real; regular
die **Richtung, -en** direction; **(in) Richtung** in the direction of, toward
riechen† smell
der **Riese, -n, -n** giant; **riesenhaft; riesig** gigantic
rings (um) round about
die **Rinne, -n** groove, channel, rivulet; **das Rinnsal, -e** little stream, rivulet
rinnen† (ist) run, flow
die **Rippe, -n** rib
der **Ritter, -** knight
der **Rock, ⁼e** coat; skirt
die **Rolle, -n** role
rosa; rosen pink, rosy; **das Rosenblatt, ⁼er** rose petal; **rosenrot** rosy red; **rosig** pink
das **Roß, -e** horse
rot red; **rotäugig** with red-rimmed eyes; **sich röten** flush (red); **rot werden**† blush
rüber = herüber
rücken (ist) move; come
der **Rücken, -** back; **die Rückkunft** return; **rücklings** backward; **die Rückseite, -n** back (side); **die Rücksichtnahme** consideration; **rücksichtslos** merciless; **rückwärts** back(ward)
der **Ruf, -e** shout; **rufen**† call, shout, cry
die **Ruhe** rest, peace, calm, quiet; **ruhen** rest; **ruhig** still, calm, quiet, peaceful
ruhig (*adv.*) just, go right ahead and . . .
der **Ruhm** fame, glory; **rühmen** praise
sich **rühren** move; bestir oneself; **rührend** touching, moving; **die Rührung** emotion, sympathy
ruh- und rastlos restless
rum = herum
rund round; **rundherum'** around (and about); **rund'umher'** round about
der **Russe, -n, -n; russisch** Russian; **(das) Rußland** Russia
rüstig vigorous
die **Rüstung, -en** armor

der **Saal, Säle** hall
der **Säbel, -** saber
die **Sache, -n** thing, matter, affair, cause
das **Sägeblatt, ⁼er** saw blade
sagen say, tell, call
das **Salz** salt
sammeln collect, gather; muster; **sich sammeln** collect oneself
der **Samstagabend, -e** Saturday evening
samt along with
sanft soft, gentle
satt haben† be sick of
der **Sattel, ⁼** saddle
der **Satz, ⁼e** sentence; leap
sauber clean; **der Saubergewaschene, -n, -n** neat and clean one
die **Säule, -n** column
der **Saum, ⁼e** hem, border
sausen rush, roar
schäbig shabby
die **Schachtel, -n** box
schad(e) too bad; **der Schaden, ⁼** damage; **schadhaft** damaged, in disrepair
das **Schaf, -e** sheep; **der Schäferhund, -e** sheep dog; **die Schafherde, -n** herd of sheep; **die Schafwolle** sheep's wool
schaffen† do; create, make
schaffen do; finish; get; transport, take
der **Schaffner, -** conductor
das **Schälchen, -** saucer; **die Schale, -n** bowl
schälen peel
die **Scham** shame; **sich schämen** be ashamed
schänden disgrace, dishonor; **schändlich** shameful, disgraceful, scandalous
die **Schar, -en** crowd, troop, band
scharf sharp
der **Schatten, -** shadow, shade; **die Schattenwand, ⁼e** shaded (dark) wall; **die Schattie'rung, -en** shade
schaudern shudder

schauen look, see
der **Schauer, -** shudder, shiver
schaukeln swing, rock
der **Schauplatz, ¨e** scene
scheiden† part, separate, divide; divorce
scheinbar seeming; **scheinen**† shine; seem
scheitern run aground, be ruined, be finished
schelten† scold, rebuke; call one a . . .
schenken give
die **Scheu** timidity, fear; **scheu** shy
schicken send
das **Schicksal, -e** fate; **der Schicksalsschlag, ¨e** blow of fate
schieben† push, shove
schief sloping
schießen† shoot
der **Schild, -e** shield
schildern portray, depict
der **Schimmer, -** gleam, glimmer, glow; **schimmern** glimmer; shimmer
schimpfen curse, swear
der **Schirm, -e** umbrella
die **Schlacht, -en** battle; **das Schlachtfeld, -er** battlefield
der **Schlaf** sleep, sleepiness
die **Schläfe, -n** temple
schlafen† sleep; **das Schlafengehen** going to sleep, bedtime; **die Schlafkammer, -n** bedroom; **schläfrig** sleepy; **der Schlafrock, ¨e** dressing gown, robe; **schlaftrunken** drugged with sleep
der **Schlag, ¨e** blow; **schlagen**† strike, hit, beat; defeat; **sich schlagen**† fight, hit one another; **das Schlagloch, ¨er** pothole
die **Schlange, -n** snake; **schlängeln** twist, wind; **der Schlangenkopf, ¨e** serpent's head; **der Schlangenschlupf, ¨e** snake's hiding place
schlank slim
schlecht bad, poor
schleichen† (ist) creep, slink, steal
schleppen drag
schleudern hurl, toss
schließen† shut, lock; end; conclude; **schließlich** finally; after all
schlimm bad
schlingen† twist, wind; throw; gulp
das **Schloß, ¨er** castle; **das Schlößchen, -** little castle; **der Schloßturm, ¨e** castle tower
die **Schlucht, -en** gorge, abyss
schlummern slumber, sleep
der **Schlupf, ¨e** hiding place; **der Schlupfwinkel, -** hidden recess, hiding place
schlurfen (ist) shuffle
der **Schluß, ¨e** close, conclusion; **Schluß machen** finish, make an end of it; **der Schlußball, ¨e** last dance (of the season)
der **Schlüssel, -** key
schmal narrow, thin; **die Schmalseite, -n** narrow end
der **Schmerz, -es** *or* **-ens, -en** pain; **schmerzen** hurt; **schmerzlich** painful, in pain; sorrowful
der **Schmied, -e** smith
der **Schmuck** ornament, jewels; **schmücken** adorn, decorate; **schmucklos** unadorned
schmutzig dirty
schnaufen puff, pant
die **Schnauze, -n** snout, muzzle
der **Schnee** snow; **schneeweiß** snow-white
schneiden† cut; **schneidig** snappy
schnell fast, quick; **die Schnelligkeit** rapidity
der **Schnitt, -e** cut, gash
schnüffeln sniff
die **Schnur, ¨e** cord, string; **schnurgerade** straight (as a string)
der **Schnurrbart, ¨e** mustache
schon already; even; all right; anyway; *etc.*
schön beautiful; good; nice; **die Schönheit, -en** beauty
schonen spare, save, take care of
der **Schotter** broken rock, gravel
schräg diagonal, slanting
das **Schreckbild, -er** frightening image (picture); **der Schrecken, -** terror, fear, horror; **schrecklich** terrible
der **Schrei, -e** scream, shout
schreiben† write; **das Schreiben, -** letter; **der Schreibtisch, -e** desk; **das Schreibzeug, -e** writing materials, pen and paper
schreien† scream, yell, shout, cry; **der Schreier, -** crier
schreiten† (ist) stride, walk, pace
die **Schrift, -en** writing; Scripture; work
der **Schritt, -e** step, pace
schubsen shove
schüchtern shy, timid, bashful
die **Schuld, -en** fault; **schulden** owe
die **Schule, -n** school; **der Schüler, -** pupil, student; **der Schuljunge, -n, -n** schoolboy; **der Schulmeister, -** schoolmaster
die **Schulter, -n** shoulder; **das Schulterblatt, ¨er** shoulderblade
der **Schuß, ¨e** shot; **die Schußwaffe, -n** firearm
der **Schutt** rubbish, rubble; **der Schuttacker, ¨** rubble field
schütteln shake
der **Schutz** protection
der **Schütze, -n, -n** marksman
schützen protect; **der Schützling, -e** protégé(e)
schwach weak
der **Schwanz, ¨e** tail; **das Schwanzende, -n** tail end

der **Schwarm, ⸚e; schwärmen** swarm
schwarz black, dark; **schwarzeisern** iron black
schweben float, hover
schweigen† be silent, say nothing
der **Schweiß** sweat
die **Schwelle, -n** threshold
schwenken swing
schwer heavy; difficult; troublesome; **schwerlich** hardly
das **Schwert, -er** sword
der **Schwerverwundete, -n, -n** serious casualty
die **Schwester, -n** sister; nurse; **das Schwesternhaus, ⸚er** deaconess home
schwierig difficult
der **Schwindel** swindle, hoax, racket; **schwindlig** dizzy
schwinden† (ist) disappear
schwingen† swing
schwitzen sweat, perspire
schwören† swear
die **Seele, -n** soul; **der Seelenkundige, -n, -n** psychologist; **der Seelenschmerz, -es, -en** pain of soul, mental suffering
der **Segen, -** blessing, benediction; grace
sehen† see, look
sich **sehnen** (*or impersonal*) long, yearn; **die Sehnsucht** longing; **sehnsüchtig** longing
sehr very (much)
die **Seide** silk; **seiden** silk(en)
sein† (ist) be; seem
die **Seinen** (*pl.*) his own people (family, men); **seinesgleichen** of his type; **seinetwegen** on his account, because of him; **der Seinige** his
seit since, for; **seitdem′** since (then)
die **Seite, -n** side; **die Seitenmauer, -n** side wall; **der Seitensatz, ⸚e** jump to the side; **der Seitensprung, ⸚e** leap to the side; **seitlich** sidewise, at an angle
selb same; **selber** oneself, *etc.;* **selbst** oneself, *etc.;* even; **das Selbst** self; **selbstgefällig** self-satisfied
die **Seligkeit** bliss, happiness
selten seldom, rare(ly)
seltsam strange
setzen set, place, put; **sich setzen** sit down
senken lower; **senkrecht** vertical
der **Sessel, -** (arm)chair
seufzen sigh; **der Seufzer, -** sigh
sich himself, *etc.;* one another
sicher certain(ly), safe, sure(ly); **die Sicherheit** certainty, assurance; safety; **sicherlich** surely, certainly; **sichern** assure, secure; watch out
die **Sicht, -en** sight
sie she; it; they; **Sie** you
der **Sieg, -e** victory; **der Sieger, -** victor; **die Sie′gestrophä′e, -n** trophy of victory
das **Silber** silver; **das Silberglöcklein, -** little silver bell; **silbern** silver
der **Sinn, -e** sense; mind; **sinnen**† **auf** think of; **das Sinnen** thoughts, aspirations; **sinnlich** sensual; **sinnlos** senseless, foolish
der **Sitz, -e** seat; **sitzen**† sit; be
der **Skat** skat
das **Skelett′, -e** skeleton
der **Sklave, -n, -n** slave
so so, thus, as, *etc.;* (*rel.*) that, who; **sobald′** as soon as; **so daß** so that; **soe′ben** just (now); **so ein (ein so)** such a; **sofort′** immediately; **sogar′** even; **sogenannt** so-called; **sogleich′** immediately
der **Sohn, ⸚e** son
solan′g(e) as long as; **solan′ge bis** until
solch such (a); **ein solch-** such a
der **Soldat′, -en, -en** soldier
solid′ solid, substantial
sollen† shall, should; be said to; be to; *etc.*
der **Sommer, -** summer; **sommergrün** summer green; **die Sommernacht, ⸚e** summer night; **der Sommerwind, -e** summer wind
sonderbar strange; **der Sonderfall, ⸚e** exception, peculiar case
sondern but
der **Sonnabend, -e** Saturday; **die Sonne, -n** sun; **sonnig** sunny; **der Sonntag, -e** Sunday; **der Sonntagvormittag, -e** Sunday morning
sonst else, otherwise
die **Sorge, -n** worry, anxiety; **(sich) sorgen** care, worry; take care, provide; **die Sorgfalt** care; **sorgfältig** careful, meticulous; **sorgsam** careful
soviel′ so much; **soweit′** in so far as; **sowie′** as well as; **sowohl′ . . . als** as much . . . as; as well as
spähen spy, peer
der **Spalt, -e** crack, fissure
sparen save
spärlich scanty, thin
der **Spaß, ⸚e** joke; **der Spaßmacher, -** prankster, joker
spät late
der **Spaten, -** spade, entrenching tool
der **Spazier′gang, ⸚e** walk
das **Speisehaus, ⸚er** restaurant
sperren close, lock up
spiegelglatt mirror-smooth; **sich spiegeln** be mirrored
das **Spiel, -e** game, play; pattern of things; **spielen** play (a game); be going on; **spielerisch** playful
spitz sharp; **die Spitze, -n** point, tip, lead
der **Splitter, -** splinter, fragment
die **Spottlust** delight in mockery; **der Spottruf, -e** mocking shout

die **Sprache, -n** language, speech; **sprachlos** silent; **sprechen**† speak
spreizen spread out
springen† (ist) jump, leap, spring; **der Sprung, ⸚e** leap
die **Spur, -en** trace; track, trail; **spüren** notice, sense
das **Staats'exa'men, -examina** state examination (university test and degree, esp. for teachers)
das **Stachelhalsband, ⸚er** spiked collar
die **Stadt, ⸚e** city
der **Stamm, ⸚e** trunk; **der Stammbaum, ⸚e** family tree, pedigree
stammeln stammer
stammen originate, come
stampfen stomp, trudge
ständig constant
stark strong; hard; considerable; **die Stärke** strength; **stärken** strengthen, gain strength; **der Starkstrom** high tension current (wire)
starr stiff, rigid, motionless, staring; **starren** stare
statt instead of; **die Statt** place, stead; **die Stätte, -n** place, site, scene; **statt-finden**† take place
der **Staub** dust; **staubig** dusty
die **Staumauer, -n** earth dam
staunen be astonished, marvel
stecken† be
stecken stick, put, *etc.*
der **Steg, -e** path, trail
stehen† stand; be; **stehen-bleiben**† (ist) stop; remain standing
steif stiff
der **Steig, -e** footpath
steigen† (ist) climb, rise
steil steep; vertical
der **Stein, -e** stone, rock, jewel; **der Steinblock, ⸚e** block of stone, boulder; **steinern** stony; **der Steinrutsch, -e** stoneslide, avalanche
die **Stelle, -n** place, spot, position; **stellen** put, set, place; **die Stellung, -en** position
stemmen brace, plant
sterben† (ist) die
der **Stern, -e** star
stets always
der **Stiefel, -** boot
der **Stierkämpfer, -** bullfighter
still still, quiet, silent; **die Stille** silence, quiet; **im stillen** silently, to oneself; **stillschweigend** tacit
der **Stimmbruch** change (breaking) of voice; **die Stimme, -n** voice
stimmen be true, be correct, agree
die **Stimmung, -en** mood
die **Stirn(e), -(e)n** forehead, brow
der **Stock, ⸚e** cane; stick; story (of house)
stocken falter, hesitate
das **Stockwerk, -e** story (of house)
stolpern stumble
der **Stolz** pride; **stolz** proud
stopfen stuff
die **Stoppel, -n** stubble
stören disturb; **die Störung, -en** being disturbed, interruption
der **Stoß, ⸚e** blow; **stoßen**† push; put; bump; throw
die **Strafe, -n** punishment, penalty, fine; **strafen** punish; chastise, censure; **die Straf'kolonie', -n** penal colony
der **Strahl, -en** ray, beam, flash; **strahlen** beam; **die Strahlung, -en** radiation
die **Straße, -n** street; **die Straßenbahn, -en** streetcar; **der Straßengraben, ⸚** (roadside) ditch; **die Straßenjugend** street urchins
sich **sträuben** resist, struggle
die **Strecke, -n** stretch, distance; **strecken** stretch
der **Streich, -e** stroke, blow; **streicheln** stroke, pat, caress; **streichen**† stroke; smooth; (ist) rove, roam
streifen graze, touch lightly, brush, strip; (ist) rove
streiten† fight
die **Strenge** severity, strictness
der **Strich, -e** line
der **Strick, -e** rope
der **Strom, ⸚e** stream, current; **strömen** pour; infuse
der **Strumpf, ⸚e** sock
struppig shaggy, bristly, tousled
die **Stube, -n** room
das **Stück, -e** piece, part, bit
der **Studienrat, ⸚e** assistant headmaster (principal); **das Studium, -ien** study
die **Stufe, -n** stair; step
der **Stuhl, ⸚e** chair
stumm silent
die **Stunde, -n** hour; moment; lesson, class; **-stündig** of . . . hours
der **Sturm, ⸚e** storm; **die Sturmflut, -en** tidal wave; **stürmisch** stormy
stürzen throw, cast; (ist) fall; rush
stützen support, prop
suchen seek, look for, try
der **Süd(en)** south
die **Summe, -n** sum
summen hum, buzz
der **Sünder, -** sinner
die **Suppe, -n** soup; bit of food
süß sweet
die **Szene, -n** scene

der **Tabak** tobacco
der **Tadel** reproach, blame; **tadellos** faultless

die **Tafel, -n** tablet, plaque, sign
der **Tag, -e** day; **tagelang** for days; **täglich** daily
der **Takt, -e** measure, beat
das **Tal, ⸚er** valley; **zu Tal** down, valleyward
das **Tannenreis, -er** fir sprig
die **Tante, -n** aunt
der **Tanz, ⸚e** dance; **tanzen** dance
tapfer brave
die **Tasche, -n** pocket; bag, purse; **das Taschentuch, ⸚er** handkerchief
die **Tasse, -n** cup
tasten grope (one's way)
die **Tat, -en** deed, act(ion); fact; **tätig** active; **die Tätigkeit, -en** activity; **die Tatsache, -n** fact; **tatsächlich** actually, in fact
der **Tau** dew
die **Taube, -n** pigeon, dove
taugen be worth
täuschen deceive, delude; **die Täuschung, -en** illusion
der (*or* das) **Teil, -e** part, share; **zum Teil** in part; **(sich) teilen** separate; **teils** partly; **teilweise** partly
der **Teller, -** plate
das **Tempo** tempo, pace
teuer expensive, dear
der **Teufel, -** devil; **teuflisch** fiendish
tief deep; down; **die Tiefe, -n** depth(s); **der Tiefflug** low altitude flight
das **Tier, -e** animal, beast; **das Tierchen, -** little animal; **tierisch** animal(-like)
die **Tinte** ink
der **Tisch, -e** table; **der Tischnachbar, -s (-n), -n** table companion; **die Tischplatte, -n** tabletop
die **Tochter, ⸚** daughter
der **Tod** death; **todbringend** death-dealing; **todernst** deadly serious; **der Todesfall, ⸚e** death; **der To'deskandidat', -en, -en** candidate for death
toll mad, wild; **tollkühn** foolhardy
der **Ton, ⸚e** tone, sound; **tönen** tone; tint
das **Tor, -e** gate; goal
tot dead; **töten** kill; **totenfahl** deathly pale; **die Totenkammer, -n** morgue, vault; **das Totenmal, -e** memorial; **die Totenstille** deathly silence; **tot machen** kill; **tot-prügeln** beat to death; **tot-schlagen†** kill; **tot-schießen†** shoot dead; **tot-schmeißen†** strike and kill, knock dead
die **Tour, -en** trip, journey
träg(e) lazy; **die Trägheit** laziness
tragen† carry, bear; wear
der **Trampelpfad, -e** (beaten) track
die **Träne, -n** tear
die **Traube, -n** grape
die **Trauer** mourning, sorrow
der **Traum, ⸚e** dream; **träumen** dream; **träumerisch** dreamy; **das Traumwerk, -e** (fabric of) dreams
traurig sad
der **Trauring, -e** wedding ring
treffen† meet; hit; hit upon; **trefflich** excellent
treiben† drive, push; do, carry on, practice; (ist) float, drift; **das Treiben** activities; drifting
(sich) **trennen** separate
die **Treppe, -n** stair(way)
treten† kick; (ist) step, walk; come
treu loyal, faithful, true
der **Trieb, -e** impulse, drive
trinken† drink
der **Tritt, -e** step; kick
der **Triumph'gesang, ⸚e** song of triumph
trocken dry; **die Trockenheit** dryness
die **Trommel, -n** drum
der **Tropfen, -** drop
der **Trost** consolation, comfort; **trösten** console; **tröstlich** consoling, comforting; **trostlos** disconsolate, wretched
der **Trotz** defiance; **trotz** in spite of; **trotzdem** nevertheless; in spite of the fact that
trüben dim, cloud; **trübfarbig** dull-colored, gloomy
die **Trümmer** (*pl.*) ruins, remains
der **Trumpf, ⸚e** trump
trunken drunk
das **Tuch, ⸚er** cloth; shawl
die **Tugend, -en** virtue (*see Keller, note* 15); **tugendlich** virtuous
der **Tumult', -e** uprising, riot
tun† do; act; make; put; utter; have; *etc.*
die **Tür(e), -(e)n** door
türkisch Turkish
der **Turm, ⸚e** tower; **das Turmgemach, ⸚er** tower room; **die Turmstube, -n** tower room
das **Turnier', -e** tourney, tournament
tuten blow a horn, toot, whistle

übel bad; **übel-nehmen†** take amiss, take offense
üben practice
über over, above; across; about; left; *etc.*
überall' everywhere
überbie'ten† exceed, (try to) surpass
überden'ken† think over
überdies' in addition
der **Überfall, ⸚e** attack
der **Übergang, ⸚e** crossing
überglücklich in an excess of joy; **übergroß** unnaturally large
überhan'gen† project

überhaupt′ at all
überho′len pass
überhö′ren fail to hear
sich **überku′geln** roll over and over, turn somersaults
überlas′sen† leave, abandon
überle′gen consider, think over
die **Überle′genheit** superiority
die **Überle′gung, -en** reflection, thought
überman′nen overcome
übermäßig extreme, excessive; **übermenschlich** superhuman; **übermorgen** day after tomorrow; **der Übermut** wild spirits, exuberance; pride; **übernächst** next but one
überneh′men† assume
überra′schen (take by) surprise
überre′den persuade
der **Überrest, -e** remnant
überrol′len roll over, overtake
überschat′ten overshadow
überschrei′ten† step over
überse′hen† overlook
übertö′nen drown out the sound of
übertra′gen† transfer, move
überwäl′tigen subdue
überzeu′gen convince
überzie′hen† cover
übrig remaining, rest of
übrig (*as verb prefix and adverb*) over; **übrigbleiben**† (ist) remain, be left (to do); **im übrigen** for the rest; **übrigens** incidentally, besides; in other respects, however
die **Übung, -en** exercise, practice
das **Ufer, -** shore, bank
die **Uhr, -en** clock, watch; o'clock; **die Uhrkette, -n** watch chain; **die Uhrmacherin, -nen** watchmaker (*fem.*)
um around, about; upon, after; for; in order (to); *etc.*
um (*as verb prefix*) around, about
umar′men embrace, throw one's arms around
um-bringen† kill
umdrän′gen press close about, surround
um-drehen turn (over); twist
um-fallen† (ist) fall (over)
der **Umfang, ⸚e** scope; **umfan′gen**† embrace
um-färben dye (a different color)
umflat′tern flutter (flap) about, hang loosely about
umflech′ten† wind around
umge′ben† surround; **die Umge′bung, -en** environment, vicinity
um-hängen throw (hang) over one's shoulder
umher′ round about
umher′ (*as verb prefix*) around
umher′-stäuben fly about, whirl
sich **umher′-treiben**† chase (each other) around
um-kehren (ist) turn around
umkrei′sen circle (around)
um-reißen† knock over
umrin′gen surround
umsäu′men rim, surround
um-schlagen† (ist) change, shift
umschlei′chen† sneak (creep) about
umschlie′ßen† surround
die **Umschrei′bung, -en** circumlocution
um so . . . (+ *compar.*) so much the . . .
umsonst′ free (of charge); in vain
der **Umstand, ⸚e** circumstance
um-wandeln transform, turn
der **Umweg, -e** roundabout way
um . . . willen for the sake of
um-winden† tie around, bind around
um-wühlen root up, disrupt
un- (*The stress of words, especially adjectives, formed with the negative prefix may vary; the one given here is not necessarily the only possibility. Note also that the obvious negative forms of a few separately listed words are not given here; see the positive form.*)
unablässig constant, incessant; **unangenehm** unpleasant; **unaufgeräumt** not yet cleared away; **unaufhalt′sam** impetuous, not to be stopped; **unaussprech′lich** indescribable; **unaussteh′lich** intolerable; **die Unbändigkeit** unruliness, lack of restraint; **unbeachtet** unnoticed; **unbedacht** rash, thoughtless; **unbedingt′** absolute, definite; **unbekümmert** unconcerned; **unbelästigt** unmolested, unencumbered; **unbeob′achtet** unobserved; **unberührt** untouched; **unbeweglich** motionless
und and
unend′lich infinite, endless; **unentbehr′lich** indispensable; **die Unentschlossenheit** indecisiveness; **unerhört′** unheard of; **unermeß′lich** immeasurable; **unermüd′lich** untiring; **unerschüt′terlich** imperturbable; indomitable; **unerträg′lich** unbearable; **unerwartet** unexpected; **unfähig** incapable; **der Unfall, ⸚e** accident; **die Unfreude** vexation, displeasure; **die Ungeduld** impatience; **ungefähr** approximately; **ungeheuer** enormous; **ungeordnet** unsystematic; **ungern** reluctantly, not like to; **ungeschickt** awkward; **ungesichert** insecure; **ungetreu** disloyal; **ungezählt** innumerable; **unglaub′lich** incredible
unheildrohend ominous
unheimlich ominous, sinister, strange; **unhör′bar** inaudible; **unnütz** useless; **die Unordnung** disorder, disarray; **unruhig** restless; **unschlüssig** indecisive, undecided; **unschön** unpleasant; **die Unschuld** innocence; **unschuldig** innocent;

unsichtbar invisible; **unsinnig** out of one's mind, irrational; **die Untat, -en** misdeed, crime
unten down, below; downstairs
unter under, below; among; *etc.;* **unter-**. . . lower
unter (*as verb prefix*) down
unterbre'chen† interrupt; **die Unterbre'chung, -en** interruption
der **Unterge'bene, -n, -n** subordinate
unter-gehen† (ist) sink, be submerged
unterhal'ten† entertain, amuse; **sich unterhal'ten**† converse; **die Unterhal'tung, -en** conversation
unterlas'sen† neglect, fail
unterle'gen inferior; **die Unterle'genheit** inferiority
unterneh'men† undertake; take; **unterneh'mend** enterprising; **die Unterneh'mung, -en** undertaking
der **Un'teroffizier', -e** non-com(missioned officer)
die **Unterre'dung, -en** conversation
der **Unterrock, ⸚e** slip
unterschei'den† distinguish, tell the difference; **sich unterschei'den**† be different, be distinguishable
der **Untertan, -en, -en** subject
unterwegs' on the way, en route, on the road, "out"
sich **unterwer'fen**† submit; **die Unterwer'fung** subjugation
unvergäng'lich imperishable, enduring; **unvergeß'lich** unforgettable; **unvergleich'lich** incomparable; **unverhältnismäßig** excessive, disproportionate; **unverse'hens** unexpectedly; **unversehrt'** undamaged; **unverständlich** incomprehensible; **unverwandt** fixed, steadfast; **unverweilt'** forthwith, directly; **unvorstellbar** unimaginable, inconceivable; **unweit** not far from; **unwillkür'lich** involuntary; **unwirsch** cross; **unzeitig** untimely; **unzufrieden** discontented, dissatisfied; **die Unzufriedenheit** discontent
uralt ancient
der **Urlaub** leave, furlough
ursprüng'lich original
das **Urteil, -e** judgment, sentence; **urteilen** judge, pass sentence

der **Vagabund', -en, -en** tramp, vagabond; **das Vagabun'denleben** life of a vagabond, homeless existence
der **Vater, ⸚** father; **das Vaterland** fatherland; **der Vati, -s** daddy
die **Verabredung, -en** agreement, date
(sich) **verabschieden** say good-bye (to)
verachten scorn, despise; **verächtlich** contemptuous
verändern change; **die Veränderung, -en** change
die **Verantwortung** responsibility
verbergen† hide, conceal; **die Verborgenheit** seclusion
sich **verbeugen** bow
verbieten† forbid
verbinden† bind, bandage; **sich verbinden**† join, ally oneself; **die Verbindung, -en** connection, combination
verbittern embitter
der **Verbrecher, -** criminal
sich **verbreiten** spread; **sich verbreiten über** enlarge upon
verbrennen† burn (up, to the ground, to death, *etc.*)
verdächtig suspicious
verdammt damn(ed), confounded
verdauen digest
das **Verdeck, -e** top; **verdecken** conceal, cover
verdienen earn; deserve
verdoppeln double
verdrießen† annoy
verdutzt baffled, dumbfounded
verenden (ist) die
verfinstern darken
verfließen† (ist) pass
verfolgen pursue, follow; persecute
sich **verfünffachen** increase fivefold
das **Vergangene** past, what is (was) past; **die Vergangenheit** past
vergeblich (in) vain; futile
vergehen† (ist) pass
vergessen† forget
das **Vergnügen, -** pleasure
vergolden gild; **die Vergoldung** gilding
vergrößern enlarge
das **Verhältnis, -se** circumstance, condition; relationship
verharren remain
verhindern prevent
verhöhnen deride, ridicule
verhüllen veil, cover, envelop
verkaufen sell; **der Verkäufer, -** seller, salesman
der **Verkehr** association; encounter; contact; traffic; **verkehren** associate, commune
verkehrt wrong; upside down
verknoten tie, knot
verlachen make fun of, mock
verlangen demand, ask; (*impersonal*) long
verlassen† leave

der **Verlauf** course, lapse; **verlaufen**† (ist) run off, run (its course)
verlegen embarrassed, perplexed, disconcerted
verleihen† grant, assign
verlernen forget (how)
verleugnen deny
sich **verlieben** fall in love; **verliebt** in love; **die Verliebtheit** (state of) being in love
verlieren† lose
sich **verloben** become engaged; **die Verlobung, -en** engagement
verloren lost, forlorn; **verloren-gehen**† (ist) be lost; **der Verlust, -e** loss
vermeiden† avoid
vermeintlich supposed, presumed
vermindern lessen
vermögen† be able
vermuten suppose, suspect; **vermutlich** presumable; **die Vermutung, -en** supposition, conjecture
vernachlässigen neglect
vernehmen† perceive, hear
sich **verneigen** bow
vernichten destroy; crush; disappoint; **die Vernichtung** devastation
vernünftig sensible
verpassen miss
verraten† betray, reveal
verrichten do, perform
verrückt crazy
versagen deny, refuse; fail
versammeln collect, gather; **die Versammlung, -en** gathering
versäumen neglect; miss
verschattet heavily shadowed
verschieden different, various
verschließen† close
(sich) **verschlimmern** worsen
verschlingen† entwine, curl
verschlossen uncommunicative, taciturn
verschränken cross
verschütten bury (*e.g.*, in rubble)
verschweigen† conceal, keep silent
verschwimmen† (ist) become blurred
verschwinden† (ist) disappear; **verschwindend** small to the point of vanishing, minute
verschwitzt sweaty
versengen scorch
versetzen move up, displace, transfer; **die Versetzung** transfer
versichern assure; insure
versinken† (ist) sink, fall, disappear
versorgen take care of; **sich versorgen** provide for oneself
verspotten mock
versprechen† promise
verspüren feel, become aware of
die **Verständnislosigkeit** incomprehension, bafflement
verstecken hide
verstehen† understand
verstört distraught, disconcerted, bewildered, agitated; **die Verstörung** consternation
verstoßen† reject, cast aside
verstreuen scatter
verstummen (ist) fall (be) silent
der **Versuch, -e** attempt; **versuchen** try
verteidigen defend
vertrauen trust, confide
der **Vertreter, -** representative
verursachen cause
verurteilen condemn, sentence
verwachsen (*participle*) overgrown
verwalten manage; **der Verwalter, -** manager, administrator
(sich) **verwandeln** change, alter; **die Verwandlung, -en** metamorphosis
der **Verwandte, -n, -n** relative; **die Verwandtschaft, -en** (family and) relatives
verweilen stay
verwildern (ist) run wild, become intractable; **verwildert** wild, savage
die **Verwirklichung** realization
verwirren confuse
verwitwet widowed
verwunden wound
verwundern amaze; **die Verwunderung** amazement
verzehren devour, consume
verzeihen† forgive
sich **verzerren** twist, be contorted
verziehen† twist, distort
die **Verzweiflung** desperation, despair
das **Vieh** beast, cattle
viel much, *etc.*; **viele** many; **vielerlei** a variety of things; **vieles** much, a lot
vielleicht′ perhaps, maybe
vielmehr′ rather
das **Viereck, -e** quadrangle; **viert-** fourth; **das Viertel, -** quarter; **die Viertelstunde, -n** quarter of an hour
der **Vogel, ⸚** bird; **die Vogelstimme, -n** bird's voice
das **Volk, ⸚er** people
voll full (of); **der Vollbart, ⸚e** full beard; **vollen′den** complete, finish; **vollends** right; on top of that; all the way; **die Vollen′dung** completion, fulfillment, perfection; **voller** full of; **völlig** complete; **vollkommen** complete, perfect; expert; **vollständig** complete; **voll-tanken** fill

with gas; **vollwichtig** in full measure; **vollzie′hen**† accomplish, complete
von of; from; by; *etc.* **von . . . aus; von . . . her** from
vor before; of; with; ago; *etc.*
vor (*as verb prefix*) ahead, forward
voran′ (*as verb prefix and adverb*) ahead
voraus′ advance, ahead
voraus′-setzen assume
vorbei′ (*as verb prefix and adverb*) past, by; **an . . . vorbei′** past
vor-bereiten prepare (the way for)
vorder- front; **das Vorderbein, -e** foreleg; **die Vorderpfote, -n** forepaw; **die Vorderstube, -n** front room; **das Vorderzimmer, -** front room
vorerst′ at first, for the time being
die **Vorfahren** (*pl.*) forefathers, ancestors
der **Vorfall, ⸚e** incident
der **Vorgänger, -** predecessor
der **Vorgarten, ⸚** front garden
das **Vorgefühl, -e** presentiment
vor-gehen† (ist) go on
vorgerückt advanced
das **Vorhaben, -** plan
(sich) **vor-halten**† hold up in front of one
vorher′ before(hand)
vorhin′ (just) before
vor-kommen† (ist) occur; seem, feel like
vorläufig temporary, for the time being
die **Vorlesung, -en** lecture
die **Vorliebe** partiality
vor-liegen† be, be present
vormals previously
der **Vormittag, -e** forenoon
vor-musizie′ren play music
vorn(e) in front
vornehm aristocratic, genteel, distinguished
vor-nehmen† question, interrogate, take under consideration; take to task; **sich vor-nehmen**† undertake, plan
der **Vorrat, ⸚e** supply, stock
der **Vorsaal, -säle** antechamber, entry
vor-sagen tell, recite
vor-schreiben† prescribe
vor-schreiten† (ist) advance
die **Vorschrift, -en** instruction
vorsichtig cautious
die **Vorstellung, -en** imagination; picture, idea
vor-strecken stretch out, stick out
der **Vortag** day before
vor-tasten grope forward
vorü′ber (*as verb prefix and adverb*) past, by
vorü′ber-gehen† (ist) pass, go by; **der Vorü′bergehende, -n, -n** passer-by
das **Vorurteil, -e** prejudice
vorwärts forward
vor-werfen† reproach for; **der Vorwurf, ⸚e** reproach

waagerecht horizontal
wach awake; **wachen** be awake, watch
wachsen† (ist) grow
das **Wachtfeuer, -** watch-fire, campfire
wacker brave, good(ly)
die **Waffe, -n** weapon; (*pl.*) arms; **der Waffenrock, ⸚e** tunic; **die Waffenrüstung** arms and armor
die **Wage (= Waage), -n** scale(s); **die Wage ist aufgehoben** the scales have been tipped; judgment has been passed
wagen dare
der **Wagen, -** carriage, coach, wagon, car
die **Wahl, -en** choice; **wählen** choose, pick
wähnen imagine; **wahnsinnig** mad, insane
wahr true, real; **nicht wahr?** right?; isn't it?; *etc.*
während during, *etc.;* while, whereas; **währenddes′sen** meanwhile
wahrhaft truly; **die Wahrheit** truth
wahr-nehmen† perceive, notice
wahr′schein′lich probable, likely; **die Wahr′schein′lichkeit** probability
der **Wald, ⸚er** wood(s), forest; **der Waldessaum, ⸚e** edge of the woods; **die Waldfrucht, ⸚e** wild fruit; **der Waldhang, ⸚e** forest slope; **der Waldhüter, -** forester; **der Waldteich, -e** forest pool
die **Walnuß, ⸚e** walnut
die **Wand, ⸚e** wall
wandeln change
wandern (ist) wander; walk, stroll; **der Wanderweg, -e** trail
die **Wange, -n** cheek
wanken stagger, stumble, waver, sway, shake
wann when
die **Wärme** warmth; **wärmen** warm; **sich warmstampfen** stamp one's feet to get warm
die **Warnung, -en** warning
warten wait
warum′ why
was what; which, that; = **etwas; was für** (ein) what sort of
waschen† wash; **die Wäsche** linen; underclothes; **der Wäschewechsel** change of linen (underclothes)
das **Wasser** water; **die Wasserkunst, ⸚e** fountain; **der Wasserstaub** mist
der **Wechsel, -** change, alternation; **wechseln** change
wecken wake
wedeln wag
weder . . . noch neither . . . nor

weg (*as verb prefix*) away
der **Weg, -e** way, path, road; distance; **sich auf den Weg machen** set out
wegen on account of, about, *etc.*
die **Wegstunde, -n** hour's walk; **der Wegweiser, -** signpost
wegwerfend disparaging, disdainful
wehen blow, wave in the wind
das **Wehgeheul** howl of misery; **die Wehmut** melancholy, sadness; **wehmütig** melancholy
sich **wehren** defend oneself, resist
weh tun† hurt
das **Weib, -er** woman (*now mostly vulgar*)
weich soft
weichen† (ist) move away, budge, retreat
die **Weide, -n** pasture
sich **weigern** hesitate; refuse
der **Weiher, -** pond
der **Weihnachtsbaum, ⁼e** Christmas tree; **die Weihnachtsfreude, -n** Christmas joy
weil because, since; while
die **Weile** while, short time; **das Weilchen** little while; **weilen** stay, sojourn
der **Wein, -e** wine
weinen cry, weep
die **Weinstube, -n** tavern
weis(e) wise
die **Weise, -n** manner, *etc.;* melody, lay
weisen† point; show; turn
weiß white; **das Weißbrot** white bread
weit far, wide; **weiter** farther, further, more, on
weiter (*as verb prefix*) on
weiter-welken wither on, continue to wither
weitläufig extensive
welch which, what, who, that
welk werden† wither
die **Welle, -n** wave; **das Wellenschlagen** wave beat
die **Welt, -en** world; **das Weltende** end of the world; **das Weltgestöhn** world-wailing; **der Weltuntergang** end of the world
wenden† turn; direct; spend; **der Wendepunkt, -e** turning point
wenig little; few; **ein wenig** a little; **wenigstens** at least
wenn if, when, whenever; **wenngleich** although
wer who; whoever, he who
werden† (ist) become, get, grow; be; shall, will
werfen† throw, cast, fling
der **Wert, -e** value; **wert** worth, worthy; **wertlos** worthless
das **Wesen, -** being, creature; thing; (whole) business; affairs; system; **wesentlich** significant, essential
der **West(en)** west
das **Wetter** weather; storm
wichtig important; **die Wichtigkeit, -en** importance, important thing
widerlich repulsive, disgusting
sich **widerset'zen** resist
widerwärtig repugnant
widmen devote, dedicate
wie how; as; like; as if; such as, the like of which
wieder again, once more; in turn
wieder (*as verb prefix*) back (again); again
wiederho'len repeat
das **Wiedersehen** reunion
wiederum again
(sich) **wiegen** rock back and forth, sway
die **Wiese, -n** meadow
wieso' what do you mean; how (come)
wild wild, savage; **das Wild** (wild) game; **der Wildschütz, -en, -en** poacher
der **Wille, -ns, -n** will; **willig** willing
wimmern whimper
windbraun wind-tanned
winden† wind, twist; **sich winden**† writhe
der **Windschatten** lee, protected side
der **Winkel, -** corner
winken wave, beckon; motion
winseln whimper
winzig tiny
der **Wipfel, -** (tree-)top
wir we
der **Wirbelwind, -e** whirlwind
wirklich real; **die Wirklichkeit** reality; **die Wirkung, -en** effect; **wirkungslos** ineffectual, without effect
wirr confused, jumbled
der **Wirt, -e** innkeeper, proprietor, hut-keeper (*fem.* **die Wirtin, -nen**); **das Wirtshaus, ⁼er** inn; **die Wirtstochter, ⁼** innkeeper's daughter
wischen wipe
wissen† know; **wissen zu** be able to; **wissenschaftlich** scientific, scholarly
die **Witwe, -n** widow; **die Witwenschaft** widowhood; **das Witwentum** widowhood
wo where; when
wo(r)- *with prepositions* where- . . . , . . . which (*relative*), . . . what (*interrogative*)
die **Woche, -n** week
woher', wo . . . her whence, where . . . from
wohin', wo . . . hin where (to)
wohl probably, indeed, no doubt; well, good; **wohlbekannt** familiar; **wohl-gefallen**† please; **das Wohlgefallen** satisfaction, pleasure; **wohlgemut** cheerful, joyous; **wohlgeneigt** well-disposed; **wohlhabend** well-to-do; **wohl-tun**† do well; do (a person) good; **das Wohlwollen** benevolence

wohnen live, dwell; **der Wohnsitz, -e** residence; **die Wohnung, -en** apartment; dwelling, home; **das Wohnzimmer, -** living room
das **Wölkchen, -** little cloud; **die Wolke, -n** cloud
wollen† want to, will, wish to; claim to; be about to; *etc.*
das **Wollkleid, -er** wool dress
womög'lich possibly
die **Wonne** joy, delight; **wonnig** delightful
worauf' on which, *etc.;* whereupon
das **Wort, -e** *or* **⸚er** word
woselbst' in which place
das **Wrack, -e (-s)** wreck
wund sore, wounded; **die Wunde, -n** wound
das **Wunder, -** surprise; miracle; **wunderbar** wonderful; surprising; **wunderhübsch** lovely; **sich wundern** wonder; **wunderschön** most lovely; **wundervoll** wonderful
der **Wunsch, ⸚e** wish; **wünschen** wish
wurmig wormy
wurzellos without roots
wüst wild, savage
die Wut fury; **wüten** rage

die **Zacke, -n** peak
die **Zahl, -en** number, figure; **zahlen** pay; **zählen** count; **zahllos** innumerable, countless
zahm tame
der **Zahn, ⸚e** tooth; **der Zahnarzt, ⸚e** dentist; **zahnlos** toothless
zart tender, delicate, slight, fine; **zärtlich** tender, fond
der **Zauber** magic, enchantment; **der Zauberer, -** magician; **der Zauberstab, ⸚e** magic wand
der **Zaun, ⸚e** fence
zehnt - tenth
das **Zeichen, -** sign
der **Zeigefinger, -** index finger; **zeigen** show; point
die **Zeit, -en** time; **(die) Zeitlang** while, time; **zeitlebens** all one's life
die **Zeitung, -en** newspaper; **das Zeitungsblatt, ⸚er** page of a paper
zerbeißen† bite in two
zerbrechen† break, shatter; **zerbrechlich** fragile
zerfallen† (ist) be ruined, become dilapidated
zerfetzen mangle, tear up, tatter
zermalmen crush
zerreißen† break, tear (to bits)
zerren drag, haul, pull
zerschmettern break (to pieces)
sich **zerstreuen** amuse oneself, provide oneself with distraction; **zerstreut** distracted; distraught
zertreten† crush (under foot); **zertreten** (*participle*) worn down
der **Zettel, -** slip of paper, note
das **Zeug, -e** stuff; thing; things (= clothes)
der **Zeuge, -n, -n** witness
zick(e) zack(e); zickzacken zigzag
ziehen† pull, draw; cultivate, raise; (ist) go, move, come, pass
das **Ziel, -e** goal, destination; **zielen** aim
ziemlich rather, fairly, relative(ly), pretty (much)
die **Zierde, -n** ornament; **zierlich** pretty, decorative, elegant
die **Ziffer, -n** figure, number; paragraph
das **Zimmer, -** room
der **Zinnbecher, -** tin (pewter) cup
die **Zinne, -n** battlement; pinnacle
der **Zipfel, -** tip
zischen hiss
zitie'ren quote
zittern tremble, shiver, flicker
zögern hesitate
der **Zögling, -e** pupil
das **Zollhaus, ⸚er** toll house, customhouse
der **Zorn** anger; **zornig** angry
zu to; at; at the sign of; to go with, *etc.;* closed
zu (*as verb prefix*) to, toward; shut
zu-bringen† spend
zucken twitch, tremble, jerk, shrug
zu-decken cover up, tuck in
zu-drücken close
zuerst' (at) first
der **Zufall, ⸚e** chance, coincidence, accident; **zufällig** (by) chance
die **Zuflucht** refuge, sanctuary
zufrie'den content; **die Zufrie'denheit** contentment
der **Zug, ⸚e** feature; expression; draught, pull; train
zu-gehen† (ist) go on
zu-gestehen† admit
zugleich' at the same time
das **Zug'personal'** train crew
zu-greifen† reach in
zugrun'de to ruin
zugun'sten in . . .'s favor, in favor of
zu-hören listen (to)
zu-kehren turn toward
die **Zukunft** future
zu-lassen† permit
zuletzt' at last, finally
zu-machen close
zumu'te sein† feel
zunächst' (at) first
zu-nehmen† increase
die **Zuneigung, -en** affection, attachment
die **Zunge, -n** tongue
zunich'te of no effect, void; ruined

zupfen tug
sich **zurecht′-finden**† adjust oneself, find one's way
zurecht′-kommen† (ist) get through, manage
zu-reden urge
zureichend adequate
zürnen be angry
zurück′ back, behind
zurück′ (*as verb prefix*) back, behind
zurück′-fahren† (ist) start back, recoil
zurück′haltend restrained, reserved
zurück′-kehren (ist) return
zurück′-legen traverse, travel
zurück′-weichen† (ist) retreat
zu-sagen agree, accept; grant
zusam′men together
zusam′men (*as verb prefix*) together, up
zusam′men-brechen† collapse; **der Zusam′menbruch** collapse
zusam′men-fahren† (ist) start (in surprise)
sich **zusam′men-finden**† gather, meet
zusam′men-klappen snap shut
zusam′men-kommen† (ist) come together, coincide
zusam′men-laufen† (ist) gather, run up
zusam′men-schlagen† close (shut)
zusam′men-sinken† (ist) sink down, collapse
zusam′men-suchen gather together, look up
zusam′men-zucken wince
der **Zuschauer, -** spectator
zu-schlagen† slam; close
zu-sehen† look (on), watch
der **Zustand, ⸚e** condition, state
zu-stehen† be the right of, belong rightfully
zu-stoßen† (ist) lunge
zuta′ge in sight
die **Zuverlässigkeit** reliability, dependability
zuviel′ too much, too many
zuvor′ before
der **Zuweg, -e** access, approach
zuwe′ge-bringen† accomplish
zuwei′len occasionally
zuwi′der repugnant, objectionable
zwar to be sure, indeed; specifically
der **Zweck, -e** purpose; **die Zwecklosigkeit** purposelessness
der **Zweifel, -** doubt; **zweifellos** doubtless, indubitable
der **Zweig, -e** branch
zweit- second; **zweitens** secondly, in the second place; **das Zwiegespräch, -e** dialogue
zwingen† force, compel, constrain
zwischen between, among; **die Zwischenzeit, -en** interval

der **Alarm′, -e**	alarm
das **Album, -s**	album
alert′	alert
der **Altar′, ¨e**	altar
der **Angler, -**	angler
der **Appetit′**	appetite
der **Applaus′, -e**	applause
das **Auto, -s**	auto
balancie′ren	balance
der **Balkon′, -e**	balcony
der **Ball, ¨e**	ball
der **Ballast′, -e**	ballast
die **Bande, -n**	band
das **Bankett′, -e**	banquet
der **Bär, -en, -en**	bear
bevor′	before
biblisch	biblical
bitter (die Bitterkeit)	bitter (bitterness)
bitterlich	bitterly
blind	blind
blond	blond
bohren	bore
die **Bombe, -n**	bomb
boxen	box
der **Boxer, -**	boxer
die **Butter**	butter
der **Campingsack, ¨e**	(camping) knapsack
der **Charak′ter, -te′re**	character
degradie′ren	degrade
der **Deserteur′, -e**	deserter
das **Dilem′ma, -s**	dilemma
die **Distanz′, -en**	distance
die **Division′, -en**	division
der **Dok′tor, -to′ren (Dr.)**	doctor (Dr.)
das **Echo, -s**	echo
das **Eis**	ice
das **Element′, -e**	element
die **Energie′, -n**	energy
existie′ren	exist
die **Fakultät′, -en**	faculty
die **Fami′lie, -n**	family
die **Fanfa′re, -n**	fanfare
die **Fassa′de, -n**	façade
der **Film, -e**	film
fischen	fish
die **Formation′, -en**	formation
die **Front, -en**	front

der **General′, -e** (*or* **¨e**)	general
geolo′gisch	geological
das **Gold**	gold
golden	golden
das **Grammophon′, -e**	gramophone
das **Gras, ¨er**	grass
die **Grimas′se, -n**	grimace
der **Hammer, ¨**	hammer
die **Hand, ¨e**	hand
hektisch	hectic
hindern	hinder
das **Horn, ¨er**	horn
der **Hunger**	hunger
die **Hyä′ne, -n**	hy(a)ena
hypnotisie′ren	hypnotize
die **Idyl′le, -n**	idyll
die **Infantrie′**	infantry
intelligent′	intelligent
interessie′ren	interest
intonie′ren	intone
die **Ironie′**	irony
das **Instrument′, -e**	instrument
der **Kaffee, -s**	coffee
die **Kamera, -s**	camera
der **Kamerad′, -en, -en**	comrade
der **Kandidat′, -en, -en**	candidate
die **Katastro′phe, -n**	catastrophe
das **Kilome′ter, -**	kilometer
die **Kolonie′, -n**	colony
die **Kommission′, -en**	commission
die **Kompagnie′, -n** = **die Kompanie′**	company
die **Kondition′, -en**	condition
die **Koral′le, -n**	coral
der **Korridor, -e**	corridor, hall
das **Kristall′**	crystal (glassware)
der **Kurier′, -e**	courier
das **Land, ¨er**	land
die **Leica, -s**	Leica (camera)
die **Letter, -n**	letter
der **Leutnant, -s**	lieutenant
die **Lippe, -n**	lip
die **Lokomoti′ve, -n**	locomotive
die **Lunge, -n**	lung
die **Madon′na, -nnen**	madonna
der **Magnet′, -en, -en**	magnet
der **Mai**	May
die **Mama′**	mama
der **Marquis′, -**	marquis

mecha'nisch	mechanical
die **Melancholie'**	melancholy
melancho'lisch	melancholy
das **Meter, -**	meter
metho'disch	methodical
die **Million', -en**	million
der **Minis'ter, -**	minister
die **Minu'te, -n**	minute
die **Musik'**	music
das **Musik'instrument', -e**	musical instrument
die **Nerve, -n**	nerve
die **Novel'le, -n**	Novelle, novella
der **Novem'ber**	November
Nr. (= Nummer)	Nr., no. (= number)
der **Page, -n, -n**	page
die **Palisa'de**	palisade
der **Park, -s**	park
passen	pass
die **Passion'**	Passion
der **Pastor, -to'ren**	pastor
die **Person', -en**	person
das **Photo, -s**	photo
das **Plateau', -s**	plateau
poli'tisch	political
die **Portion', -en**	portion
präsent'	present
pressen	press
die **Promena'de, -n**	promenade
die **Provinz', -en**	province
der **Pullover, -**	pullover
der **Puls, -e**	pulse
die **Pupil'le, -n**	pupil
das **Radio, -s**	radio
rammen	ram
religiös'	religious
die **Revolution', -en**	revolution
der **Ring, -e**	ring
der **Riva'le, -n, -n**	rival
rollen (ist)	roll
die **Rose, -n**	rose
das **Rudiment', -e**	rudiment
ruinie'ren	ruin
der **Sack, ⸚e**	sack
der **Sand**	sand
schnappen	snap
schrill	shrill
der **Schuh, -e**	shoe
schwimmen† (ist)	swim
senden†	send
das **Signal', -e**	signal
singen†	sing
sinken† (ist)	sink
die **Socke, -n**	sock
das **Sofa, -s**	sofa
die **Sohle, -n**	sole
souverän'	sovereign
der **Speer, -e**	spear
die **Station', -en**	station
das **Statut', -en**	statute
die **Steppe, -n**	steppe
stoppen (ist)	stop
der **Student', -en, -en**	student
studie'ren	study
das **System', -e**	system
die **Tablet'te, -n**	tablet
der **Tee**	tea
das **Telefon', -e**	(tele)phone
telephonie'ren	telephone
die **Theologie'**	theology
die **Toma'te**	tomato
der **Triumph', -e**	triumph
trotten (ist)	trot
der **Tumult', -e**	tumult
die **Uniform', -en**	uniform
die **Universität', -en**	university
der **Vagabund', -en, -en**	vagabond
die **Variation', -en**	variation
violett'	violet
die **Viper, -n**	viper
das **Visier', -e**	visor
warm	warm
warnen	warn
der **Wind, -e**	wind
der **Winter, -**	winter
der **Wolf, ⸚e**	wolf
die **Zigaret'te, -n**	cigarette
die **Zone, -n**	zone

Principal Parts of Strong and Irregular Verbs

backen	backte (buk)	gebacken	bäckt
befehlen	befahl	befohlen	befiehlt
beginnen	begann	begonnen	beginnt
beißen	biß	gebissen	beißt
bergen	barg	geborgen	birgt
biegen	bog	gebogen	biegt
bieten	bot	geboten	bietet
binden	band	gebunden	bindet
bitten	bat	gebeten	bittet
blasen	blies	geblasen	bläst
bleiben	blieb	geblieben	bleibt
braten	briet	gebraten	brät
brechen	brach	gebrochen	bricht
brennen	brannte	gebrannt	brennt
bringen	brachte	gebracht	bringt
denken	dachte	gedacht	denkt
dreschen	drosch (drasch)	gedroschen	drischt
dringen	drang	gedrungen	dringt
dürfen	durfte	gedurft	darf
empfehlen	empfahl	empfohlen	empfiehlt
empfinden	empfand	empfunden	empfindet
erschrecken	erschrak	erschrocken	erschrickt
essen	aß	gegessen	ißt
fahren	fuhr	gefahren	fährt
fallen	fiel	gefallen	fällt
fangen	fing	gefangen	fängt
finden	fand	gefunden	findet
flechten	flocht	geflochten	flicht
fliegen	flog	geflogen	fliegt
fliehen	floh	geflohen	flieht
fließen	floß	geflossen	fließt
fressen	fraß	gefressen	frißt
frieren	fror	gefroren	friert
geben	gab	gegeben	gibt
gedeihen	gedieh	gediehen	gedeiht
gehen	ging	gegangen	geht
gelingen	gelang	gelungen	gelingt
gelten	galt	gegolten	gilt
genesen	genas	genesen	genest
geschehen	geschah	geschehen	geschieht
gewinnen	gewann	gewonnen	gewinnt
gleichen	glich	geglichen	gleicht
gleiten	glitt	geglitten	gleitet
glimmen	glomm	geglommen	glimmt
graben	grub	gegraben	gräbt
greifen	griff	gegriffen	greift
haben	hatte	gehabt	hat
halten	hielt	gehalten	hält

hängen (hangen)	hing	gehangen, gehängt	hängt
hauen	hieb, haute	gehauen	haut
heben	hob (hub)	gehoben	hebt
heißen	hieß	geheißen	heißt
helfen	half	geholfen	hilft
kennen	kannte	gekannt	kennt
klingen	klang	geklungen	klingt
kneifen	kniff	gekniffen	kneift
kommen	kam	gekommen	kommt
können	konnte	gekonnt	kann
kriechen	kroch	gekrochen	kriecht
laden	lud	geladen	lädt
lassen	ließ	gelassen	läßt
laufen	lief	gelaufen	läuft
leiden	litt	gelitten	leidet
leihen	lieh	geliehen	leiht
lesen	las	gelesen	liest
liegen	lag	gelegen	liegt
löschen	losch	geloschen	lischt
lügen	log	gelogen	lügt
meiden	mied	gemieden	meidet
messen	maß	gemessen	mißt
mißlingen	mißlang	mißlungen	mißlingt
mögen	mochte	gemocht	mag
müssen	mußte	gemußt	muß
nehmen	nahm	genommen	nimmt
nennen	nannte	genannt	nennt
pfeifen	pfiff	gepfiffen	pfeift
pflegen	pflegte, pflog	gepflegt, gepflogen	pflegt
raten	riet	geraten	rät
reiben	rieb	gerieben	reibt
reißen	riß	gerissen	reißt
reiten	ritt	geritten	reitet
rennen	rannte	gerannt	rennt
riechen	roch	gerochen	riecht
ringen	rang	gerungen	ringt
rinnen	rann	geronnen	rinnt
rufen	rief	gerufen	ruft
saufen	soff	gesoffen	säuft
schaffen	schuf	geschaffen	schafft
scheiden	schied	geschieden	scheidet
scheinen	schien	geschienen	scheint
schelten	schalt	gescholten	schilt
schieben	schob	geschoben	schiebt
schießen	schoß	geschossen	schießt
schinden	schund	geschunden	schindet
schlafen	schlief	geschlafen	schläft

schlagen	schlug	geschlagen	schlägt
schleichen	schlich	geschlichen	schleicht
schließen	schloß	geschlossen	schließt
schlingen	schlang	geschlungen	schlingt
schmeißen	schmiß	geschmissen	schmeißt
schneiden	schnitt	geschnitten	schneidet
schreiben	schrieb	geschrieben	schreibt
schreien	schrie	geschrieen, geschrien	schreit
schreiten	schritt	geschritten	schreitet
schweigen	schwieg	geschwiegen	schweigt
schwimmen	schwamm	geschwommen	schwimmt
schwinden	schwand	geschwunden	schwindet
schwingen	schwang	geschwungen	schwingt
schwören	schwur, schwor	geschworen	schwört
sehen	sah	gesehen	sieht
sein	war	gewesen	ist
senden	sandte, sendete	gesandt, gesendet	sendet
singen	sang	gesungen	singt
sinken	sank	gesunken	sinkt
sinnen	sann	gesonnen	sinnt
sitzen	saß	gesessen	sitzt
sollen	sollte	gesollt	soll
spinnen	spann	gesponnen	spinnt
sprechen	sprach	gesprochen	spricht
springen	sprang	gesprungen	springt
stechen	stach	gestochen	sticht
stecken	steckte, stak	gesteckt	steckt
stehen	stand	gestanden	steht
steigen	stieg	gestiegen	steigt
sterben	starb	gestorben	stirbt
stieben	stob	gestoben	stiebt
stoßen	stieß	gestoßen	stößt
streichen	strich	gestrichen	streicht
streiten	stritt	gestritten	streitet
tragen	trug	getragen	trägt
treffen	traf	getroffen	trifft
treiben	trieb	getrieben	treibt
treten	trat	getreten	tritt
trinken	trank	getrunken	trinkt
trügen	trog	getrogen	trügt
tun	tat	getan	tut
verdrießen	verdroß	verdrossen	verdrießt
vergessen	vergaß	vergessen	vergißt
verlieren	verlor	verloren	verliert
wachsen	wuchs	gewachsen	wächst
waschen	wusch	gewaschen	wäscht
weichen	wich	gewichen	weicht
weisen	wies	gewiesen	weist
wenden	wandte, wendete	gewandt, gewendet	wendet
werben	warb	geworben	wirbt
werden	wurde(ward)	geworden	wird

werfen	warf	geworfen	wirft
winden	wand	gewunden	windet
wissen	wußte	gewußt	weiß
wollen	wollte	gewollt	will
zeihen	zieh	geziehen	zeiht
ziehen	zog	gezogen	zieht
zwingen	zwang	gezwungen	zwingt